Designing Linear Control Systems with MATLAB®

KATSUHIKO OGATA

University of Minnesota

MATLAB® Curriculum Series

PRENTICE HALL, Englewood Cliffs, New Jersey 07632

Library of Congress Cataloging-in-Publication Data

Ogata, Katsuhiko.
   Designing linear control systems with MATLAB / by Katsuhiko
Ogata.
      p. cm.
   Includes bibliographical references (p.   ) and index.
   ISBN 0-13-293226-1
   1. Automatic control.   2. Linear systems—Design and
construction—Data processing.   3. MATLAB.   I. Title.
TJ213.027   1993
629.8'32'02855369—dc20   93-34429
                                                         CIP

Acquisitions Editor: Don Fowley
Editorial/Production Supervision: Lynda Griffiths
Buyer: Linda Behrens
Cover Design: Perrapin Graphics

Printed in the United States of America

10 9 8 7 6 5 4 3 2 1

ISBN 0-13-293226-1

PRENTICE-HALL INTERNATIONAL (UK) LIMITED, *London*
PRENTICE-HALL OF AUSTRALIA PTY. LIMITED, *Sydney*
PRENTICE-HALL CANADA INC., *Toronto*
PRENTICE-HALL HISPANOAMERICANA, S.A., *Mexico*
PRENTICE-HALL OF INDIA PRIVATE LIMITED, *New Delhi*
PRENTICE-HALL OF JAPAN, INC., *Tokyo*
SIMON & SCHUSTER ASIA PTE. LTD., *Singapore*
EDITORA PRENTICE-HALL DO BRASIL, LTDA., *Rio de Janeiro*

Contents

Preface

This book is intended to aid engineering students (at the senior/first-year graduate level) and practicing engineers in their study of MATLAB for use in designing control systems. The major topics presented in this book are design of control systems via pole placement, design of state observers, and design of quadratic optimal control systems. Both continuous-time and discrete-time systems are treated.

In writing this book, it is assumed that the reader is familiar with the materials presented in my companion book *Solving Control Engineering Problems with MATLAB* or its equivalent.

The Student Edition of MATLAB has many commands that can be directly used in analyzing and designing control systems. If the reader is using the professional version of MATLAB, these commands are included in the Control System Toolbox.

In this book, theoretical background materials for designing control systems are discussed in detail. Once theoretical aspects are understood, the reader can use MATLAB with advantage to obtain numerical solutions that involve various types of vector-matrix operations. Many examples presented in this book are taken from two of my earlier books: *Modern Control Engineering,* 2nd edition (Prentice Hall), and *Discrete-Time Control Systems* (Prentice Hall).

All of the MATLAB programs presented in this book are written with user-friendly comments so that the reader can follow each step easily. The routines that appear in this book work with the Student Edition of MATLAB and MATLAB versions 3.5 and 4.0. The plots shown in this book were produced from PostScript files created with version 3.5 of MATLAB. The Student Edition of MATLAB can produce the same plots but only with screen dump hardcopy output.

Finally, I would like to thank The MathWorks, Inc. for their permission to use some of the basic MATLAB materials presented in *Student Edition of MATLAB* (published by Prentice Hall) in this book.

Katsuhiko Ogata

Chapter 1 Basic Background Materials

1-1 INTRODUCTION*

This chapter deals with the necessary background materials for designing control systems with MATLAB. MATLAB (an abbreviation for MATrix LABoratory) is a matrix-based system for mathematical and engineering calculations. We may think of MATLAB as a kind of language designed solely to do matrix manipulations. All variables handled in MATLAB are matrices. That is, MATLAB has only one data type, a matrix, or a rectangular array of numbers. MATLAB has an extensive set of routines for obtaining graphical outputs.

MATLAB commands and matrix functions that are frequently used in analyzing and designing control systems

MATLAB has many predefined functions that can be called by the user to solve many different types of control problems.

In Table 1-1, we list such commands and matrix functions.

Accessing and exiting MATLAB

On most systems, once MATLAB has been installed, to invoke MATLAB, execute the command MATLAB. To exit MATLAB, execute the command exit or quit.

How MATLAB is used

MATLAB is usually used in a command-driven mode. When single-line commands are entered, MATLAB processes them immediately and displays the results. MATLAB is also capable of executing sequences of command that are stored in files.

The commands that are typed may be accessed later by using the *up-arrow* key. It is possible to scroll through some of the latest commands that are entered and recall a particular command line.

Variables in MATLAB

A convenient feature of MATLAB is that the variables need not be dimensioned before use. In MATLAB, variables are generated automatically once they are used.

---

*The material presented in this chapter is an abbreviated version of Chapters 1 and 2 of *Solving Control Engineering Problems with MATLAB*, by Katsuhiko Ogata, published by Prentice Hall, Englewood Cliffs, New Jersey.

Table 1-1 MATLAB COMMANDS AND MATRIX FUNCTIONS

Commands and matrix functions commonly used in solving control engineering problems	Explanations of what commands do, matrix functions mean, or statements mean
abs	Absolute value, complex magnitude
angle	Phase angle
ans	Answer when expression is not assigned
atan	Arctangent
axis	Manual axis scaling
bode	Plot Bode diagram
clear	Clear workspace
clg	Clear graph screen
computer	Type of computer
conj	Complex conjugate
conv	Convolution, multiplication
corrcoef	Correlation coefficients
cos	Cosine
cosh	Hyperbolic cosine
cov	Covariance
deconv	Deconvolution, division
det	Determinant
diag	Diagonal matrix
eig	Eigenvalues and eigenvectors
exit	Terminate program
exp	Exponential base e
expm	Matrix exponential
eye	Identity matrix
filter	Direct filter implementation
format long	15-Digit scaled fixed point (Example: 1.33333333333333)
format long e	15-Digit floating point (Example: 1.33333333333333e+000)
format short	5-Digit scaled fixed point (Example: 1.3333)
format short e	5-Digit floating point (Example: 1.3333e+000)
freqs	Laplace transform frequency response
freqz	z-Transform frequency response
grid	Draw grid lines
hold	Hold current graph on the screen
i	$\sqrt{-1}$
imag	Imaginary part
inf	Infinity (∞)
inv	Inverse

(Continued)

Table 1-1 (*Continued*)

j	$\sqrt{-1}$
length	Vector length
linspace	Linearly spaced vectors
log	Natural logarithm
loglog	Loglog $x-y$ plot
logm	Matrix logarithm
logspace	Logarithmically spaced vectors
log10	Log base 10
lqe	Linear quadratic estimator design
lqr	Linear quadratric regulator design
max	Maximum value
mean	Mean value
median	Median value
min	Minimum value
NaN	Not-a-number
nyquist	Plot Nyquist frequency response
ones	constant
pi	Pi (π)
plot	Linear $x-y$ plot
polar	Polar plot
poly	Characteristic polynomial
polyfit	Polynomial curve fitting
polyval	Polynomial evaluation
polyvalm	Matrix polynomial evaluation
prod	Product of elements
quit	Terminate program
rand	Generate random numbers and matrices
rank	Calculate the rank of a matrix
real	Real part
rem	Remainder or modulus
residue	Partial-fraction expansion
rlocus	Plot root loci
roots	Polynomial roots
semilogx	Semilog $x-y$ plot (x-axis logarithmic)
semilogy	Semilog $x-y$ plot (y-axis logarithmic)
sign	Signum function
sin	Sine
sinh	Hyperbolic sine
size	Row and column dimensions
sqrt	Square root
sqrtm	Matrix square root
std	Standard deviation
step	Plot unit-step response
sum	Sum of elements

(Continued)

Table 1-1 (*Continued*)

Commands and matrix functions commonly used in solving control engineering problems	Explanations of what commands do, matrix functions mean, or statements mean
tan tanh text title trace	Tangent Hyperbolic tangent Arbitrarily positioned text Plot title Trace of a matrix
who	Lists all variables currently in memory
xlabel	*x*-Axis label
ylabel	*y*-Axis label
zeros	Zero

(The dimensions of the variables can be altered later if necessary.) Such variables remain in memory until the command exit or quit is entered.

To obtain a list of the variables in the workspace, simply type the command who. Then all variables currently in the workspace appear on the screen.

The command clear will clear all nonpermanent variables from the workspace. If it is desired to clear only a particular variable, say 'x', from the workspace, enter the command clear x.

Program line beginning with '%'

Throughout this book, many MATLAB programs are written with comments and remarks that explain particular steps taken in the programs. Program lines in MATLAB beginning with '%' are comments or remarks. The notation '%' is similar to 'REM' in BASIC. A line beginning with % is used to store the programmer's comments or remarks, and such comments or remarks are not executed. That is, everything appearing after % on a MATLAB program line is ignored. If comments or remarks require more than one program line, each line must begin with %.

Use of semicolon operator

The semicolon is used to suppress printing. If the last character of a statement is a semicolon, the printing is suppressed; but the command is still executed, only the result is not displayed. This is a useful feature, since printing of intermediate results may not be needed. Also, in entering a matrix, a semicolon is used to indicate the end of the row, except at the last row.

Use of colon operator

The colon operator plays an important role in MATLAB. This operator may be used to create vectors, to subscript matrices, and to specify *for* iterations. For example, j:k is the same as $[j \quad j+1 \quad \cdots \quad k]$, A(:, j) is the *j*th column of **A**, and A(i, :) is the *i*th row of **A**. For 'for' iterations, see, for example, MATLAB Program 4-9.

Entering a long statement that will not fit on one line

A statement is normally terminated with the carriage return or enter key. If the statement being entered is too long for one line, an ellipsis consisting of three or more periods (...), followed by the carriage return, can be used to indicate that the statement continues on the next line. An example is

$$x = 1.234 + 2.345 + 3.456 + 4.567 + 5.678 + 6.789\ldots$$
$$+ 7.890 + 8.901 - 9.012;$$

Note that the blank spaces around the $=$, $+$, and $-$ signs are optional. Such spaces are often provided to improve readability.

Entering several statements on one line

Several statements can be placed on one line if they are separated by commas or semicolons. Examples are

plot(x,y,'o'), text(1,20,'System 1'), text(1,15,'System 2')

and

plot(x,y,'o'); text(1,20,'System 1'); text(1,15,'System 2')

Selecting output format

All computations in MATLAB are performed in double precision. However, the displayed output may have a fixed point with four decimal places. For example, for the vector

$$\mathbf{x} = [1/3 \quad 0.00002]$$

MATLAB exhibits the following output:

x =

0.3333   0.0000

If at least one element of a matrix is not an exact integer, there are four possible output formats. The displayed output can be controlled by use of the following commands:

format short
format long
format short e
format long e

Once invoked, the chosen format remains in effect until changed.

For control systems analysis, format short and format long are commonly used. Whenever MATLAB is invoked and no format command is entered, MATLAB shows the numerical results in format short. If all elements of a matrix or vector are exact integers, then format short and format long yield the same result.

How to save variables when exiting from MATLAB

When 'exit' or 'quit' is typed, all variables in MATLAB are lost. If the command save is entered before exiting, then all variables can be kept in a disk file named matlab.mat. When we later reenter MATLAB, the command load will restore the workspace to its former state.

1-2 PLOTTING RESPONSE CURVES

MATLAB has an extensive set of routines for obtaining graphical output. The plot command creates linear x–y plots. (Logarithmic and polar plots are created by substituting the words loglog, semilogx, semilogy, or polar plot.) All such commands are used the same way: they only affect how the axis is scaled and how the data are displayed.

x–y plot

If $\mathbf{x}$ and $\mathbf{y}$ are vectors of the same length, the command

$$\text{plot(x,y)}$$

plots the values in y against the values in x.

Plotting multiple curves

To plot multiple curves on a single graph, use the plot command with multiple arguments.

$$\text{plot(X1, Y1, X2, Y2,} \ldots \text{, Xn, Yn)}$$

The variables X1, Y1, X2, Y2, and so on, are pairs of vectors. Each x–y pair is graphed, generating multiple curves on the plot. Multiple arguments have the benefit of allowing vectors of different lengths to be displayed on the same graph. Each pair uses a different line type.

Plotting more than one curve on a single graph may also be accomplished by using the command hold. The *hold* command freezes the current plot and inhibits erasure and rescaling. Hence subsequent curves will be overplotted on the original curve. Entering the command hold again releases the current plot.

Adding grid lines, title of the graph, x-axis label, and y-axis label

Once a graph is on the screen, grid lines may be drawn, the graph may be titled, and x and y axes may be labeled. MATLAB commands for grid, title, x-axis label, and y-axis label are

grid	(grid lines)
title	(graph title)
xlabel	(x-axis label)
ylabel	(y-axis label)

Note that, once the command display has been brought back, grid lines, graph title, and x and y labels can be put on the plot by successively entering the commands.

Writing text on the graphic screen

To write text beginning at point (X, Y) on the graphic screen, use the command

$$\text{text(X,Y,'text')}$$

For example, the statement

$$\text{text(3,0.45,'sin t')}$$

will write sin t horizontally beginning at point $(3, 0.45)$. Also, the statements

$$\text{plot(x1,y1,x2,y2), text(x1,y1,'1'), text(x2,y2,'2')}$$

mark two curves so that they can be distinguished easily.

Plot type

$$\text{plot(X,Y,'x')}$$

draws a point plot using $\times$ mark symbols, while

$$\text{plot(X1, Y1, ':', X2, Y2, '+')}$$

uses a dotted line for the first curve and the plus symbol $(+)$ for the second curve. Available line and point types are as follows:

Line types		Point types	
solid	–	point	•
dashed	– –	plus	+
dotted	:	star	*
dash-dot	–•	circle	○
		$\times$-mark	$\times$

Color

Statements

$$\text{plot(X,Y,'r')}$$
$$\text{plot(X,Y,'+g')}$$

indicate the use of a red line on the first graph and green + marks on the second. Available colors are

red	r
green	g
blue	b
white	w
invisible	i

Automatic plotting algorithms

In MATLAB the plot is automatically scaled. This plot remains as the current plot until another is plotted, in which case the old plot is erased and the axis is automatically rescaled. The automatic plotting algorithms for transient-response curves, root loci, Bode diagrams, Nyquist plots, and the like, are designed to work with a wide range of systems but are not always perfect. Thus, in certain situations it may become desirable to override the automatic axis scaling feature of the plot command and to manually select the plotting limits.

Manual axis scaling

If it is desired to plot a curve in a region specified by

$$v = [\text{x-min} \quad \text{x-max} \quad \text{y-min} \quad \text{y-max}]$$

enter the command axis(v). axis(v), where v is a four-element vector, sets the axis scaling to the prescribed limits. For logarithmic plots, the elements of v are $\log_{10}$ of the minimums and maximums.

Executing axis(v) freezes the current axis scaling for subsequent plots. Typing axis again resumes autoscaling.

axis('square') sets the plot region on the screen to be square. With a square aspect ratio, a line with slope 1 is at a true 45°, not skewed by the irregular shape of the screen. axis('normal') sets the aspect ratio back to normal.

1-3 COMPUTING MATRIX FUNCTIONS

In this section we shall discuss computations of norms, eigenvalues, eigenvectors, generalized eigenvalues, generalized eigenvectors, and polynomial evaluation, among others.

Norms

The norm of a matrix is a scalar that gives some measure of the size of the matrix. Several different definitions are commonly used. One such definition is

$$\text{norm}(\mathbf{A}) = \text{largest singular value of } \mathbf{A}$$

Similarly, several definitions are available for the norm of a vector. One commonly used definition for the norm of a vector $\mathbf{x}$ is

$$\text{norm(x)} = \text{sum(abs(x).}^\wedge 2)^\wedge 0.5$$

See the following example.

```
x = [2   3   6];
norm(x)
ans =

        7
```

Eigenvalues and eigenvectors

If $\mathbf{A}$ is an $n \times n$ matrix, then the n numbers λ that satisfy

$$\mathbf{Ax} = \lambda\mathbf{x}$$

are the eigenvalues of $\mathbf{A}$. They are found using the command

eig(A)

which returns the eigenvalues in a column vector.

If $\mathbf{A}$ is real and symmetric, the eigenvalues will be real. But if $\mathbf{A}$ is not symmetric, the eigenvalues are frequently complex numbers.

For example, with

$$\mathbf{A} = \begin{bmatrix} 0 & 1 \\ -1 & 0 \end{bmatrix}$$

the command

eig(A)

produces

ans =

0 + 1.0000i
0 − 1.0000i

MATLAB functions may have single- or multiple-output arguments. For example, as seen above, eig(A) produces a column vector consisting of the eigenvalues of $\mathbf{A}$, while a double-assignment statement

[X,D] = eig(A)

produces eigenvalues and eigenvectors. The diagonal elements of diagonal matrix $\mathbf{D}$ are the eigenvalues, and the columns of $\mathbf{X}$ are the corresponding eigenvectors such that

$$\mathbf{AX} = \mathbf{XD}$$

For example, if

$$\mathbf{A} = \begin{bmatrix} 0 & 1 & 0 \\ 0 & 0 & 1 \\ -6 & -11 & -6 \end{bmatrix}$$

then the statement

[X,D] = eig(A)

gives the following result:

```
[X,D] = eig(A)

X =

      -0.5774          0.2182         -0.1048
       0.5774         -0.4364          0.3145
      -0.5774          0.8729         -0.9435


D =

      -1.0000               0               0
            0         -2.0000               0
            0               0         -3.0000
```

The eigenvectors are scaled so that the norm of each is 1.

If the eigenvalues of a matrix are distinct, the eigenvectors are always independent, and the eigenvector matrix **X** will diagonalize the original matrix **A** if applied as a similarity transformation. However, if a matrix has repeated eigenvalues, it is not diagonalizable unless it has a full (independent) set of eigenvectors. If the eigenvectors are not independent, the original matrix is said to be defective. Even if a matrix is defective, the solution from eig satisfies the relationship **AX = XD**.

Generalized eigenvalues and generalized eigenvectors

If **A** and **B** are square matrices, then the command

$$eig(A,B)$$

returns a vector containing the generalized eigenvalues solving the equation

$$\mathbf{Ax} = \lambda\,\mathbf{Bx}$$

where λ is a scalar. The values of λ that satisfy the equation are the generalized eigenvalues, and the corresponding values of **x** are the generalized eigenvectors.

To obtain eigenvectors, use the double-assignment command as follows:

$$[X,D] = eig(A,B)$$

This produces a diagonal matrix **D** of generalized eigenvalues and a square matrix **X** whose columns are corresponding eigenvectors so that

$$\mathbf{AX = BXD}$$

For example, if

$$\mathbf{A} = \begin{bmatrix} 0 & 1 & 0 \\ 0 & 0 & 1 \\ -4 & -6 & -4 \end{bmatrix}$$

$$\mathbf{B} = \begin{bmatrix} 1 & 0 & 1 \\ 0 & 1 & 0 \\ 0 & 0 & 1 \end{bmatrix}$$

then eig(A,B) gives

```
eig(A,B)

ans =

        0.3129 − 2.5087i
        0.3129 + 2.5087i
       −0.6258 − 0.0000i
```

and [X,D] = eig(A,B) gives

```
[X,D] = eig(A,B)

X =

     0.7309 + 0.0144i   −0.6720 + 0.2880i   −0.2390 + 0.5893i
    −0.0178 − 0.2503i   −0.0776 − 0.2387i    0.2459 − 0.6062i
    −0.6336 − 0.0336i    0.5745 − 0.2693i   −0.1539 + 0.3794i


D =

     0.3129 − 2.5087i            0                    0
          0             0.3129 + 2.5087i            0
          0                     0           −0.6258 − 0.0000i
```

The eigenvectors are scaled so that the norm of each is 1.0.

Characteristic equation

The roots of the characteristic equation are the same as the eigenvalues of matrix **A**. The characteristic equation of matrix **A** is computed with

$$p = poly(A)$$

For example, if matrix **A** is given by

$$\mathbf{A} = \begin{bmatrix} 0 & 1 & 0 \\ 0 & 0 & 1 \\ -6 & -11 & -6 \end{bmatrix}$$

then the command poly(A) will yield

```
p = poly(A)

p =

     1.0000      6.0000      11.0000      6.0000
```

This is the MATLAB representation of the polynomial

$$s^3 + 6s^2 + 11s + 6 = 0$$

The roots of the characteristic equation $p = 0$ can be obtained by entering the command r = roots(p):

```
r = roots(p)

r =

   -3.0000
   -2.0000
   -1.0000
```

The roots of the characteristic equation may be reassembled back into the original polynomial with the command q = poly(r).

```
q = poly(r)

q =

     1.0000     6.0000    11.0000     6.0000
```

Product of polynomials

Consider

$$a(s) = s^2 - 20.6$$

$$b(s) = s^2 + 19.6s + 151.2$$

The product of the polynomials is the convolution of the coefficients. The product of polynomials $a(s)$ and $b(s)$ can be obtained by entering the command c = conv(a, b).

```
a = [1   0   -20.6]; b = [1   19.6   151.2];
c = conv(a,b)

c =

  1.0e + 003 *

    0.0010    0.0196    0.1306    -0.4038    -3.1147
```

This is the MATLAB representation of the polynomial

$$c(s) = s^4 + 19.6s^3 + 130.6s^2 - 403.8s - 3114.7$$

Deconvolution (division of polynomials)

To divide polynomial $c(s)$ by $a(s)$, use the deconvolution command, $[q,r] =$ deconv(c,a).

```
[q,r] = deconv(c,a)

q =

        1.0000   19.6000   151.2000


r =

         0      0      0      0      0
```

Polynomial evaluation

If p is a vector whose elements are the coefficients of a polynomial in descending powers, then polyval(p,s) is the value of the polynomial evaluated at s. For example, to evaluate the polynomial

$$p(s) = 3s^2 + 2s + 1$$

at $s = 5$, enter the command

$$p = [3 \quad 2 \quad 1];$$

$$polyval(p,5)$$

then we get

$$ans =$$

$$86$$

The command polyvalm(p,A) evaluates the polynomial p in a matrix sense. Consider the following matrix **J**:

$$\mathbf{J} = \begin{bmatrix} -2 + j2\sqrt{3} & 0 & 0 \\ 0 & -2 - j2\sqrt{3} & 0 \\ 0 & 0 & -10 \end{bmatrix}$$

The command poly(J) gives the characteristic polynomial for **J**.

```
p = poly(J)

p =

      1.0000    14.0000    56.0000    160.0000
```

This is the MATLAB expression for the characteristic polynomial for **J**.

$$\text{poly}(\mathbf{J}) = \phi(\mathbf{J}) = \mathbf{J}^3 + 14\mathbf{J}^2 + 56\mathbf{J} + 160\mathbf{I}$$

where **I** is the identity matrix. For the matrix

$$\mathbf{A} = \begin{bmatrix} 0 & 1 & 0 \\ 0 & 0 & 1 \\ -6 & -11 & -6 \end{bmatrix}$$

the command polyvalm(poly(J),A) evaluates the following $\phi(\mathbf{A})$:

$$\phi(\mathbf{A}) = \mathbf{A}^3 + 14\mathbf{A}^2 + 56\mathbf{A} + 160\mathbf{I} = \begin{bmatrix} 154 & 45 & 8 \\ -48 & 66 & -3 \\ 18 & -15 & 84 \end{bmatrix}$$

See the following MATLAB output.

```
polyvalm(poly( J),A)

ans =

   154.0000    45.0000     8.0000
   -48.0000    66.0000    -3.0000
    18.0000   -15.0000    84.0000
```

Obtaining squares of entries of vector *x*

For a vector **x**, x.$^\wedge$2 gives the vector of the square of each element. For example, for

$$\mathbf{x} = \begin{bmatrix} 1 & 2 & 3 \end{bmatrix}$$

x.$^\wedge$2 is given as shown in the following MATLAB output.

```
x = [1   2   3];
x.^2

ans =

        1     4     9
```

Also, for the vector **y**,

$$\mathbf{y} = \begin{bmatrix} 2 + 5j & 3 + 4j & 1 - j \end{bmatrix}$$

y. $^\wedge$ 2 is given as follows:

```
y = [2+5*i   3+4*i   1−i];
y.^2

ans =

   −21.0000 + 20.0000i   −7.0000 + 24.0000i        0 − 2.0000i
```

Obtaining squares of entries of matrix A

For a matrix **A**, A. $^\wedge$ 2 gives the matrix consisting of the square of each element. For example, for matrices **A** and **B**, where

$$\mathbf{A} = \begin{bmatrix} 1 & 2 \\ 3 & 4 \end{bmatrix}, \qquad \mathbf{B} = \begin{bmatrix} 1 + j & 2 - 2j \\ 3 + 4j & 5 - j \end{bmatrix}$$

A. $^\wedge$ 2 and B. $^\wedge$ 2 are given as follows:

```
A = [1   2;3   4];
A.^2

ans =

        1      4
        9     16

B = [1+i   2−2*i;3+4*i   5−i];
B.^2

ans =

        0 +   2.0000i        0 −   8.0000i
   −7.0000 + 24.0000i   24.0000 − 10.0000i
```

Absolute values

abs(A) gives the matrix consisting of the absolute value of each element of **A**. If **A** is complex, abs(A) returns the complex modulus (magnitude):

$$abs(A) = sqrt(real(A).^\wedge 2 + imag(A).^\wedge 2)$$

angle(A) returns the phase angles, in radians, of the elements of complex matrix **A**. The angles lie between $-\pi$ and π. See the following example.

```
A = [2+2*i   1+3*i;4+5*i   6−i];
abs(A)

ans =

        2.8284          3.1623

        6.4031          6.0828

angle(A)

ans =

        0.7854          1.2490
        0.8961         −0.1651
```

Magnitude and phase angle of a complex number

The magnitude and phase angle of a complex number $z = x + iy = re^{i\theta}$ are given by

$$r = \text{abs}(z)$$

$$\text{theta} = \text{angle}(z)$$

and the statement

$$z = r*\exp(i*\text{theta})$$

converts back to the original complex number z.

Matrix exponential

expm(A) is the matrix exponential of an $n \times n$ matrix **A**. That is

$$\text{expm}(\mathbf{A}) = \mathbf{I} + \mathbf{A} + \frac{\mathbf{A}^2}{2!} + \frac{\mathbf{A}^3}{3!} + \cdots$$

Note that a transcendental function is interpreted as a matrix function if an "m" is appended to the function name, as in expm(A) or sqrtm(A).

Utility matrices

In MATLAB, the functions

```
ones(n)
ones(m,n)
ones(A)
zeros
```

generate special matrices. That is, ones(n) produces an $n \times n$ matrix of ones. ones(m,n) produces an $m \times n$ matrix of ones. Similarly, zeros(n) produces an $n \times n$ matrix of zeros, while zeros(m,n) produces an $m \times n$ matrix of zeros. zeros(A) produces a matrix of zeros of the same size as A, except when A is a scalar.

Identity matrix

We often need to enter an identity matrix **I** in MATLAB programs. A statement eye(n) gives an $n \times n$ identity matrix. That is,

```
eye(5)

ans =

      1    0    0    0    0
      0    1    0    0    0
      0    0    1    0    0
      0    0    0    1    0
      0    0    0    0    1
```

Diagonal matrix

If **x** is a vector, a statement diag(x) produces a diagonal matrix with **x** on the diagonal line. For example, for a vector

$$x = [ones(1,n)]$$

diag([ones(1,n)]) gives an $n \times n$ identity matrix as follows:

```
diag([ones(1,5)])

ans =

      1    0    0    0    0
      0    1    0    0    0
      0    0    1    0    0
      0    0    0    1    0
      0    0    0    0    1
```

If **A** is a square matrix, then diag(A) is a vector consisting of the diagonal of **A**, and diag(diag(A)) is a diagonal matrix with elements of diag(A) appearing on the diagonal line. See the following MATLAB output.

```
A = [1   2   3;4   5   6;7   8   9];
diag(A)

ans =

      1
      5
      9

diag(diag(A))
```

```
ans =

    1    0    0
    0    5    0
    0    0    9
```

Note that diag(1:5) gives

```
diag(1:5)

ans =

    1    0    0    0    0
    0    2    0    0    0
    0    0    3    0    0
    0    0    0    4    0
    0    0    0    0    5
```

Also, diag(0:4) gives

```
diag(0:4)

ans =

    0    0    0    0    0
    0    1    0    0    0
    0    0    2    0    0
    0    0    0    3    0
    0    0    0    0    4
```

Hence diag(1:5) − diag(0:4) is an identity matrix.

It is important to note that diag(0,n) is quite different from diag(0:n). diag(0,n) is an $(n + 1) \times (n + 1)$ matrix consisting of all zero elements. See the following MATLAB output.

```
diag(0,4)

ans =

    0    0    0    0    0
    0    0    0    0    0
    0    0    0    0    0
    0    0    0    0    0
    0    0    0    0    0
```

1-4 MATHEMATICAL MODELS OF LINEAR SYSTEMS

MATLAB has useful commands to transform a mathematical model of a linear system to another model. Such linear system transformations useful for solving control engineering problems are listed in the following.

Transfer function to state space

The command

$$[A,B,C,D] = tf2ss(num,den)$$

converts the system in the transfer function form

$$\frac{Y(s)}{U(s)} = \frac{num}{den} = \mathbf{C}(s\mathbf{I} - \mathbf{A})^{-1}\mathbf{B} + D$$

to the state-space form:

$$\dot{\mathbf{x}} = \mathbf{A}\mathbf{x} + \mathbf{B}u$$

$$y = \mathbf{C}\mathbf{x} + Du$$

State space to transfer function

If the system has one input and one output, the command

$$[num,den] = ss2tf(A,B,C,D)$$

yields the transfer function $Y(s)/U(s)$.

If the system involves more than one input, use the following command:

$$[num,den] = ss2tf(A,B,C,D,iu)$$

This command converts the system in state space

$$\dot{\mathbf{x}} = \mathbf{A}\mathbf{x} + \mathbf{B}\mathbf{u}$$

$$y = \mathbf{C}\mathbf{x} + \mathbf{D}\mathbf{u}$$

to the transfer function

$$\frac{Y(s)}{U_i(s)} = i\text{th element of } [\mathbf{C}(s\mathbf{I} - \mathbf{A})^{-1}\mathbf{B} + \mathbf{D}]$$

Note that the scalar 'iu' is an index into the inputs of the system and specifies which input is to be used for the response.

Consider, for example, the following system, which has two inputs, u_1 and u_2.

$$\begin{bmatrix} \dot{x}_1 \\ \dot{x}_2 \end{bmatrix} = \begin{bmatrix} 0 & 1 \\ -2 & -3 \end{bmatrix} \begin{bmatrix} x_1 \\ x_2 \end{bmatrix} + \begin{bmatrix} 1 & 0 \\ 0 & 1 \end{bmatrix} \begin{bmatrix} u_1 \\ u_2 \end{bmatrix}$$

$$y = \begin{bmatrix} 1 & 0 \end{bmatrix} \begin{bmatrix} x_1 \\ x_2 \end{bmatrix} + \begin{bmatrix} 0 & 0 \end{bmatrix} \begin{bmatrix} u_1 \\ u_2 \end{bmatrix}$$

Two transfer functions may be obtained for this system. One relates the output y and input u_1, and the other relates the output y and input u_2. (When considering input u_1, we assume that input u_2 is zero, and vice versa.) See the following MATLAB output.

```
A = [0   1;-2   -3];
B = [1   0;0   1];
C = [1   0];
D = [0   0];

[num,den] = ss2tf(A,B,C,D,1)

num =

        0     1     3


den =

        1     3     2

[num,den] = ss2tf(A,B,C,D,2)

num =

        0     0     1


den =

        1     3     2
```

From the MATLAB output, we have

$$\frac{Y(s)}{U_1(s)} = \frac{s + 3}{s^2 + 3s + 2}$$

and

$$\frac{Y(s)}{U_2(s)} = \frac{1}{s^2 + 3s + 2}$$

Partial-fraction expansion of the transfer function

Consider the transfer function

$$\frac{B(s)}{A(s)} = \frac{num}{den} = \frac{b(1)s^n + b(2)s^{n-1} + \cdots + b(n)}{a(1)s^n + a(2)s^{n-1} + \cdots + a(n)}$$

where $a(1) \neq 0$, but some of $a(i)$ and $b(j)$ may be zero.

Row vectors num and den specify the coefficients of the numerator and denominator of the transfer function. That is,

$$\text{num} = [b(1) \quad b(2) \quad \cdots \quad b(n)]$$

$$\text{den} = [a(1) \quad a(2) \quad \cdots \quad a(n)]$$

The command

$$[r,p,k] = \text{residue(num,den)}$$

finds the residues, poles, and direct terms of a partial-fraction expansion of the ratio of two polynomials $B(s)$ and $A(s)$. The partial-fraction expansion of $B(s)/A(s)$ is given by

$$\frac{B(s)}{A(s)} = \frac{r(1)}{s - p(1)} + \frac{r(2)}{s - p(2)} + \cdots + \frac{r(n)}{s - p(n)} + k(s)$$

As an example, consider the following transfer function:

$$\frac{B(s)}{A(s)} = \frac{2s^3 + 5s^2 + 3s + 6}{s^3 + 6s^2 + 11s + 6}$$

For this function,

$$\text{num} = [2 \quad 5 \quad 3 \quad 6]$$

$$\text{den} = [1 \quad 6 \quad 11 \quad 6]$$

The command

$$[r,p,k] = \text{residue(num,den)}$$

gives the following result:

```
[r,p,k] = residue(num,den)

r =

    -6.0000
    -4.0000
     3.0000


p =

    -3.0000
    -2.0000
    -1.0000


k =

     2
```

Note that the residues are returned in column vector r, the pole locations in column vector p, and the direct term in row vector k. This is the MATLAB representation of the following partial-fraction expansion of $B(s)/A(s)$;

$$\frac{B(s)}{A(s)} = \frac{2s^3 + 5s^2 + 3s + 6}{(s + 1)(s + 2)(s + 3)}$$

$$= \frac{-6}{s + 3} + \frac{-4}{s + 2} + \frac{3}{s + 1} + 2$$

The command

$$[num,den] = residue(r,p,k)$$

where r, p, and k are as given in the previous MATLAB output, converts the partial-fraction expansion back to the polynomial ratio $B(s)/A(s)$ as follows:

```
[num,den] = residue(r,p,k)

num =

    2.0000      5.0000      3.0000      6.0000


den =

    1.0000      6.0000     11.0000      6.0000
```

Conversion from continuous time to discrete time

The command

$$[G,H] = c2d(A,B,Ts)$$

where Ts is the sampling period in seconds, converts the state-space model from continuous time to discrete time, assuming a zero-order hold on the inputs. That is, with this command

$$\dot{\mathbf{x}} = \mathbf{Ax} + \mathbf{Bu}$$

is converted to

$$\mathbf{x}(k + 1) = \mathbf{Gx}(k) + \mathbf{Hu}(k)$$

Consider, for example, the following continuous-time system:

$$\begin{bmatrix} \dot{x}_1 \\ \dot{x}_2 \end{bmatrix} = \begin{bmatrix} 0 & 1 \\ -25 & -4 \end{bmatrix} \begin{bmatrix} x_1 \\ x_2 \end{bmatrix} + \begin{bmatrix} 0 \\ 1 \end{bmatrix} u$$

An equivalent discrete-time system can be obtained by use of the command $[G,H] = c2d(A,B,Ts)$. The sampling period Ts is assumed to be 0.05 sec. See the following MATLAB output.

```
A = [0   1;−25   −4];
B = [0;1];
format long
[G,H] = c2d(A,B,0.05)

G =

        0.97088325381929   0.04484704238264
       −1.12117605956599   0.79149508428874


H =

        0.00116466984723
        0.04484704238264
```

The equivalent discrete-time state space equation is given by

$$\begin{bmatrix} x_1(k+1) \\ x_2(k+1) \end{bmatrix} = \begin{bmatrix} 0.9709 & 0.04485 \\ -1.1212 & 0.7915 \end{bmatrix} \begin{bmatrix} x_1(k) \\ x_2(k) \end{bmatrix} + \begin{bmatrix} 0.001165 \\ 0.04485 \end{bmatrix} u(k)$$

1-5 OUTLINE OF THE BOOK

This book deals with control system design with MATLAB. The outline of the book is as follows: Chapter 1 has presented introductory material. Chapters 2 and 3 discuss pole placement and observer design problems solved with MATLAB. Specifically, Chapter 2 deals with continuous-time systems, whereas Chapter 3 treats discrete-time systems. Chapter 4 is concerned with the design of optimal control systems; here we solve quadratic optimal control problems with MATLAB. Both continuous- and discrete-time systems are treated. Also, minimum-energy control of discrete-time systems is discussed in this chapter.

Chapter 2 Pole Placement and Design of Observers for Continuous-Time Systems

2-1 INTRODUCTION

In this chapter we shall first present the pole-placement approach to the design of closed-loop control systems. Then we shall discuss the design of state observers. This chapter is concerned with continuous-time control systems only. Discrete-time control systems are treated separately in Chapter 3.

Design via pole placement

In the conventional approach to the design of a single-input, single-output control system, we design a controller (compensator) such that the dominant closed-loop poles have a desired damping ratio ζ and undamped natural frequency ω_n. In this approach, the order of the system may be raised by 1 or 2 unless pole–zero cancellation takes place. Note that in this approach we assume the effects on the responses of nondominant closed-loop poles to be negligible.

Different from specifying only dominant closed-loop poles (conventional design approach), the pole-placement approach specifies all closed-loop poles. The desired closed-loop poles are determined based on the transient-response and/or frequency-response requirements. By choosing an appropriate gain matrix for state feedback, it is possible to force the system to have closed-loop poles at the desired locations. There is a cost associated with placing all closed-loop poles, however, because such placement requires successful measurements of all state variables or else the inclusion of a state observer in the system. There is also a requirement on the part of the system for the closed-loop poles to be placed at arbitrarily chosen locations. The requirement is that the system be completely state controllable.

In the pole-placement approach to the design of control systems, we assume that all state variables are available for feedback. In practice, however, this is not so. Then we need to estimate unavailable state variables. It is important to note that we should avoid differentiating a state variable to generate another one. Differentiation of a signal always decreases the signal-to-noise ratio because noise generally fluctuates more rapidly than the command signal. Sometimes the signal-to-noise ratio may be decreased by several times by a single differentiation process. Methods are available to estimate unmeasurable state variables without a differentiation process. Estimation of unmeasurable state variables is commonly called *observation*.

A device (or a computer program) that estimates or observes the state variables is called a *state observer*, or simply an *observer*. If the state observer observes all state variables of the system, regardless of whether some state variables are available for direct measurement, it is called a *full-order state observer*. There are times when this will not be necessary, when we will need observation of only the unmeasurable state variables, but not of those that are directly measurable as well. For example, since the output variables are observable and they are linearly related to the state variables, we need not observe all state variables, but observe only $n - m$ state variables, where n is the dimension of the state vector and m is the dimension of the output vector. The state observer that observes only the minimum number of state variables is called a *minimum-order state observer* or, simply, *minimum-order observer*. In this chapter, we shall discuss both the full-order state observer and the minimum-order state observer.

Note that state observers can be designed if and only if the observability condition is satisfied. In many practical cases, the observed state vector is used in the state feedback to generate the desired control vector.

In the pole-placement approach, the designer wishes to examine several different sets of desired closed-loop poles and determine the corresponding state feedback gain matrices **K**. After making computer simulations of the system and examining response curves, choose the **K** matrix that gives the best overall system performance. The criterion for the best overall system performance depends on the particular situation, including economic considerations. Similar comments apply to the design of state observers.

Outline of the chapter

The outline of this chapter is as follows: Section 2-1 has presented introductory material. Section 2-2 discusses the pole-placement technique. We derive equations for the determination of state feedback gain matrix **K**. Section 2-3 presents case studies dealing with the design of type 1 servo systems. Section 2-4 treats full-order state observers. We give equations for the determination of the gain matrix $\mathbf{K}_e$ for full-order state observers. Finally, Section 2-5 discusses the minimum-order state observer; here we derive equations for gain matrix $\mathbf{K}_e$ for minimum-order state observers. MATLAB programs are presented to solve pole-placement problems and to design state observers. All MATLAB programs are written in such a way that the reader can follow each step easily.

2-2 POLE PLACEMENT

Consider a control system

$$\dot{\mathbf{x}} = \mathbf{A}\mathbf{x} + \mathbf{B}u \tag{2-1}$$

where $\mathbf{x}$ = state vector (n-vector)
u = control signal (scalar)
$\mathbf{A} = n \times n$ constant matrix
$\mathbf{B} = n \times 1$ constant matrix

We shall choose the control signal to be

$$u = -\mathbf{K}\mathbf{x} \tag{2-2}$$

This means that the control signal is determined by an instantaneous state. Such a scheme is called *state feedback*. The $1 \times n$ matrix $\mathbf{K}$ is called the state feedback gain matrix. In the following analysis we assume that u is unconstrained.

Substituting Eq. (2-2) into Eq. (2-1) gives

$$\dot{\mathbf{x}}(t) = (\mathbf{A} - \mathbf{BK})\mathbf{x}(t)$$

The solution of this equation is given by

$$\mathbf{x}(t) = e^{(\mathbf{A} - \mathbf{BK})t}\mathbf{x}(0) \tag{2-3}$$

where $\mathbf{x}(0)$ is the initial state caused by external disturbances. The stability and transient response characteristics are determined by the eigenvalues of matrix $\mathbf{A} - \mathbf{BK}$. If matrix $\mathbf{K}$ is chosen properly, then matrix $\mathbf{A} - \mathbf{BK}$ can be made an asymptotically stable matrix, and for all $\mathbf{x}(0) \neq \mathbf{0}$ it is possible to make $\mathbf{x}(t)$ approach $\mathbf{0}$ as t approaches infinity. The eigenvalues of matrix $\mathbf{A} - \mathbf{BK}$ are called the regulator poles. If these regulator poles are located in the left-half s plane, then $\mathbf{x}(t)$ approaches $\mathbf{0}$ as t approaches infinity. The problem of placing the closed-loop poles at the desired location is called a pole-placement problem.

Figure 2-1(a) shows the system defined by Eq. (2-1). It is an open-loop control system, because the state $\mathbf{x}$ is not fed back to the control signal u. Figure 2-1(b) shows the system with state feedback. This is a closed-loop control system, because the state $\mathbf{x}$ is fed back to the control signal u.

It is possible to prove that arbitrary pole placement for a given system is possible if and only if the system is completely state controllable.

Theoretical background

We shall present two approaches for obtaining the state feedback gain matrix $\mathbf{K}$. The first approach is to use a transformation matrix $\mathbf{T}$ to transform the state equation to a controllable canonical form and then to compare the desired characteristic equation and the characteristic equation involving gain $\mathbf{K}$. By equating the coefficients of the corresponding terms of the two equations, the state feedback gain matrix $\mathbf{K}$ can be determined.

The second approach is based on the Caylay–Hamilton theorem, which states that matrix $\mathbf{A} - \mathbf{BK} = \hat{\mathbf{A}}$ satisfies its own characteristic equation. By modifying the matrix characteristic polynomial $\phi(\hat{\mathbf{A}})$, an equation for the gain matrix can be derived. The equation for the determination of gain $\mathbf{K}$ based on this approach is commonly called Ackermann's formula.

In what follows, we shall give detailed derivations of the state feedback gain

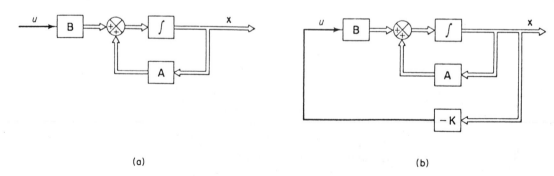

(a)   (b)

Figure 2-1

matrix $\mathbf{K}$, since good knowledge of these derivations is necessary for understanding the MATLAB programs presented in this chapter.

In the following discussions we assume that the system is completely state controllable. (This is the necessary and sufficient condition for arbitrary pole placement for linear time-invariant systems. For the proof, see, for example, Reference 4 listed at the end of the book.)

Method based on transformation to controllable canonical form

The system equation and control equation we deal with are given by Eqs. (2-1) and (2-2), respectively. Define a transformation matrix $\mathbf{T}$ by

$$\mathbf{T} = \mathbf{MW} \tag{2-4}$$

where $\mathbf{M}$ is the controllability matrix

$$\mathbf{M} = [\mathbf{B} \vdots \mathbf{AB} \vdots \cdots \vdots \mathbf{A}^{n-1}\mathbf{B}] \tag{2-5}$$

and $\mathbf{W}$ is given by

$$\mathbf{W} = \begin{bmatrix} a_{n-1} & a_{n-2} & \cdots & a_1 & 1 \\ a_{n-2} & a_{n-3} & \cdots & 1 & 0 \\ \vdots & \vdots & & \vdots & \vdots \\ a_1 & 1 & \cdots & 0 & 0 \\ 1 & 0 & \cdots & 0 & 0 \end{bmatrix} \tag{2-6}$$

where the a_i's are coefficients of the characteristic polynomial

$$|s\mathbf{I} - \mathbf{A}| = s^n + a_1 s^{n-1} + \cdots + a_{n-1}s + a_n$$

Define a new state vector $\hat{\mathbf{x}}$ by

$$\mathbf{x} = \mathbf{T}\hat{\mathbf{x}}$$

Since the system is assumed to be completely state controllable, the rank of the controllability matrix $\mathbf{M}$ is n. Thus the inverse of matrix $\mathbf{T}$ exists and Eq. (2-1) can be modified to

$$\dot{\hat{\mathbf{x}}} = \mathbf{T}^{-1}\mathbf{AT}\hat{\mathbf{x}} + \mathbf{T}^{-1}\mathbf{B}u \tag{2-7}$$

where

$$\mathbf{T}^{-1}\mathbf{AT} = \begin{bmatrix} 0 & 1 & 0 & \cdots & 0 \\ 0 & 0 & 1 & \cdots & 0 \\ \vdots & \vdots & \vdots & & \vdots \\ 0 & 0 & 0 & \cdots & 1 \\ -a_n & -a_{n-1} & -a_{n-2} & \cdots & -a_1 \end{bmatrix} \tag{2-8}$$

$$\mathbf{T}^{-1}\mathbf{B} = \begin{bmatrix} 0 \\ 0 \\ \vdots \\ 0 \\ 1 \end{bmatrix} \tag{2-9}$$

Let us choose a set of the desired eigenvalues as $\mu_1, \mu_2, \ldots, \mu_n$. Then the desired characteristic equation becomes

$$(s - \mu_1)(s - \mu_2) \cdots (s - \mu_n) = s^n + \alpha_1 s^{n-1} + \cdots + \alpha_{n-1} s + \alpha_n \qquad (2\text{-}10)$$

Let us write

$$\hat{\mathbf{K}} = \mathbf{KT} = [\delta_n \quad \delta_{n-1} \quad \cdots \quad \delta_1] \qquad (2\text{-}11)$$

When $u = -\hat{\mathbf{K}}\hat{\mathbf{x}} = -\mathbf{KT}\hat{\mathbf{x}}$ is used to control the system given by Eq. (2-7), the system equation becomes

$$\dot{\hat{\mathbf{x}}} = \mathbf{T}^{-1}\mathbf{AT}\hat{\mathbf{x}} - \mathbf{T}^{-1}\mathbf{BKT}\hat{\mathbf{x}}$$

The characteristic equation is

$$|s\mathbf{I} - \mathbf{T}^{-1}\mathbf{AT} + \mathbf{T}^{-1}\mathbf{BKT}| = 0$$

This characteristic equation is the same as the characteristic equation for the system, defined by Eq. (2-1), when $u = -\mathbf{Kx}$ is used as the control signal. This can be seen as follows: Since

$$\dot{\mathbf{x}} = \mathbf{Ax} + \mathbf{Bu} = (\mathbf{A} - \mathbf{BK})\mathbf{x}$$

the characteristic equation for this system is

$$|s\mathbf{I} - \mathbf{A} + \mathbf{BK}| = |\mathbf{T}^{-1}(s\mathbf{I} - \mathbf{A} + \mathbf{BK})\mathbf{T}| = |s\mathbf{I} - \mathbf{T}^{-1}\mathbf{AT} + \mathbf{T}^{-1}\mathbf{BKT}|$$

Now let us simplify the characteristic equation of the system in the controllable canonical form. Referring to Eqs. (2-8), (2-9), and (2-11), we have

$$|s\mathbf{I} - \mathbf{T}^{-1}\mathbf{AT} + \mathbf{T}^{-1}\mathbf{BKT}|$$

$$= \left| s\mathbf{I} - \begin{bmatrix} 0 & 1 & \cdots & 0 \\ \vdots & \vdots & & \vdots \\ 0 & 0 & \cdots & 1 \\ -a_n & -a_{n-1} & \cdots & -a_1 \end{bmatrix} + \begin{bmatrix} 0 \\ \vdots \\ 0 \\ 1 \end{bmatrix} [\delta_n \quad \delta_{n-1} \quad \cdots \quad \delta_1] \right|$$

$$= \begin{vmatrix} s & -1 & \cdots & 0 \\ 0 & s & \cdots & 0 \\ \vdots & \vdots & & \vdots \\ a_n + \delta_n & a_{n-1} + \delta_{n-1} & \cdots & s + a_1 + \delta_1 \end{vmatrix}$$

$$= s^n + (a_1 + \delta_1)s^{n-1} + \cdots + (a_{n-1} + \delta_{n-1})s + (a_n + \delta_n) = 0 \qquad (2\text{-}12)$$

This is the characteristic equation for the system with state feedback. Therefore, it must be equal to Eq. (2-10), the desired characteristic equation. By equating the coefficients of like powers of s, we get

$$a_1 + \delta_1 = \alpha_1$$
$$a_2 + \delta_2 = \alpha_2$$
$$\vdots$$
$$a_n + \delta_n = \alpha_n$$

Solving the preceding equations for the δ_i's and substituting them into Eq. (2-11), we obtain

$$\mathbf{K} = \hat{\mathbf{K}}\mathbf{T}^{-1} = [\delta_n \quad \delta_{n-1} \quad \cdots \quad \delta_1]\mathbf{T}^{-1}$$

$$= [\alpha_n - a_n \vdots \alpha_{n-1} - a_{n-1} \vdots \cdots \vdots \alpha_2 - a_2 \vdots \alpha_1 - a_1]\mathbf{T}^{-1} \qquad (2\text{-}13)$$

Thus, if the system is completely state controllable, all eigenvalues can be placed at the desired locations by choosing matrix $\mathbf{K}$ according to Eq. (2-13).

Based on the above derivations for matrix $\mathbf{K}$, design steps for pole placement may be stated as follows:

Step 1: Check the controllability matrix. The rank of the controllability matrix must be n. Otherwise, Eq. (2-13) cannot be used.

Step 2: From the characteristic polynomial for matrix $\mathbf{A}$,

$$|s\mathbf{I} - \mathbf{A}| = s^n + a_1 s^{n-1} + \cdots + a_{n-1}s + a_n$$

determine the values of $a_1, a_2, \ldots, a_n$.

Step 3: Determine the transformation matrix $\mathbf{T}$ that transforms the system state equation into the controllable canonical form. (If the given system equation is already in the controllable canonical form, then $\mathbf{T} = \mathbf{I}$.) It is not necessary to write the state equation in the controllable canonical form. All we need here is to find the matrix $\mathbf{T}$. The transformation matrix $\mathbf{T}$ is given by Eq. (2-4), or

$$\mathbf{T} = \mathbf{MW}$$

where $\mathbf{M}$ is given by Eq. (2-5) and $\mathbf{W}$ is given by Eq. (2-6).

Step 4: Using the desired eigenvalues (desired closed-loop poles), write the desired characteristic polynomial:

$$(s - \mu_1)(s - \mu_2) \cdots (s - \mu_n) = s^n + \alpha_1 s^{n-1} + \cdots + \alpha_{n-1}s + \alpha_n$$

and determine the values of $\alpha_1, \alpha_2, \ldots, \alpha_n$.

Step 5: The required state feedback gain matrix $\mathbf{K}$ can be determined from the following equation:

$$\mathbf{K} = [\alpha_n - a_n \vdots \alpha_{n-1} - a_{n-1} \vdots \cdots \vdots \alpha_2 - a_2 \vdots \alpha_1 - a_1]\mathbf{T}^{-1}$$

Ackermann's formula

The system equation and control equation we consider here are given by Eqs. (2-1) and (2-2), respectively. By substituting Eq. (2-2) into Eq. (2-1), we obtain

$$\dot{\mathbf{x}} = (\mathbf{A} - \mathbf{BK})\mathbf{x}$$

Let us define

$$\hat{\mathbf{A}} = \mathbf{A} - \mathbf{BK}$$

The desired characteristic equation is

$$|s\mathbf{I} - \mathbf{A} + \mathbf{BK}| = |s\mathbf{I} - \hat{\mathbf{A}}| = (s - \mu_1)(s - \mu_2) \cdots (s - \mu_n)$$

$$= s^n + \alpha_1 s^{n-1} + \cdots + \alpha_{n-1}s + \alpha_n = 0$$

Define

$$\phi(s) = s^n + \alpha_1 s^{n-1} + \cdots + \alpha_{n-1} s + \alpha_n$$

Then

$$\phi(\mathbf{A}) = \mathbf{A}^n + \alpha_1 \mathbf{A}^{n-1} + \cdots + \alpha_{n-1} \mathbf{A} + \alpha_n \mathbf{I} \qquad (2\text{-}14)$$

Since the Cayley–Hamilton theorem states that $\hat{\mathbf{A}}$ satisfies its own characteristic equation, we have

$$\phi(\hat{\mathbf{A}}) = \hat{\mathbf{A}}^n + \alpha_1 \hat{\mathbf{A}}^{n-1} + \cdots + \alpha_{n-1} \hat{\mathbf{A}} + \alpha_n \mathbf{I} = \mathbf{0} \qquad (2\text{-}15)$$

We shall utilize Eq. (2-15) to derive Ackermann's formula. To simplify the derivation, we consider the case where $n = 3$. (For any other positive integer n, the following derivation can be easily extended.)

Consider the following identities:

$$\mathbf{I} = \mathbf{I}$$
$$\hat{\mathbf{A}} = \mathbf{A} - \mathbf{BK}$$
$$\hat{\mathbf{A}}^2 = (\mathbf{A} - \mathbf{BK})^2 = \mathbf{A}^2 - \mathbf{ABK} - \mathbf{BK}\hat{\mathbf{A}}$$
$$\hat{\mathbf{A}}^3 = (\mathbf{A} - \mathbf{BK})^3 = \mathbf{A}^3 - \mathbf{A}^2\mathbf{BK} - \mathbf{ABK}\hat{\mathbf{A}} - \mathbf{BK}\hat{\mathbf{A}}^2$$

Multiplying the preceding equations in order by $\alpha_3, \alpha_2, \alpha_1, \alpha_0$ (where $\alpha_0 = 1$), respectively, and adding the results, we obtain

$$\alpha_3 \mathbf{I} + \alpha_2 \hat{\mathbf{A}} + \alpha_1 \hat{\mathbf{A}}^2 + \hat{\mathbf{A}}^3$$
$$= \alpha_3 \mathbf{I} + \alpha_2 (\mathbf{A} - \mathbf{BK}) + \alpha_1 (\mathbf{A}^2 - \mathbf{ABK} - \mathbf{BK}\hat{\mathbf{A}}) + \mathbf{A}^3 - \mathbf{A}^2\mathbf{BK}$$
$$\quad - \mathbf{ABK}\hat{\mathbf{A}} - \mathbf{BK}\hat{\mathbf{A}}^2$$
$$= \alpha_3 \mathbf{I} + \alpha_2 \mathbf{A} + \alpha_1 \mathbf{A}^2 + \mathbf{A}^3 - \alpha_2 \mathbf{BK} - \alpha_1 \mathbf{ABK} - \alpha_1 \mathbf{BK}\hat{\mathbf{A}} - \mathbf{A}^2\mathbf{BK}$$
$$\quad - \mathbf{ABK}\hat{\mathbf{A}} - \mathbf{BK}\hat{\mathbf{A}}^2 \qquad (2\text{-}16)$$

Referring to Eq. (2-15), we have

$$\alpha_3 \mathbf{I} + \alpha_2 \hat{\mathbf{A}} + \alpha_1 \hat{\mathbf{A}}^2 + \hat{\mathbf{A}}^3 = \phi(\hat{\mathbf{A}}) = \mathbf{0}$$

Also, we have

$$\alpha_3 \mathbf{I} + \alpha_2 \mathbf{A} + \alpha_1 \mathbf{A}^2 + \mathbf{A}^3 = \phi(\mathbf{A}) \neq \mathbf{0}$$

Substituting the last two equations into Eq. (2-16), we get

$$\phi(\hat{\mathbf{A}}) = \phi(\mathbf{A}) - \alpha_2 \mathbf{BK} - \alpha_1 \mathbf{BK}\hat{\mathbf{A}} - \mathbf{BK}\hat{\mathbf{A}}^2 - \alpha_1 \mathbf{ABK} - \mathbf{ABK}\hat{\mathbf{A}} - \mathbf{A}^2\mathbf{BK}$$

Since $\phi(\hat{\mathbf{A}}) = \mathbf{0}$, we obtain

$$\phi(\mathbf{A}) = \mathbf{B}(\alpha_2 \mathbf{K} + \alpha_1 \mathbf{K}\hat{\mathbf{A}} + \mathbf{K}\hat{\mathbf{A}}^2) + \mathbf{AB}(\alpha_1 \mathbf{K} + \mathbf{K}\hat{\mathbf{A}}) + \mathbf{A}^2\mathbf{BK}$$
$$= [\mathbf{B} \vdots \mathbf{AB} \vdots \mathbf{A}^2\mathbf{B}] \begin{bmatrix} \alpha_2 \mathbf{K} + \alpha_1 \mathbf{K}\hat{\mathbf{A}} + \mathbf{K}\hat{\mathbf{A}}^2 \\ \alpha_1 \mathbf{K} + \mathbf{K}\hat{\mathbf{A}} \\ \mathbf{K} \end{bmatrix} \qquad (2\text{-}17)$$

Since the system is completely state controllable, the inverse of the controllability matrix

$$[\mathbf{B} \vdots \mathbf{AB} \vdots \mathbf{A}^2 \mathbf{B}]$$

exists. Premultiplying the inverse of the controllability matrix to both sides of Eq. (2-17), we obtain

$$[\mathbf{B} \vdots \mathbf{AB} \vdots \mathbf{A}^2\mathbf{B}]^{-1} \phi(\mathbf{A}) = \begin{bmatrix} \alpha_2 \mathbf{K} + \alpha_1 \mathbf{K}\hat{\mathbf{A}} + \mathbf{K}\hat{\mathbf{A}}^2 \\ \alpha_1 \mathbf{K} + \mathbf{K}\hat{\mathbf{A}} \\ \mathbf{K} \end{bmatrix}$$

Premultiplying both sides of this last equation by $[0 \quad 0 \quad 1]$, we obtain

$$[0 \quad 0 \quad 1][\mathbf{B} \vdots \mathbf{AB} \vdots \mathbf{A}^2 \mathbf{B}]^{-1}\phi(\mathbf{A}) = [0 \quad 0 \quad 1] \begin{bmatrix} \alpha_2 \mathbf{K} + \alpha_1 \mathbf{K}\hat{\mathbf{A}} + \mathbf{K}\hat{\mathbf{A}}^2 \\ \alpha_1 \mathbf{K} + \mathbf{K}\hat{\mathbf{A}} \\ \mathbf{K} \end{bmatrix} = \mathbf{K}$$

which can be rewritten as

$$\mathbf{K} = [0 \quad 0 \quad 1][\mathbf{B} \vdots \mathbf{AB} \vdots \mathbf{A}^2 \mathbf{B}]^{-1}\phi(\mathbf{A})$$

This last equation gives the required state feedback gain matrix $\mathbf{K}$.

For an arbitrary positive integer n, we have

$$\mathbf{K} = [0 \quad 0 \quad \cdots \quad 0 \quad 1][\mathbf{B} \vdots \mathbf{AB} \vdots \cdots \vdots \mathbf{A}^{n-1}\mathbf{B}]^{-1}\phi(\mathbf{A})$$

$$= [0 \quad 0 \quad \cdots \quad 0 \quad 1]\mathbf{M}^{-1}\phi(\mathbf{A}) \tag{2-18}$$

where

$$\mathbf{M} = [\mathbf{B} \vdots \mathbf{AB} \vdots \cdots \vdots \mathbf{A}^{n-1}\mathbf{B}]$$

Equation (2-18) is known as Ackermann's formula for the determination of the state feedback gain matrix $\mathbf{K}$.

EXAMPLE 2-1

A regulator system has a plant

$$\frac{Y(s)}{U(s)} = \frac{10}{(s+1)(s+2)(s+3)}$$

Define state variables as

$$x_1 = y$$
$$x_2 = \dot{x}_1$$
$$x_3 = \dot{x}_2$$

By use of the state feedback control $u = -\mathbf{Kx}$, it is desired to place the closed-loop poles at $s = \mu_i \ (i = 1, 2, 3)$, where

$$\mu_1 = -2 + j2\sqrt{3}, \qquad \mu_2 = -2 - j2\sqrt{3}, \qquad \mu_3 = -10$$

Determine the necessary state feedback gain matrix $\mathbf{K}$.

The state-space equations for the system are

$$\begin{bmatrix} \dot{x}_1 \\ \dot{x}_2 \\ \dot{x}_3 \end{bmatrix} = \begin{bmatrix} 0 & 1 & 0 \\ 0 & 0 & 1 \\ -6 & -11 & -6 \end{bmatrix} \begin{bmatrix} x_1 \\ x_2 \\ x_3 \end{bmatrix} + \begin{bmatrix} 0 \\ 0 \\ 10 \end{bmatrix} u$$

$$y = \begin{bmatrix} 1 & 0 & 0 \end{bmatrix} \begin{bmatrix} x_1 \\ x_2 \\ x_3 \end{bmatrix} + 0u$$

Hence

$$\mathbf{A} = \begin{bmatrix} 0 & 1 & 0 \\ 0 & 0 & 1 \\ -6 & -11 & -6 \end{bmatrix}, \qquad \mathbf{B} = \begin{bmatrix} 0 \\ 0 \\ 10 \end{bmatrix}$$

$$\mathbf{C} = \begin{bmatrix} 1 & 0 & 0 \end{bmatrix}, \qquad\qquad \mathbf{D} = [0]$$

Define the controllability matrix as $\mathbf{M}$.

$$\mathbf{M} = [\mathbf{B} \quad \mathbf{AB} \quad \mathbf{A}^2\mathbf{B}]$$

The first step in the design is to find the rank of matrix $\mathbf{M}$. In this case

$$\text{rank } \mathbf{M} = \begin{bmatrix} 0 & 0 & 10 \\ 0 & 10 & -60 \\ 10 & -60 & 250 \end{bmatrix} = 3$$

The next step is to find the coefficients a_1, a_2, and a_3 of the characteristic equation $|s\mathbf{I} - \mathbf{A}| = 0$. This can be done by entering the statement

$$P = \text{poly}(A)$$

into the computer. Then the coefficients will appear on the screen as follows:

```
A = [0  1  0;0  0  1;-6  -11  -6];
P = poly(A)

P =

     1.0000     6.0000     11.0000     6.0000
```

Then $a_1 = a1 = P2$, $a_2 = a2 = P3$, and $a_3 = a3 = P4$.

Define matrix $\mathbf{W}$, where

$$\mathbf{W} = \begin{bmatrix} a_2 & a_1 & 1 \\ a_1 & 1 & 0 \\ 1 & 0 & 0 \end{bmatrix} = \begin{bmatrix} 11 & 6 & 1 \\ 6 & 1 & 0 \\ 1 & 0 & 0 \end{bmatrix}$$

Then multiply $\mathbf{M}$ and $\mathbf{W}$, which can be done quite easily on the MATLAB.

$$\mathbf{T} = \mathbf{MW}$$

Now obtain the desired characteristic equation. This can be done by first defining matrix $\mathbf{J}$ such that

$$\mathbf{J} = \begin{bmatrix} \mu_1 & 0 & 0 \\ 0 & \mu_2 & 0 \\ 0 & 0 & \mu_3 \end{bmatrix} = \begin{bmatrix} -2+j2\sqrt{3} & 0 & 0 \\ 0 & -2-j2\sqrt{3} & 0 \\ 0 & 0 & -10 \end{bmatrix}$$

and then using the *poly*(J) command, as follows:

```
J = [-2+2*sqrt(3)*i  0  0;0  -2-2*sqrt(3)*i  0;0  0  -10];
Q = poly(J)

Q =

       1.0000    14.0000    56.0000    160.0000
```

Hence we have

$$\alpha_1 = aa1 = Q2, \qquad \alpha_2 = aa2 = Q3, \qquad \alpha_3 = aa3 = Q4$$

(We use aai for α_i.)

The required state feedback gain matrix $\mathbf{K}$ can be determined from

$$\mathbf{K} = [\alpha_3 - a_3 \quad \alpha_2 - a_2 \quad \alpha_1 - a_1]\mathbf{T}^{-1}$$
$$= [aa3 - a3 \quad aa2 - a2 \quad aa1 - a1]\mathbf{T}^{-1}$$

Two MATLAB programs for solving this example problem are given. MATLAB Program 2-1 utilizes the transformation matrix $\mathbf{T}$, and MATLAB Program 2-2 is based on Ackermann's formula.

```
MATLAB Program 2-1

% ---------- Pole placement ----------

% ***** Determination of state feedback gain matrix K by
% use of transformation matrix T *****

% ***** Enter matrices A and B *****

A = [0  1  0;0  0  1;-6  -11  -6];
B = [0;0;10];

% ***** Obtain the coefficients of the characteristic
% polynomial |sI - A|.  This can be done by entering
% statement poly(A) *****

JA =  poly(A)

JA =

       1.0000    6.0000    11.0000    6.0000
```

```
a1=  JA(2); a2 = JA(3); a3 = JA(4);

% ***** Define the controllability matrix M *****

M = [B  A*B  A^2*B];

% ***** Check the rank of matrix M *****

rank(M)

ans =

      3

% ***** Since the rank of M is 3, arbitrary pole
% placement is possible *****

% ***** Define matrices W and T as follows *****

W = [a2  a1  1;a1  1  0;1  0  0];
T = M*W;

% ***** Obtain the desired characteristic polynomial by
% defining the following matrix J and entering statement
% poly (J) *****

J = [-2+2*sqrt(3)*i        0        0
        0        -2-2*sqrt(3)*i        0
        0                   0      -10];

JJ = poly(J)

JJ =
    1.0000      14.0000      56.0000      160.0000

aa1 = JJ(2); aa2 = JJ(3); aa3 = JJ(4);

% ***** State feedback gain matrix can be given by *****

K = [aa3-a3  aa2-a2  aa1-a1]*(inv(T))

K =

   15.4000      4.5000      0.8000

% ***** Hence, k1, k2, and k3 are given by *****

k1 = K(1), k2 = K(2), k3 = K(3)

k1 =

    15.4000
```

```
k2 =

    4.5000


k3 =

    0.8000
```

Now we determine the state feedback gain matrix **K** by use of Ackermann's formula. This formula requires the computation of a matrix characteristic polynomial $\phi(\mathbf{A})$ given by Eq. (2-14), where for this system

$$\phi(\mathbf{A}) = \mathbf{A}^3 + \alpha_1 \mathbf{A}^2 + \alpha_2 \mathbf{A} + \alpha_3 \mathbf{I}$$

In MATLAB, polyvalm computes the matrix polynomial $\phi(\mathbf{A})$. For the given **J**, poly(J) computes the coefficients of the characteristic polynomial, as follows:

```
J =

   -2.0000 + 3.4641i          0                  0
          0           -2.0000 - 3.4641i          0
          0                  0           -10.0000

poly(J)

ans =

    1.0000    14.0000    56.0000    160.0000
```

For

$$\mathbf{A} = \begin{bmatrix} 0 & 1 & 0 \\ 0 & 0 & 1 \\ -6 & -11 & -6 \end{bmatrix}$$

the command polyvalm(poly(J),A) computes the following $\phi(\mathbf{A})$:

$$\phi(\mathbf{A}) = \mathbf{A}^3 + 14\mathbf{A}^2 + 56\mathbf{A} + 160\mathbf{I} = \begin{bmatrix} 154 & 45 & 8 \\ -48 & 66 & -3 \\ 18 & -15 & 84 \end{bmatrix}$$

In fact,

```
polyvalm(poly(J),A)

ans =

    154.0000    45.0000     8.0000
    -48.0000    66.0000    -3.0000
     18.0000   -15.0000    84.0000
```

MATLAB Program 2–2

```
% ---------- Pole placement ----------

% ***** Determination of state feedback gain matrix K by
% use of Ackermann's formula *****

% ***** Enter matrices A and B *****

A = [0  1  0;0  0  1;-6  -11  -6];
B = [0;0;10];

% ***** Define the controllability matrix M *****

M = [B  A*B  A^2*B];

% ***** Check the rank of matrix M *****

rank(M)

ans =

      3

% ***** Since the rank of M is 3, the system is
% completely state controllable.  Hence, arbitrary
% pole placement is possible *****

% ***** Obtain the desired characteristic polynomial by
% defining the following matrix J and entering statement
% poly(J) *****

J = [-2+2*sqrt(3)*i      0      0
        0     -2-2*sqrt(3)*i      0
        0                0  -10];

poly(J)

ans =

      1.0000    14.0000    56.0000    160.0000

% ***** Compute the characteristic polynomial Phi
% = polyvalm(poly(J),A) *****

Phi = polyvalm(poly(J),A);

% ***** State feedback gain matrix K can be given by *****

K = [0  0  1]*(inv(M))*Phi

K =

      15.4000     4.5000     0.8000
```

% ***** Hence, k1, k2, and k3 are given by *****

k1 = K(1), k2 = K(2), k3 = K(3)

k1 =

    15.4000

k2 =

    4.5000

k3 =

    0.8000

2-3 CASE STUDIES: DESIGN OF TYPE 1 SERVO SYSTEMS

In this section we shall give detailed discussions of a problem of designing type 1 servo systems. We shall first design a type 1 servo system in which the plant involves an integrator. Then we shall discuss the design of a type 1 servo system in which the plant has no integrator.

Type 1 servo system in which plant has an integrator

Assume that the plant is defined by

$$\dot{\mathbf{x}} = \mathbf{A}\mathbf{x} + \mathbf{B}u \tag{2-19}$$

$$y = \mathbf{C}\mathbf{x} \tag{2-20}$$

where $\mathbf{x}$ = state vector for the plant (n-vector)
  u = control signal (scalar)
  y = output signal (scalar)
  $\mathbf{A}$ = $n \times n$ constant matrix
  $\mathbf{B}$ = $n \times 1$ constant matrix
  $\mathbf{C}$ = $1 \times n$ constant matrix

We assume that both the control signal u and the output signal y are scalars. By a proper choice of a set of state variables, it is possible to choose the output to be equal to one of the state variables.

Figure 2-2 shows a general configuration of the type 1 servo system in which the plant has an integrator. Here we assume that $y = x_1$. In the present analysis we assume that the reference input r is a step function. In this system we use the following state feedback control scheme:

$$u = -[0 \quad k_2 \quad k_3 \quad \cdots \quad k_n]\begin{bmatrix} x_1 \\ x_2 \\ \vdots \\ x_n \end{bmatrix} + k_1(r - x_1) \tag{2-21}$$

$$= -\mathbf{K}\mathbf{x} + k_1 r$$

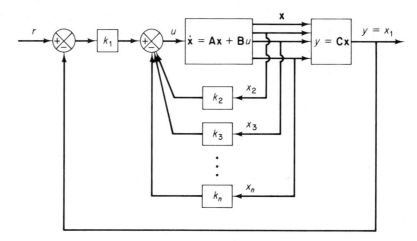

Figure 2-2

where

$$\mathbf{K} = [k_1 \quad k_2 \quad \cdots \quad k_n] \tag{2-22}$$

Assume that the reference input (step function) is applied at $t = 0$. Then, for $t > 0$, the system dynamics can be described by Eqs. (2-19) and (2-21), or

$$\dot{\mathbf{x}} = \mathbf{A}\mathbf{x} + \mathbf{B}u = (\mathbf{A} - \mathbf{B}\mathbf{K})\mathbf{x} + \mathbf{B}k_1 r \tag{2-23}$$

We shall design the type 1 servo system such that the closed-loop poles are located at desired positions. The designed system will be an asymptotically stable system, and $y(\infty)$ will approach constant value r and $u(\infty)$ will approach zero.

Notice that at steady state we have

$$\dot{\mathbf{x}}(\infty) = (\mathbf{A} - \mathbf{B}\mathbf{K})\mathbf{x}(\infty) + \mathbf{B}k_1 r(\infty) \tag{2-24}$$

Noting that $r(t)$ is a step input, we have $r(\infty) = r(t) = r$(constant) for $t > 0$. By subtracting Eq. (2-24) from Eq. (2-23), we obtain

$$\dot{\mathbf{x}}(t) - \dot{\mathbf{x}}(\infty) = (\mathbf{A} - \mathbf{B}\mathbf{K})[\mathbf{x}(t) - \mathbf{x}(\infty)] \tag{2-25}$$

Define

$$\mathbf{x}(t) - \mathbf{x}(\infty) = \mathbf{e}(t)$$

Then Eq. (2-25) becomes

$$\dot{\mathbf{e}} = (\mathbf{A} - \mathbf{B}\mathbf{K})\mathbf{e} \tag{2-26}$$

Equation (2-26) describes the error dynamics.

The design of the type 1 servo system here is converted to the design of an asymptotically stable regulator system such that $\mathbf{e}(t)$ approaches zero, given any initial condition $\mathbf{e}(0)$. If the system defined by Eq. (2-19) is completely state controllable, then, by specifying the desired eigenvalues $\mu_1, \mu_2, \ldots, \mu_n$ for the matrix $\mathbf{A} - \mathbf{B}\mathbf{K}$, matrix $\mathbf{K}$ can be determined by the pole-placement technique presented in Section 2-2.

The steady-state values of $\mathbf{x}(t)$ and $u(t)$ can be found as follows: At steady state $(t = \infty)$, we have, from Eq. (2-23),

$$\dot{\mathbf{x}}(\infty) = \mathbf{0} = (\mathbf{A} - \mathbf{BK})\mathbf{x}(\infty) + \mathbf{B}k_1 r$$

Since the desired eigenvalues of $\mathbf{A} - \mathbf{BK}$ are all in the left-half s plane, the inverse of matrix $\mathbf{A} - \mathbf{BK}$ exists. Consequently, $\mathbf{x}(\infty)$ can be determined as

$$\mathbf{x}(\infty) = -(\mathbf{A} - \mathbf{BK})^{-1}\mathbf{B}k_1 r \qquad (2\text{-}27)$$

Also, $u(\infty)$ can be obtained as

$$u(\infty) = -\mathbf{K}\mathbf{x}(\infty) + k_1 r = 0$$

(See Example 2-2 to verify this last equation.)

EXAMPLE 2-2

Consider the design of a type 1 servo system in which the plant transfer function has the integrator

$$\frac{Y(s)}{U(s)} = \frac{1}{s(s + 1)(s + 2)}$$

It is desired to design a type 1 servo system such that the closed-loop poles are at $-2 \pm j2\sqrt{3}$ and -10. Assume that the system configuration is the same as that shown in Fig. 2-2 and the reference input r is a step function.

Define state variables x_1, x_2, and x_3 as follows:

$$x_1 = y$$
$$x_2 = \dot{x}_1$$
$$x_3 = \dot{x}_2$$

Then the state-space representation of the system becomes

$$\dot{\mathbf{x}} = \mathbf{A}\mathbf{x} + \mathbf{B}u \qquad (2\text{-}28)$$
$$y = \mathbf{C}\mathbf{x} \qquad (2\text{-}29)$$

where

$$\mathbf{A} = \begin{bmatrix} 0 & 1 & 0 \\ 0 & 0 & 1 \\ 0 & -2 & -3 \end{bmatrix}, \quad \mathbf{B} = \begin{bmatrix} 0 \\ 0 \\ 1 \end{bmatrix}, \quad \mathbf{C} = \begin{bmatrix} 1 & 0 & 0 \end{bmatrix}$$

Referring to Fig. 2-2 and noting that $n = 3$, the control signal u is given by

$$u = -(k_2 x_2 + k_3 x_3) + k_1(r - x_1) = -\mathbf{K}\mathbf{x} + k_1 r \qquad (2\text{-}30)$$

where

$$\mathbf{K} = \begin{bmatrix} k_1 & k_2 & k_3 \end{bmatrix}$$

Our problem here is to determine the state feedback gain matrix $\mathbf{K}$ by the pole-placement approach.

Let us examine the controllability matrix for the system. The rank of

$$\mathbf{M} = [\mathbf{B} \vdots \mathbf{AB} \vdots \mathbf{A}^2\mathbf{B}] = \begin{bmatrix} 0 & 0 & 1 \\ 0 & 1 & -3 \\ 1 & -3 & 7 \end{bmatrix}$$

is 3. Hence the plant is completely state controllable. The characteristic equation for the system is

$$\begin{aligned} |s\mathbf{I} - \mathbf{A}| &= \begin{vmatrix} s & -1 & 0 \\ 0 & s & -1 \\ 0 & 2 & s+3 \end{vmatrix} \\ &= s^3 + 3s^2 + 2s \\ &= s^3 + a_1 s^2 + a_2 s + a_3 = 0 \end{aligned}$$

Hence

$$a_1 = 3, \qquad a_2 = 2, \qquad a_3 = 0$$

Since the desired eigenvalues of $\mathbf{A} - \mathbf{BK}$ are

$$\mu_1 = -2 + j2\sqrt{3}, \qquad \mu_2 = -2 - j2\sqrt{3}, \qquad \mu_3 = -10$$

we have the desired characteristic equation as follows:

$$\begin{aligned} (s - \mu_1)(s - \mu_2)(s - \mu_3) &= (s + 2 - j2\sqrt{3})(s + 2 + j2\sqrt{3})(s + 10) \\ &= s^3 + 14s^2 + 56s + 160 \\ &= s^3 + \alpha_1 s^2 + \alpha_2 s + \alpha_3 = 0 \end{aligned}$$

Hence

$$\alpha_1 = 14, \qquad \alpha_2 = 56, \qquad \alpha_3 = 160$$

For the determination of the matrix $\mathbf{K}$ by the pole-placement approach, we may use Eq. (2-13), rewritten as

$$\mathbf{K} = [\alpha_3 - a_3 \vdots \alpha_2 - a_2 \vdots \alpha_1 - a_1]\mathbf{T}^{-1} \tag{2-31}$$

Since the state equation for the system, Eq. (2-28), is already in the controllable canonical form, we have $\mathbf{T} = \mathbf{I}$.

Then the state feedback gain matrix $\mathbf{K}$ is given by

$$\begin{aligned} \mathbf{K} &= [\alpha_3 - a_3 \vdots \alpha_2 - a_2 \vdots \alpha_1 - a_1]\mathbf{T}^{-1} \\ &= [160 - 0 \vdots 56 - 2 \vdots 14 - 3]\mathbf{I} \\ &= [160 \quad 54 \quad 11] \end{aligned}$$

If we use Ackermann's formula, we may refer to Eq. (2-18). Since we have

$$\mathbf{M}^{-1} = \begin{bmatrix} 0 & 0 & 1 \\ 0 & 1 & -3 \\ 1 & -3 & 7 \end{bmatrix}^{-1} = \begin{bmatrix} 2 & 3 & 1 \\ 3 & 1 & 0 \\ 1 & 0 & 0 \end{bmatrix}$$

and

$$\phi(\mathbf{A}) = \mathbf{A}^3 + 14\mathbf{A}^2 + 56\mathbf{A} + 160\mathbf{I} = \begin{bmatrix} 160 & 54 & 11 \\ 0 & 138 & 21 \\ 0 & -42 & 75 \end{bmatrix}$$

we obtain

$$\mathbf{K} = \begin{bmatrix} 0 & 0 & 1 \end{bmatrix}\mathbf{M}^{-1}\phi(\mathbf{A}) = \begin{bmatrix} 160 & 54 & 11 \end{bmatrix}$$

Now we shall design the type 1 servo system discussed in Example 2-2 using MATLAB Program 2-3. Here we use Ackermann's formula for pole placement.

MATLAB Program 2–3

```
% ---------- Design of a type 1 servo system ----------

% ***** In this program we use Ackermann's formula for
% pole placement *****

% ***** Enter state matrix A, control matrix B, output
% matrix C, and direct transmission matrix D *****

A = [0  1  0;0  0  1;0  -2  -3];
B = [0;0;1];
C = [1  0  0];
D = [0];

% ***** Define the controllability matrix M *****

M = [B  A*B  A^2*B];

% ***** Check the rank of matrix M *****

rank(M)

ans =

        3

% ***** Since the rank of M is 3, the system is
% completely state controllable.  Hence, arbitrary
% pole placement is possible *****

% ***** Obtain the desired characteristic polynomial by
% defining the following matrix J and entering statement
% poly(J) *****

J = [-2+2*sqrt(3)*i        0        0
        0         -2-2*sqrt(3)*i     0
        0                  0       -10];

poly(J)
```

```
ans =

    1.0000    14.0000    56.0000    160.0000

% ***** Compute the characteristic polynomial Phi
% = polyvalm(poly(J),A) *****

Phi = polyvalm(poly(J),A);

% ***** Based on Ackermann's formula for pole placement,
% state feedback gain matrix K can be given by *****

K = [0  0  1]*(inv(M))*Phi

K =

    160.0000    54.0000    11.0000

k1 = K(1), k2 = K(2), k3 = K(3)

k1 =

    160.0000


k2 =

    54


k3 =

    11
```

Step-response characteristics of the designed system. Next we shall investigate the step-response characteristics of the designed system. Since

$$\mathbf{A} - \mathbf{BK} = \begin{bmatrix} 0 & 1 & 0 \\ 0 & 0 & 1 \\ 0 & -2 & -3 \end{bmatrix} - \begin{bmatrix} 0 \\ 0 \\ 1 \end{bmatrix} [160 \quad 54 \quad 11] = \begin{bmatrix} 0 & 1 & 0 \\ 0 & 0 & 1 \\ -160 & -56 & -14 \end{bmatrix}$$

the state equation for the designed system is

$$\begin{bmatrix} \dot{x}_1 \\ \dot{x}_2 \\ \dot{x}_3 \end{bmatrix} = \begin{bmatrix} 0 & 1 & 0 \\ 0 & 0 & 1 \\ -160 & -56 & -14 \end{bmatrix} \begin{bmatrix} x_1 \\ x_2 \\ x_3 \end{bmatrix} + \begin{bmatrix} 0 \\ 0 \\ 160 \end{bmatrix} r$$

and the output equation is

$$y = [1 \quad 0 \quad 0] \begin{bmatrix} x_1 \\ x_2 \\ x_3 \end{bmatrix}$$

Since

$$(\mathbf{A} - \mathbf{BK})^{-1} = \begin{bmatrix} 0 & 1 & 0 \\ 0 & 0 & 1 \\ -160 & -56 & -14 \end{bmatrix}^{-1} = \begin{bmatrix} -\dfrac{7}{20} & -\dfrac{7}{80} & -\dfrac{1}{160} \\ 1 & 0 & 0 \\ 0 & 1 & 0 \end{bmatrix}$$

referring to Eq. (2-27) we have

$$\mathbf{x}(\infty) = -(\mathbf{A} - \mathbf{BK})^{-1}\mathbf{B}k_1 r = -\begin{bmatrix} -\dfrac{7}{20} & -\dfrac{7}{80} & -\dfrac{1}{160} \\ 1 & 0 & 0 \\ 0 & 1 & 0 \end{bmatrix} \begin{bmatrix} 0 \\ 0 \\ 1 \end{bmatrix}(160)r$$

$$= \begin{bmatrix} \dfrac{1}{160} \\ 0 \\ 0 \end{bmatrix}(160)r = \begin{bmatrix} 1 \\ 0 \\ 0 \end{bmatrix}r = \begin{bmatrix} r \\ 0 \\ 0 \end{bmatrix}$$

Clearly, $x_1(\infty) = y(\infty) = r$. There is no steady-state error in the step response.
Note that since

$$u(\infty) = -\mathbf{Kx}(\infty) + k_1 r(\infty) = -\mathbf{Kx}(\infty) + k_1 r$$

we have

$$u(\infty) = -[160 \quad 54 \quad 11] \begin{bmatrix} x_1(\infty) \\ x_2(\infty) \\ x_3(\infty) \end{bmatrix} + 160r$$

$$= -[160 \quad 54 \quad 11] \begin{bmatrix} r \\ 0 \\ 0 \end{bmatrix} + 160r$$

$$= -160r + 160r = 0$$

At steady state the control signal u becomes zero.

MATLAB Program 2-4 may be used for obtaining the unit-step response of the designed system.

Figure 2-3 shows the unit-step response curve y versus t (where $y = x1$). The output y approaches unity. Figure 2-4 shows a plot of curves $x1$, $x2$, and $x3$ versus t on one diagram. Figure 2-5 shows the curve $x2$ versus t. ($x2$ is the output velocity $\dot{y}$.) Figure 2-6 gives a plot of $x3$ versus t. ($x3$ corresponds to the acceleration $\ddot{y}$.)

MATLAB Program 2–4

```
% ---------- Unit-step response ----------

% ***** Finding the unit-step response of the designed system *****

% ***** The state feedback gain matrix K was obtained in MATLAB
% Program 2-3. (Matrices A, B, C, and D are given in MATLAB
% Program 2-3)*****

% ***** The state equation for the designed state feedback system
% is xdot = Ax + B(-Kx + k1r) = (A - BK)x + Bk1r *****

A - B*K

ans =

          0     1.0000          0
          0          0     1.0000
  -160.0000   -56.0000   -14.0000

B*k1

ans =

          0
          0
   160.0000

% ***** Define AA = A - BK, BB = Bk1, CC = C, and DD = D *****

AA = A - B*K;
BB = B*k1;
CC = C;
DD = D;

% ***** To obtain the unit-step response, enter the following
% command *****

[y,x,t] = step(AA,BB,CC,DD);

% ***** To plot y(t) versus t, enter the following command *****

plot(t,y)
grid
title('Unit-Step Response of the Designed Servo System')
xlabel('Sec')
ylabel('Output y')

% ***** To plot curves x1, x2, x3 versus t on one diagram
% enter the following command *****
```

```
plot(t,x)
grid
title('Step-Response Curves for x1, x2, x3')
xlabel('Sec')
ylabel('x1, x2, x3')
text(1.2,1.25,'x1')
text(0.45,2,'x2')
text(0.25,6,'x3')

% ***** To plot curve x2 versus t, enter the following
% command *****

x2 = [0   1   0]*x'; plot(t,x2)
grid
title('Response x2 versus t')
xlabel('Sec')
ylabel('x2')

% ***** To plot curve x3 versus t, enter the following
% command *****

x3 = [0   0   1]*x'; plot(t,x3)
grid
title('Response x3 versus t')
xlabel('Sec')
ylabel('x3')
```

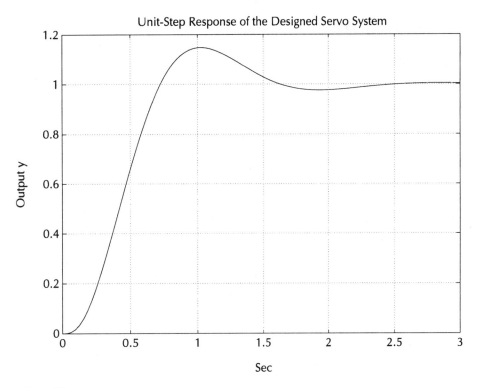

Figure 2-3

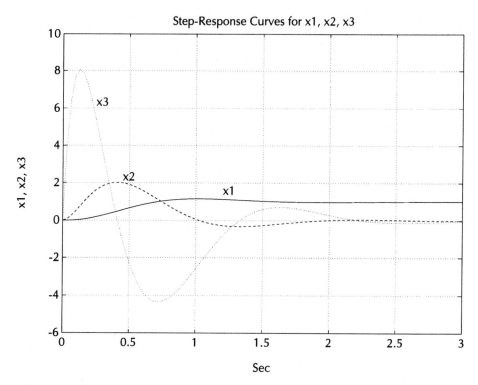

Figure 2-4

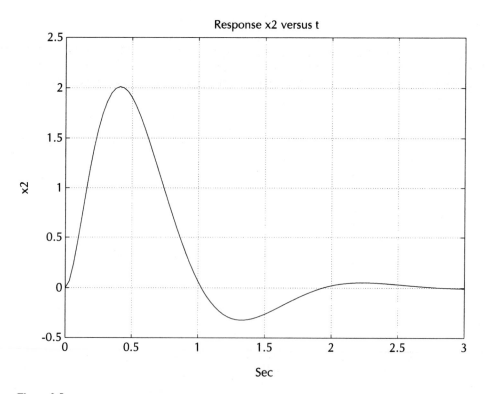

Figure 2-5

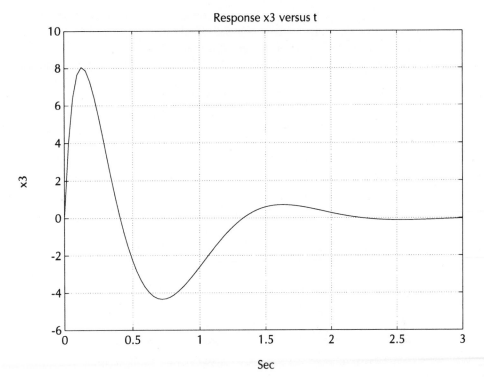

Figure 2-6

Type 1 servo system in which plant has no integrator

Since the plant has no integrator (type 0 plant), the basic principle of the design of a type 1 servo system is to insert an integrator in the feedforward path between the error comparator and the plant as shown in Figure 2-7. (The block diagram of Figure 2-7 is a basic form of the type 1 servo system in which the plant has no integrator.) From the diagram we obtain

$$\dot{\mathbf{x}} = \mathbf{Ax} + \mathbf{B}u \tag{2-32}$$

$$y = \mathbf{Cx} \tag{2-33}$$

$$u = -\mathbf{Kx} + k_I\xi \tag{2-34}$$

$$\dot{\xi} = r - y = r - \mathbf{Cx} \tag{2-35}$$

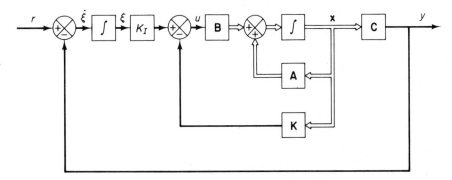

Figure 2-7

where $\mathbf{x}$ = state vector of the plant (n-vector)
  u = control signal (scalar)
  y = output signal (scalar)
  ξ = output of the integrator (state variable of the system, scalar)
  r = reference input signal (step function, scalar)
  $\mathbf{A}$ = $n \times n$ constant matrix
  $\mathbf{B}$ = $n \times 1$ constant matrix
  $\mathbf{C}$ = $1 \times n$ constant matrix

We assume that the plant given by Eq. (2-32) is completely state controllable. The transfer function of the plant can be given by

$$G_p(s) = \mathbf{C}(s\mathbf{I} - \mathbf{A})^{-1}\mathbf{B}$$

We assume that there is no cancellation of the inserted integrator by the plant zero(s).

Assume that the reference input (step function) is applied at $t = 0$. Then, for $t > 0$, the system dynamics can be described by an equation that is a combination of Eqs. (2-32) and (2-35):

$$\begin{bmatrix} \dot{\mathbf{x}}(t) \\ \dot{\xi}(t) \end{bmatrix} = \begin{bmatrix} \mathbf{A} & \mathbf{0} \\ -\mathbf{C} & 0 \end{bmatrix}\begin{bmatrix} \mathbf{x}(t) \\ \xi(t) \end{bmatrix} + \begin{bmatrix} \mathbf{B} \\ 0 \end{bmatrix}u(t) + \begin{bmatrix} \mathbf{0} \\ 1 \end{bmatrix}r(t) \qquad (2\text{-}36)$$

We shall design an asymptotically stable system such that $\mathbf{x}(\infty)$, $\xi(\infty)$, and $u(\infty)$ approach constant values, respectively. Then, at steady state $\dot{\xi}(\infty) = 0$, and we get $y(\infty) = r$.

Notice that at steady state we have

$$\begin{bmatrix} \dot{\mathbf{x}}(\infty) \\ \dot{\xi}(\infty) \end{bmatrix} = \begin{bmatrix} \mathbf{A} & \mathbf{0} \\ -\mathbf{C} & 0 \end{bmatrix}\begin{bmatrix} \mathbf{x}(\infty) \\ \xi(\infty) \end{bmatrix} + \begin{bmatrix} \mathbf{B} \\ 0 \end{bmatrix}u(\infty) + \begin{bmatrix} \mathbf{0} \\ 1 \end{bmatrix}r(\infty) \qquad (2\text{-}37)$$

Noting that $r(t)$ is a step input, we have $r(\infty) = r(t) = r$(constant) for $t > 0$. By subtracting Eq. (2-37) from Eq. (2-36), we obtain

$$\begin{bmatrix} \dot{\mathbf{x}}(t) - \dot{\mathbf{x}}(\infty) \\ \dot{\xi}(t) - \dot{\xi}(\infty) \end{bmatrix} = \begin{bmatrix} \mathbf{A} & \mathbf{0} \\ -\mathbf{C} & 0 \end{bmatrix}\begin{bmatrix} \mathbf{x}(t) - \mathbf{x}(\infty) \\ \xi(t) - \xi(\infty) \end{bmatrix} + \begin{bmatrix} \mathbf{B} \\ 0 \end{bmatrix}[u(t) - u(\infty)] \qquad (2\text{-}38)$$

Define

$$\mathbf{x}_e(t) = \mathbf{x}(t) - \mathbf{x}(\infty)$$

$$\xi_e(t) = \xi(t) - \xi(\infty)$$

$$u_e(t) = u(t) - u(\infty)$$

Then Eq. (2-38) can be written as

$$\begin{bmatrix} \dot{\mathbf{x}}_e(t) \\ \dot{\xi}_e(t) \end{bmatrix} = \begin{bmatrix} \mathbf{A} & \mathbf{0} \\ -\mathbf{C} & 0 \end{bmatrix}\begin{bmatrix} \mathbf{x}_e(t) \\ \xi_e(t) \end{bmatrix} + \begin{bmatrix} \mathbf{B} \\ 0 \end{bmatrix}u_e(t) \qquad (2\text{-}39)$$

where

$$u_e(t) = -\mathbf{K}\mathbf{x}_e(t) + K_I \xi_e(t) \qquad (2\text{-}40)$$

Define a new $(n + 1)$th-order error vector $\mathbf{e}(t)$ by

$$\mathbf{e}(t) = \begin{bmatrix} \mathbf{x}_e(t) \\ \xi_e(t) \end{bmatrix} = (n + 1)\text{-vector}$$

Then Eq. (2-39) becomes

$$\dot{\mathbf{e}} = \hat{\mathbf{A}}\mathbf{e} + \hat{\mathbf{B}}u_e \tag{2-41}$$

where

$$\hat{\mathbf{A}} = \begin{bmatrix} \mathbf{A} & \mathbf{0} \\ -\mathbf{C} & 0 \end{bmatrix}, \qquad \hat{\mathbf{B}} = \begin{bmatrix} \mathbf{B} \\ 0 \end{bmatrix}$$

and Eq. (2-40) becomes

$$u_e = -\hat{\mathbf{K}}\mathbf{e} \tag{2-42}$$

where

$$\hat{\mathbf{K}} = [\mathbf{K} \mathbin{\vdots} -K_I]$$

The basic idea in designing the type 1 servo system here is to design a stable $(n + 1)$th-order regulator system that will bring the new error vector $\mathbf{e}(t)$ to zero, given any initial condition $\mathbf{e}(0)$.

Equations (2-41) and (2-42) describe the dynamics of the $(n + 1)$th-order regulator system. If the system defined by Eq. (2-41) is completely state controllable, then, by specifying the desired characteristic equation for the system, matrix $\hat{\mathbf{K}}$ can be determined by the pole-placement technique presented in Section 2-2.

The steady-state values of $\mathbf{x}(t)$, $\xi(t)$, and $u(t)$ can be found as follows: At steady state $(t = \infty)$, from Eqs. (2-32) and (2-35), we have

$$\dot{\mathbf{x}}(\infty) = \mathbf{0} = \mathbf{A}\mathbf{x}(\infty) + \mathbf{B}u(\infty)$$

$$\dot{\xi}(\infty) = 0 = r - \mathbf{C}\mathbf{x}(\infty)$$

which can be combined into one vector–matrix equation:

$$\begin{bmatrix} \mathbf{0} \\ 0 \end{bmatrix} = \begin{bmatrix} \mathbf{A} & \mathbf{B} \\ -\mathbf{C} & 0 \end{bmatrix} \begin{bmatrix} \mathbf{x}(\infty) \\ u(\infty) \end{bmatrix} + \begin{bmatrix} \mathbf{0} \\ r \end{bmatrix}$$

If matrix $\mathbf{P}$, defined by

$$\mathbf{P} = \begin{bmatrix} \mathbf{A} & \mathbf{B} \\ -\mathbf{C} & 0 \end{bmatrix} \tag{2-43}$$

is of rank $n + 1$, then its inverse exists and

$$\begin{bmatrix} \mathbf{x}(\infty) \\ u(\infty) \end{bmatrix} = \begin{bmatrix} \mathbf{A} & \mathbf{B} \\ -\mathbf{C} & 0 \end{bmatrix}^{-1} \begin{bmatrix} \mathbf{0} \\ -r \end{bmatrix}$$

Also, from Eq. (2-34) we have

$$u(\infty) = -\mathbf{K}\mathbf{x}(\infty) + K_I \xi(\infty)$$

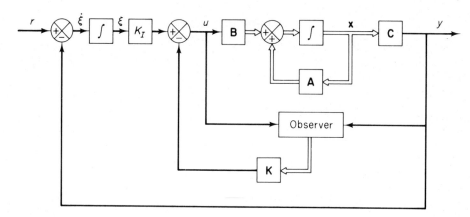

Figure 2-8

and therefore we have

$$\xi(\infty) = \frac{1}{K_I}[u(\infty) + \mathbf{K}\mathbf{x}(\infty)]$$

It is noted that, if matrix $\mathbf{P}$ given by Eq. (2-43) has rank $n + 1$, then the system defined by Eq. (2-41) becomes completely state controllable. Therefore, if the rank of matrix $\mathbf{P}$ is $n + 1$, the solution to this problem can be obtained by the pole-placement approach.

The state error equation can be obtained by substituting Eq. (2-42) into Eq. (2-41).

$$\dot{\mathbf{e}} = (\hat{\mathbf{A}} - \hat{\mathbf{B}}\hat{\mathbf{K}})\mathbf{e} \qquad (2\text{-}44)$$

If the desired eigenvalues of matrix $\hat{\mathbf{A}} - \hat{\mathbf{B}}\hat{\mathbf{K}}$ (that is, the desired closed-loop poles) are specified as $\mu_1, \mu_2, \ldots, \mu_{n+1}$, then the state feedback gain matrix $\mathbf{K}$ and the integral gain constant K_I can be determined. In the actual design, it is necessary to consider several different matrices $\hat{\mathbf{K}}$ (which correspond to several different sets of desired eigenvalues) and carry out computer simulations to find the one that yields the best overall system performance. Then choose the best one as the matrix $\hat{\mathbf{K}}$.

As is usually the case, not all state variables can be directly measurable. If this is the case, we need to use a state observer. Figure 2-8 shows a block diagram of a type 1 servo system with a state observer.

EXAMPLE 2-3

In this example we shall consider the design of an inverted pendulum control system. We shall first derive a mathematical model of the inverted pendulum system. Then we shall design a controller to keep the pendulum upright at steady state after transient periods (due to input or disturbance) are over.

Consider the inverted pendulum mounted on a motor-driven cart as shown in Figure 2-9. This is a model of the attitude control of a space booster on takeoff. (The objective of the attitude control problem is to keep the space booster in a vertical position.) The inverted pendulum is unstable in that it may fall over any time in any direction unless a suitable control force is applied. Here we consider only a two-dimensional problem in which the pendulum moves only in the plane of the page. Assume that the pendulum mass is concentrated at the end of the rod, as shown in the figure. (The rod is massless.) The control force u is applied to the cart.

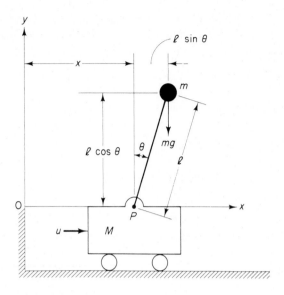

Figure 2-9

Define the angle of the rod from the vertical line as θ. (Since we want to keep the inverted pendulum vertical, angle θ is assumed to be small.) Define also the (x, y) coordinates of the center of gravity of the mass as (x_G, y_G). Then

$$x_G = x + l \sin\theta$$

$$y_G = l \cos\theta$$

Applying Newton's second law to the x direction of motion yields

$$M\frac{d^2 x}{dt^2} + m\frac{d^2 x_G}{dt^2} = u$$

or

$$M\frac{d^2 x}{dt^2} + m\frac{d^2}{dt^2}(x + l \sin\theta) = u \tag{2-45}$$

Noting that

$$\frac{d}{dt} \sin\theta = (\cos\theta)\dot\theta$$

$$\frac{d^2}{dt^2} \sin\theta = -(\sin\theta)\dot\theta^2 + (\cos\theta)\ddot\theta$$

$$\frac{d}{dt} \cos\theta = -(\sin\theta)\dot\theta$$

$$\frac{d^2}{dt^2} \cos\theta = -(\cos\theta)\dot\theta^2 - (\sin\theta)\ddot\theta$$

Equation (2-45) can be written as

$$(M + m)\ddot x - ml(\sin\theta)\dot\theta^2 + ml(\cos\theta)\ddot\theta = u \tag{2-46}$$

The equation of motion of the mass m in the y direction cannot be written without considering the motion of the mass m in the x direction. Therefore, instead of considering the motion of the mass m in the y direction, we consider the rotational motion of the mass m around point P. Applying Newton's second law to the rotational motion, we obtain

$$m \frac{d^2 x_G}{dt^2} l \cos \theta - m \frac{d^2 y_G}{dt^2} l \sin \theta = mgl \sin \theta$$

or

$$\left[m \frac{d^2}{dt^2}(x + l \sin \theta) \right] l \cos \theta - \left[m \frac{d^2}{dt^2}(l \cos \theta) \right] l \sin \theta = mgl \sin \theta$$

which can be simplified as follows:

$$m[\ddot{x} - l(\sin \theta)\dot{\theta}^2 + l(\cos \theta) \ddot{\theta}]l \cos \theta - m[-l(\cos \theta)\dot{\theta}^2 - l(\sin \theta) \ddot{\theta}]l \sin \theta = mgl \sin \theta$$

Further simplification results in

$$m\ddot{x} \cos \theta + ml \ddot{\theta} = mg \sin \theta \qquad (2\text{-}47)$$

Clearly, Eqs. (2-46) and (2-47) are nonlinear differential equations. Since we must keep the inverted pendulum vertical, we can assume that $\theta(t)$ and $\dot{\theta}(t)$ are small quantities such that $\sin \theta \doteq \theta$, $\cos \theta \doteq 1$, and $\theta\dot{\theta}^2 \doteq 0$. Then Eqs. (2-46) and (2-47) can be linearized as follows:

$$(M + m)\ddot{x} + ml \ddot{\theta} = u \qquad (2\text{-}48)$$

$$m\ddot{x} + ml \ddot{\theta} = mg\theta \qquad (2\text{-}49)$$

These linearized equations are valid as long as θ and $\dot{\theta}$ are small. Equations (2-48) and (2-49) define a mathematical model of the inverted pendulum system.

The linearized system equations, Eqs. (2-48) and (2-49), can be modified to

$$Ml \ddot{\theta} = (M + m)g\theta - u \qquad (2\text{-}50)$$

$$M\ddot{x} = u - mg\theta \qquad (2\text{-}51)$$

Equation (2-50) was obtained by eliminating $\ddot{x}$ from Eqs. (2-48) and (2-49). Equation (2-51) was obtained by eliminating $\ddot{\theta}$ from Eqs. (2-48) and (2-49). Define state variables x_1, x_2, x_3, and x_4 by

$$x_1 = \theta$$
$$x_2 = \dot{\theta}$$
$$x_3 = x$$
$$x_4 = \dot{x}$$

Note that angle θ indicates the rotation of the pendulum rod about point P, and x is the location of the cart. We consider x as the output of the system, or

$$y = x = x_3$$

Then, from the definition of the state variables and Eqs. (2-50) and (2-51), we obtain

$$\dot{x}_1 = x_2$$

$$\dot{x}_2 = \frac{M + m}{Ml} g x_1 - \frac{1}{Ml} u$$

$$\dot{x}_3 = x_4$$

$$\dot{x}_4 = -\frac{m}{M} g x_1 + \frac{1}{M} u$$

In terms of vector–matrix equations, we have

$$
\begin{bmatrix} \dot{x}_1 \\ \dot{x}_2 \\ \dot{x}_3 \\ \dot{x}_4 \end{bmatrix} = \begin{bmatrix} 0 & 1 & 0 & 0 \\ \dfrac{M+m}{Ml}g & 0 & 0 & 0 \\ 0 & 0 & 0 & 1 \\ -\dfrac{m}{M}g & 0 & 0 & 0 \end{bmatrix} \begin{bmatrix} x_1 \\ x_2 \\ x_3 \\ x_4 \end{bmatrix} + \begin{bmatrix} 0 \\ -\dfrac{1}{Ml} \\ 0 \\ \dfrac{1}{M} \end{bmatrix} u \tag{2-52}
$$

$$
y = \begin{bmatrix} 0 & 0 & 1 & 0 \end{bmatrix} \begin{bmatrix} x_1 \\ x_2 \\ x_3 \\ x_4 \end{bmatrix} \tag{2-53}
$$

Equations (2-52) and (2-53) give a state-space representation of the inverted pendulum system. (Note that the state-space representation of the system is not unique. There are infinitely many such representations.)

It is desired to keep the inverted pendulum upright as much as possible and yet control the position of the cart, for instance, by moving the cart in a step fashion. To control the position of the cart, we need to build a type 1 servo system. The inverted-pendulum system mounted on a cart does not have an integrator. Therefore, we feed the position signal y (which indicates the position of the cart) back to the input and insert an integrator in the feedforward path, as shown in Figure 2-10.

In this example, we assume the following numerical values for M, m, and l:

$$
M = 2 \text{ kg}, \qquad m = 0.1 \text{ kg}, \qquad l = 0.5 \text{ m}
$$

By substituting these values, we obtain

$$
\frac{M+m}{Ml}g = 20.601, \qquad \frac{m}{M}g = 0.4905, \qquad \frac{1}{Ml} = 1, \qquad \frac{1}{M} = 0.5
$$

Then Eqs. (2-52) and (2-53) can be written as

$$
\dot{\mathbf{x}} = \mathbf{A}\mathbf{x} + \mathbf{B}u
$$

$$
y = \mathbf{C}\mathbf{x} + Du
$$

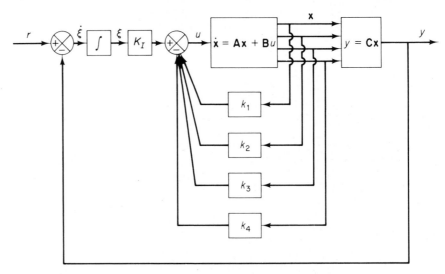

Figure 2-10

where

$$\mathbf{A} = \begin{bmatrix} 0 & 1 & 0 & 0 \\ 20.601 & 0 & 0 & 0 \\ 0 & 0 & 0 & 1 \\ -0.4905 & 0 & 0 & 0 \end{bmatrix}, \quad \mathbf{B} = \begin{bmatrix} 0 \\ -1 \\ 0 \\ 0.5 \end{bmatrix}, \quad \mathbf{C} = [0 \;\; 0 \;\; 1 \;\; 0], \quad D = 0$$

Then, referring to Fig. 2-10, the equations for the inverted pendulum control system are

$$\dot{\mathbf{x}} = \mathbf{A}\mathbf{x} + \mathbf{B}u \tag{2-54}$$

$$y = \mathbf{C}\mathbf{x} \tag{2-55}$$

$$u = -\mathbf{K}\mathbf{x} + K_I \xi \tag{2-56}$$

$$\dot{\xi} = r - y = r - \mathbf{C}\mathbf{x} \tag{2-57}$$

For the type 1 servo system, we have the state error equation as given by Eq. (2-41):

$$\dot{\mathbf{e}} = \hat{\mathbf{A}}\mathbf{e} + \hat{\mathbf{B}}u_e \tag{2-58}$$

where

$$\hat{\mathbf{A}} = \begin{bmatrix} \mathbf{A} & \mathbf{0} \\ -\mathbf{C} & 0 \end{bmatrix} = \begin{bmatrix} 0 & 1 & 0 & 0 & 0 \\ 20.601 & 0 & 0 & 0 & 0 \\ 0 & 0 & 0 & 1 & 0 \\ -0.4905 & 0 & 0 & 0 & 0 \\ 0 & 0 & -1 & 0 & 0 \end{bmatrix}, \quad \hat{\mathbf{B}} = \begin{bmatrix} \mathbf{B} \\ 0 \end{bmatrix} = \begin{bmatrix} 0 \\ -1 \\ 0 \\ 0.5 \\ 0 \end{bmatrix}, \quad \mathbf{e} = \begin{bmatrix} \mathbf{x}_e \\ \xi_e \end{bmatrix}$$

and the control signal is given by Eq. (2-42):

$$u_e = -\hat{\mathbf{K}}\mathbf{e}$$

where

$$\hat{\mathbf{K}} = [\mathbf{K} \;\vdots\; -K_I] = [k_1 \quad k_2 \quad k_3 \quad k_4 \;\vdots\; -K_I]$$

We shall determine the necessary state feedback gain matrix $\hat{\mathbf{K}}$ by use of the pole-placement technique. We shall first use Eq. (2-13) to obtain the gain matrix $\mathbf{K}$. Then we shall demonstrate the use of Eq. (2-18) to obtain the same solution.

Before we proceed further, we must examine the rank of matrix $\mathbf{P}$, where

$$\mathbf{P} = \begin{bmatrix} \mathbf{A} & \mathbf{B} \\ -\mathbf{C} & 0 \end{bmatrix}$$

Matrix $\mathbf{P}$ is given by

$$\mathbf{P} = \begin{bmatrix} \mathbf{A} & \mathbf{B} \\ -\mathbf{C} & 0 \end{bmatrix} = \begin{bmatrix} 0 & 1 & 0 & 0 & 0 \\ 20.601 & 0 & 0 & 0 & -1 \\ 0 & 0 & 0 & 1 & 0 \\ -0.4905 & 0 & 0 & 0 & 0.5 \\ 0 & 0 & -1 & 0 & 0 \end{bmatrix} \tag{2-59}$$

The rank of this matrix is 5. Therefore, the system defined by Eq. (2-58) is completely state controllable and arbitrary pole placement is possible. We shall next obtain the characteristic equation for the system given by Eq. (2-58).

$$\left| s\mathbf{I} - \hat{\mathbf{A}} \right| = \begin{bmatrix} s & -1 & 0 & 0 & 0 \\ -20.601 & s & 0 & 0 & 0 \\ 0 & 0 & s & -1 & 0 \\ 0.4905 & 0 & 0 & s & 0 \\ 0 & 0 & 1 & 0 & s \end{bmatrix}$$

$$= s^3(s^2 - 20.601)$$

$$= s^5 - 20.601s^3$$

$$= s^5 + a_1 s^4 + a_2 s^3 + a_3 s^2 + a_4 s + a_5 = 0$$

Hence

$$a_1 = 0, \quad a_2 = -20.601, \quad a_3 = 0, \quad a_4 = 0, \quad a_5 = 0$$

To obtain a reasonable speed and damping in the response of the designed system (for example, a settling time of approximately 4 to 5 sec and the maximum overshoot of 15% to 16% in the step response of the cart), let us choose the desired closed-loop poles at $s = \mu_i \, (i = 1, 2, 3, 4, 5)$, where

$$\mu_1 = -1 + j\sqrt{3}, \quad \mu_2 = -1 - j\sqrt{3}, \quad \mu_3 = -5, \quad \mu_4 = -5, \quad \mu_5 = -5$$

(This is a possible set of desired closed-loop poles. Other sets can be chosen.) Then the desired characteristic equation becomes

$$(s - \mu_1)(s - \mu_2)(s - \mu_3)(s - \mu_4)(s - \mu_5)$$

$$= (s + 1 - j\sqrt{3})(s + 1 + j\sqrt{3})(s + 5)(s + 5)(s + 5)$$

$$= s^5 + 17s^4 + 109s^3 + 335s^2 + 550s + 500$$

$$= s^5 + \alpha_1 s^4 + \alpha_2 s^3 + \alpha_3 s^2 + \alpha_4 s + \alpha_5 = 0$$

Hence

$$\alpha_1 = 17, \quad \alpha_2 = 109, \quad \alpha_3 = 335, \quad \alpha_4 = 550, \quad \alpha_5 = 500$$

The next step is to obtain the transformation matrix $\mathbf{T}$ given by Eq. (2-4):

$$\mathbf{T} = \mathbf{M}\mathbf{W}$$

where $\mathbf{M}$ and $\mathbf{W}$ are given by Eqs. (2-5) and (2-6), respectively:

$$\mathbf{M} = [\hat{\mathbf{B}} \vdots \hat{\mathbf{A}}\hat{\mathbf{B}} \vdots \hat{\mathbf{A}}^2\hat{\mathbf{B}} \vdots \hat{\mathbf{A}}^3\hat{\mathbf{B}} \vdots \hat{\mathbf{A}}^4\hat{\mathbf{B}}]$$

$$= \begin{bmatrix} 0 & -1 & 0 & -20.601 & 0 \\ -1 & 0 & -20.601 & 0 & -(20.601)^2 \\ 0 & 0.5 & 0 & 0.4905 & 0 \\ 0.5 & 0 & 0.4905 & 0 & 10.1048 \\ 0 & 0 & -0.5 & 0 & -0.4905 \end{bmatrix}$$

$$\mathbf{W} = \begin{bmatrix} a_4 & a_3 & a_2 & a_1 & 1 \\ a_3 & a_2 & a_1 & 1 & 0 \\ a_2 & a_1 & 1 & 0 & 0 \\ a_1 & 1 & 0 & 0 & 0 \\ 1 & 0 & 0 & 0 & 0 \end{bmatrix} = \begin{bmatrix} 0 & 0 & -20.601 & 0 & 1 \\ 0 & -20.601 & 0 & 1 & 0 \\ -20.601 & 0 & 1 & 0 & 0 \\ 0 & 1 & 0 & 0 & 0 \\ 1 & 0 & 0 & 0 & 0 \end{bmatrix}$$

Then

$$\mathbf{T} = \mathbf{MW} = \begin{bmatrix} 0 & 0 & 0 & -1 & 0 \\ 0 & 0 & 0 & 0 & -1 \\ 0 & -9.81 & 0 & 0.5 & 0 \\ 0 & 0 & -9.81 & 0 & 0.5 \\ 9.81 & 0 & -0.5 & 0 & 0 \end{bmatrix}$$

The inverse of matrix $\mathbf{T}$ is

$$\mathbf{T}^{-1} = \begin{bmatrix} 0 & -\dfrac{0.25}{(9.81)^2} & 0 & -\dfrac{0.5}{(9.81)^2} & \dfrac{1}{9.81} \\ -\dfrac{0.5}{9.81} & 0 & -\dfrac{1}{9.81} & 0 & 0 \\ 0 & -\dfrac{0.5}{9.81} & 0 & -\dfrac{1}{9.81} & 0 \\ -1 & 0 & 0 & 0 & 0 \\ 0 & -1 & 0 & 0 & 0 \end{bmatrix}$$

Referring to Eq. (2-13), matrix $\hat{\mathbf{K}}$ is given by

$$\begin{aligned} \hat{\mathbf{K}} &= [\alpha_5 - a_5 \vdots \alpha_4 - a_4 \vdots \alpha_3 - a_3 \vdots \alpha_2 - a_2 \vdots \alpha_1 - a_1]\mathbf{T}^{-1} \\ &= [500 - 0 \vdots 550 - 0 \vdots 335 - 0 \vdots 109 + 20.601 \vdots 17 - 0]\mathbf{T}^{-1} \\ &= [500 \vdots 550 \vdots 335 \vdots 129.601 \vdots 17]\mathbf{T}^{-1} \\ &= [-157.6336 \quad -35.3733 \quad -56.0652 \quad -36.7466 \quad 50.9684] \\ &= [k_1 \quad k_2 \quad k_3 \quad k_4 \quad -K_I] \end{aligned}$$

Thus we get

$$\mathbf{K} = [k_1 \quad k_2 \quad k_3 \quad k_4] = [-157.6336 \quad -35.3733 \quad -56.0652 \quad -36.7466] \tag{2-60}$$

and

$$K_I = -50.9684 \tag{2-61}$$

Another approach to obtain $\hat{\mathbf{K}}$ is to use Ackermann's formula given by Eq. (2-18), rewritten as follows:

$$\hat{\mathbf{K}} = [0 \quad 0 \quad 0 \quad 0 \quad 1]\mathbf{M}^{-1}\phi(\hat{\mathbf{A}})$$

where

$$\mathbf{M}^{-1} = \begin{bmatrix} 0 & 0.05 & 0 & 2.10 & 0 \\ 0.05 & 0 & 2.10 & 0 & 0 \\ 0 & 0.0025 & 0 & 0.0051 & -2.1 \\ -0.051 & 0 & -0.1019 & 0 & 0 \\ 0 & -0.0026 & 0 & -0.0052 & 0.1019 \end{bmatrix}$$

and

$$\begin{aligned} \phi(\hat{\mathbf{A}}) &= \hat{\mathbf{A}}^5 + 17\hat{\mathbf{A}}^4 + 109\hat{\mathbf{A}}^3 + 335\hat{\mathbf{A}}^2 + 550\hat{\mathbf{A}} + 500\hat{\mathbf{I}} \\ &= \begin{bmatrix} 14{,}616 & 3{,}220 & 0 & 0 & 0 \\ 66{,}333 & 14{,}616 & 0 & 0 & 0 \\ -336 & -64 & 500 & 550 & 0 \\ -1{,}579 & -336 & 0 & 500 & 0 \\ 64 & 8 & -550 & -335 & 500 \end{bmatrix} \end{aligned}$$

Hence

$$\hat{\mathbf{K}} = [0 \quad 0 \quad 0 \quad 0 \quad 1]\mathbf{M}^{-1}\phi(\hat{\mathbf{A}})$$
$$= [-157.6336 \quad -35.3733 \quad -56.0652 \quad -36.7466 \quad 50.9684]$$

or

$$\mathbf{K} = [k_1 \quad k_2 \quad k_3 \quad k_4]$$
$$= [-157.6336 \quad -35.3733 \quad -56.0652 \quad -36.7466]$$
$$K_I = -50.9684$$

MATLAB Program 2-5 may be used to design the inverted pendulum control system considered. Note in the program that we use notations A1, B1, and KK for $\hat{\mathbf{A}}$, $\hat{\mathbf{B}}$, and $\hat{\mathbf{K}}$, respectively. That is,

$$A1 = \hat{\mathbf{A}} = \begin{bmatrix} \mathbf{A} & \mathbf{0} \\ -\mathbf{C} & 0 \end{bmatrix}, \qquad B1 = \hat{\mathbf{B}} = \begin{bmatrix} \mathbf{B} \\ 0 \end{bmatrix}, \qquad KK = \hat{\mathbf{K}}$$

MATLAB Program 2–5

```
% ---------- Design of an inverted pendulum control system ----------

% ***** In this program we use Ackermann's formula for
% pole placement *****

% ***** This program determines the state feedback gain matrix
% K = [k1   k2   k3   k4] and integral gain constant KI *****

% ***** Enter matrices A, B, C, and D *****

A =  [0          1  0  0
      20.601  0  0  0
      0          0  0  1
      -0.4905  0  0  0];
B =  [0;-1;0;0.5];
C =  [0  0  1  0];
D =  [0];

% ***** Enter matrices A1 and B1 *****

A1 = [A   zeros(4,1);-C   0];
B1 = [B;0];

% ***** Define the controllability matrix M *****

M = [B1   A1*B1   A1^2*B1   A1^3*B1   A1^4*B1];

% ***** Check the rank of matrix M *****

rank(M)
```

```
ans =

      5
```

% ***** Since the rank of M is 5, the system is completely
% state controllable. Hence, arbitrary pole placement is
% possible *****

% ***** Enter the desired characteristic polynomial, which
% can be obtained by defining the following matrix J and
% entering statement poly(J) *****

```
J = [-1+sqrt(3)*i    0    0    0    0
        0    -1-sqrt(3)*i    0    0    0
        0               0   -5    0    0
        0               0    0   -5    0
        0               0    0    0   -5];
JJ = poly(J)

JJ =

    1.0000    17.0000    109.0000    335.0000    550.0000    500.0000
```

% ***** Enter characteristic polynomial Phi *****

```
Phi = polyvalm(poly(J),A1);
```

% ***** State feedback gain matrix K and integral gain constant
% KI can be determined from *****

```
KK = [0   0   0   0   1]*(inv(M))*Phi

KK =

  -157.6336    -35.3733    -56.0652    -36.7466    50.9684
```

k1 = KK(1), k2 = KK(2), k3 = KK(3), k4 = KK(4), KI = -KK(5)

```
k1 =

  -157.6336


k2 =

  -35.3733


k3 =

  -56.0652
```

k4 =

   -36.7466

KI =

   -50.9684

Unit step-response characteristics of the designed system.   Once we determine the feedback gain matrix **K** and the integral gain constant K_I, the step response in the cart position can be obtained by solving the following equation:

$$\begin{bmatrix} \dot{\mathbf{x}} \\ \dot{\xi} \end{bmatrix} = \begin{bmatrix} \mathbf{A} & 0 \\ -\mathbf{C} & 0 \end{bmatrix} \begin{bmatrix} \mathbf{x} \\ \xi \end{bmatrix} + \begin{bmatrix} \mathbf{B} \\ 0 \end{bmatrix} u + \begin{bmatrix} 0 \\ 1 \end{bmatrix} r \qquad (2\text{-}62)$$

Since

$$u = -\mathbf{K}\mathbf{x} + K_I \xi$$

Equation (2-62) can be written as follows:

$$\begin{bmatrix} \dot{\mathbf{x}} \\ \dot{\xi} \end{bmatrix} = \begin{bmatrix} \mathbf{A} - \mathbf{BK} & \mathbf{B}K_I \\ -\mathbf{C} & 0 \end{bmatrix} \begin{bmatrix} \mathbf{x} \\ \xi \end{bmatrix} + \begin{bmatrix} 0 \\ 1 \end{bmatrix} r \qquad (2\text{-}63)$$

The output of the system is $x_3(t)$, or

$$y = [0 \quad 0 \quad 1 \quad 0 \quad 0] \begin{bmatrix} \mathbf{x} \\ \xi \end{bmatrix} + [0] r \qquad (2\text{-}64)$$

Define the state matrix, control matrix, output matrix, and direct transmission matrix of the system given by Eqs. (2-63) and (2-64) as AA, BB, CC, and DD, respectively. Matrices AA, BB, CC, and DD are obtained as follows:

AA = [A−B*K   B*kI;−C   0]

AA =

0	1.0000	0	0	0
−137.0326	−35.3733	−56.0652	−36.7466	50.9684
0	0	0	1.0000	0
78.3263	17.6867	28.0326	18.3733	−25.4842
0	0	−1.0000	0	0

BB = [0;0;0;0;1]

BB =

    0
    0
    0
    0
    1

```
CC = [0   0   1   0   0]

CC =

       0   0   1   0   0

DD = [0]

DD =

       0
```

MATLAB Program 2-6 may be used to obtain the step-response curves of the designed system. Notice that, to obtain the unit-step response, we entered the command

$$[y, x, t] = step(AA,BB,CC,DD)$$

```
MATLAB Program 2–6

% ---------- Step response of the designed system ----------

% ***** The following program is to obtain step response
% of the inverted pendulum system just designed *****

% ***** Enter necessary matrices *****

A = [0          1   0   0
      20.601    0   0   0
      0         0   0   1
      -0.4905   0   0   0];
B = [0;-1;0;0.5];
C = [0   0   1   0];
D = [0];
K = [-157.6336  -35.3733  -56.0652  -36.7466];
KI = -50.9684;
AA = [A-B*K   B*KI;-C   0];
BB = [0;0;0;0;1];
CC = [C   0];
DD = [0];

% ***** Enter the ranges for the x axis and y axis *****

v = [0   5   -0.4   1.4];
axis(v);

% ***** Next, enter the following command *****

[y,x,t] = step(AA,BB,CC,DD);

% ***** To obtain the output curve y versus t, enter the
% following command *****

plot(t,y)
```

```
grid
title('Output y versus Time t')
xlabel('Sec')
ylabel('Output y = x3')

% ***** To obtain response curves x1, x2, x3, x4, x5 versus t
% on one diagram, enter the following command *****

plot(t,x,'-g')
grid
title('Response Curves x1, x2, x3, x4, x5 versus Time t')
xlabel('Sec')
ylabel('x1, x2, x3, x4, x5')
text(1.2,0.02,'x1')
text(1.2,-0.38,'x2')
text(1.2,0.3,'x3')
text(2.2,0.25,'x4')
text(1.5,1.25,'x5')

% ***** To obtain x1 versus t, enter the following command *****

x1 = [1  0  0  0  0]*x';
plot(t,x1)
grid
title('Response x1 versus t')
xlabel('Sec')
ylabel('x1')

% ***** To obtain x2 versus t, enter the following command *****

x2 = [0  1  0  0  0]*x';
plot(t,x2)
grid
title('Response x2 versus t')
xlabel('Sec')
ylabel('x2')

% ***** To obtain x4 versus t, enter the following command *****

x4 = [0  0  0  1  0]*x';
plot(t,x4)
grid
title('Response x4 versus t')
xlabel('Sec')
ylabel('x4')

% ***** To obtain x5 versus t, enter the following command *****

x5 = [0  0  0  0  1]*x';
plot(t,x5)
grid
title('Response x5 versus t')
xlabel('Sec')
ylabel('x5')
```

It is important to note that if we do not specify the x–y region (the range of the x axis and y axis) and enter the command

$$\text{plot(y)}$$

then the computer will generate the plot shown in Figure 2-11. The abscissa is not time but computation points (152 points = 5 sec). To plot a curve $y(t)$ versus t, we need to enter the command

$$\text{plot(t,y)}$$

In MATLAB Program 2-6, the x–y region is specified as

$$v = [0 \quad 5 \quad -0.4 \quad 1.4]; \text{ axis(v)}$$

The output curve y versus t is obtained by entering the command plot(t,y). See Figure 2-12. Note that $y = x3 = x$.

The output y shows the settling time of approximately 4.5 sec and the maximum overshoot of approximately 14.8%. An interesting point in the position curve is that the cart moves backward for the first 0.6 sec or so to make the pendulum fall forward. Then the cart accelerates to move in the positive direction.

To plot curves $x_1(t)$, $x_2(t)$, $x_3(t)$, $x_4(t)$, and $\xi(t)$ versus t on one diagram, enter the following command:

$$\text{plot(t, x)}$$

The resulting plot is shown in Figure 2-13.

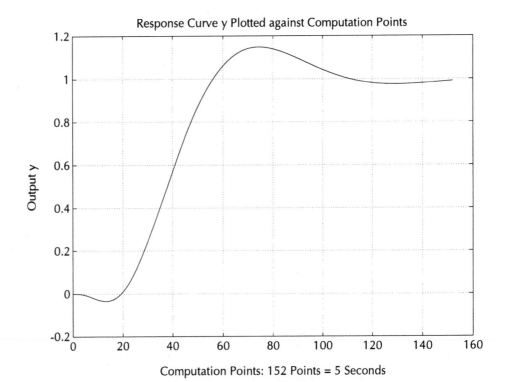

Figure 2-11

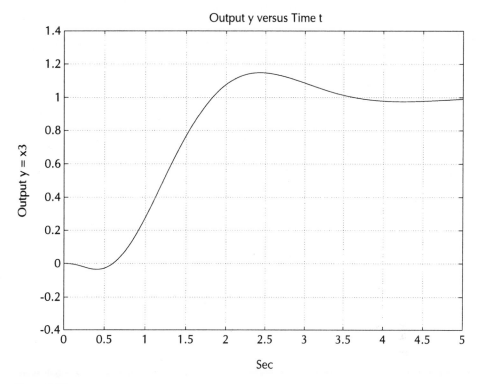

Figure 2-12

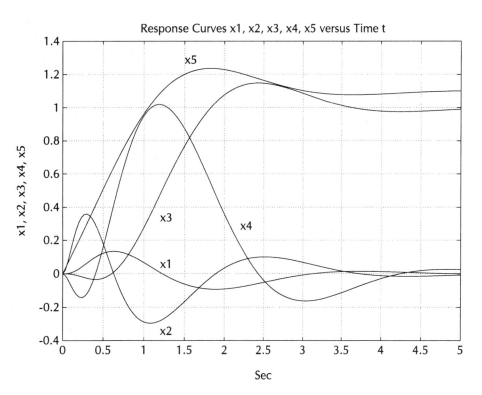

Figure 2-13

Figures 2-14, 2-15, 2-16, and 2-17 show curves $x1$ versus t, $x2$ versus t, $x4$ versus t, and $x5$ versus t, respectively. The response curve $x3\,(\,=y)$ versus t shows that $x3(\infty)$ approaches r. Also, $x1(\infty)=0$, $x2(\infty)=0$, $x4(\infty)=0$, and $\xi(\infty)=x5(\infty)=1.1$. This result can be verified by the analytical approach given next.

At steady state we have

$$\dot{\mathbf{x}}(\infty)=\mathbf{0}=\mathbf{A}\mathbf{x}(\infty)+\mathbf{B}u(\infty)$$

$$\dot{\xi}(\infty)=0=r-\mathbf{C}\mathbf{x}(\infty)$$

which can be combined into

$$\begin{bmatrix}\mathbf{0}\\0\end{bmatrix}=\begin{bmatrix}\mathbf{A}&\mathbf{B}\\-\mathbf{C}&0\end{bmatrix}\begin{bmatrix}\mathbf{x}(\infty)\\u(\infty)\end{bmatrix}+\begin{bmatrix}0\\r\end{bmatrix}$$

Since we earlier found that the rank of matrix

$$\begin{bmatrix}\mathbf{A}&\mathbf{B}\\-\mathbf{C}&0\end{bmatrix}$$

is 5, it has the inverse. Hence

$$\begin{bmatrix}\mathbf{x}(\infty)\\u(\infty)\end{bmatrix}=\begin{bmatrix}\mathbf{A}&\mathbf{B}\\-\mathbf{C}&0\end{bmatrix}^{-1}\begin{bmatrix}0\\-r\end{bmatrix}$$

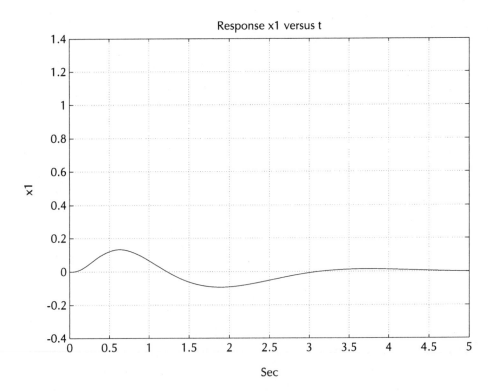

Figure 2-14

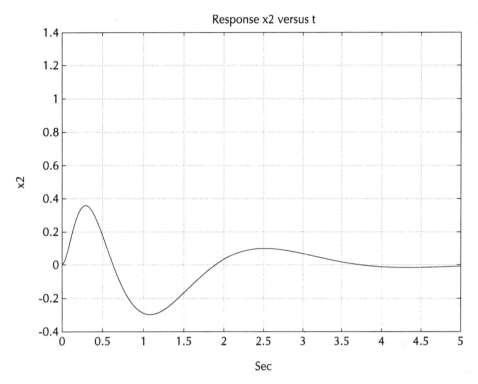

Figure 2-15

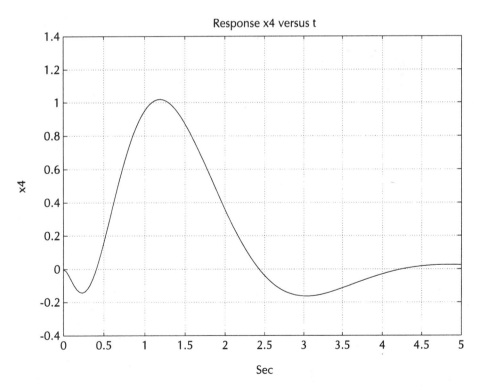

Figure 2-16

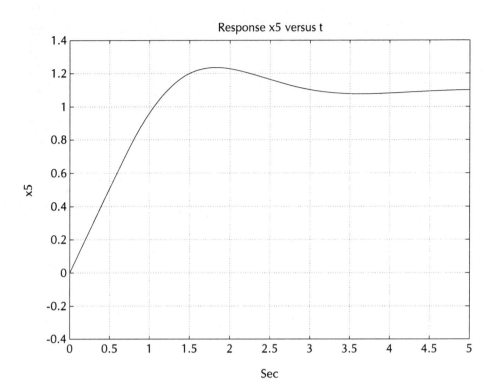

Figure 2-17

Referring to Eq. (2-59), we have

$$
\begin{bmatrix} \mathbf{A} & \mathbf{B} \\ -\mathbf{C} & 0 \end{bmatrix}^{-1} = \begin{bmatrix} 0 & \dfrac{0.5}{9.81} & 0 & \dfrac{1}{9.81} & 0 \\ 1 & 0 & 0 & 0 & 0 \\ 0 & 0 & 0 & 0 & -1 \\ 0 & 0 & 1 & 0 & 0 \\ 0 & 0.05 & 0 & 2.1 & 0 \end{bmatrix}
$$

Hence

$$
\begin{bmatrix} x_1(\infty) \\ x_2(\infty) \\ x_3(\infty) \\ x_4(\infty) \\ u(\infty) \end{bmatrix} = \begin{bmatrix} 0 & \dfrac{0.5}{9.81} & 0 & \dfrac{1}{9.81} & 0 \\ 1 & 0 & 0 & 0 & 0 \\ 0 & 0 & 0 & 0 & -1 \\ 0 & 0 & 1 & 0 & 0 \\ 0 & 0.05 & 0 & 2.1 & 0 \end{bmatrix} \begin{bmatrix} 0 \\ 0 \\ 0 \\ 0 \\ -r \end{bmatrix} = \begin{bmatrix} 0 \\ 0 \\ r \\ 0 \\ 0 \end{bmatrix}
$$

Consequently,

$$
y(\infty) = \mathbf{C}\mathbf{x}(\infty) = \begin{bmatrix} 0 & 0 & 1 & 0 \end{bmatrix} \begin{bmatrix} x_1(\infty) \\ x_2(\infty) \\ x_3(\infty) \\ x_4(\infty) \end{bmatrix} = x_3(\infty) = r
$$

Since

$$
\dot{\mathbf{x}}(\infty) = \mathbf{0} = \mathbf{A}\mathbf{x}(\infty) + \mathbf{B}u(\infty)
$$

or

$$\begin{bmatrix} 0 \\ 0 \\ 0 \\ 0 \end{bmatrix} = \begin{bmatrix} 0 & 1 & 0 & 0 \\ 20.601 & 0 & 0 & 0 \\ 0 & 0 & 0 & 1 \\ -0.4905 & 0 & 0 & 0 \end{bmatrix} \begin{bmatrix} 0 \\ 0 \\ r \\ 0 \end{bmatrix} + \begin{bmatrix} 0 \\ -1 \\ 0 \\ 0.5 \end{bmatrix} u(\infty)$$

we get

$$u(\infty) = 0$$

Since $u(\infty) = 0$, we have, from Eq. (2-56),

$$u(\infty) = 0 = -\mathbf{K}\mathbf{x}(\infty) + K_I \xi(\infty)$$

and so

$$\xi(\infty) = \frac{1}{K_I} [\mathbf{K}\mathbf{x}(\infty)] = \frac{1}{K_I} k_3 x_3(\infty) = \frac{-56.0652}{-50.9684} r = 1.1r$$

Hence, for $r = 1$, we have

$$\xi(\infty) = 1.1$$

(See Figure 2-17, where $x_5 = \xi$.)

In concluding this design example, it is noted that, as in any design problem, if the speed and damping are not quite satisfactory, we must modify the desired characteristic equation and determine a new matrix $\hat{\mathbf{K}}$. MATLAB solutions must be repeated until a satisfactory result is obtained.

2-4 DESIGN OF FULL-ORDER STATE OBSERVERS

This section deals with the design of state observers. We shall first review theoretical analysis and then present MATLAB programs to design state observers. We discuss full-order state observers in this section and minimum-order state observers in Section 2-5.

Design of full-order state observers

Consider the system defined by

$$\dot{\mathbf{x}} = \mathbf{A}\mathbf{x} + \mathbf{B}u \qquad (2\text{-}65)$$

$$y = \mathbf{C}\mathbf{x} \qquad (2\text{-}66)$$

where $\mathbf{x}$ = state vector (n-vector)
u = control signal (scalar)
y = output signal (scalar)
$\mathbf{A} = n \times n$ constant matrix
$\mathbf{B} = n \times 1$ constant matrix
$\mathbf{C} = 1 \times n$ constant matrix

We assume that the system is completely observable. We assume further that the system configuration is the same as that shown in Figure 2-18.

In designing the full-order state observer, it is convenient if we transform the system equations given by Eqs. (2-65) and (2-66) into the observable canonical form. This can be done as follows: Define a transformation matrix $\mathbf{Q}$ by

$$\mathbf{Q} = (\mathbf{WN'})^{-1} \tag{2-67}$$

where $\mathbf{N}$ is the observability matrix

$$\mathbf{N} = [\mathbf{C'} \vdots \mathbf{A'C'} \vdots \cdots \vdots (\mathbf{A'})^{n-1} \mathbf{C'}] \tag{2-68}$$

and $\mathbf{W}$ is defined by Eq. (2-6), rewritten thus:

$$\mathbf{W} = \begin{bmatrix} a_{n-1} & a_{n-2} & \cdots & a_1 & 1 \\ a_{n-2} & a_{n-3} & \cdots & 1 & 0 \\ \vdots & \vdots & & \vdots & \vdots \\ a_1 & 1 & \cdots & 0 & 0 \\ 1 & 0 & \cdots & 0 & 0 \end{bmatrix}$$

where $a_1, a_2, \ldots, a_{n-1}$ are coefficients in the characteristic equation of the original state equation given by Eq. (2-65):

$$|s\mathbf{I} - \mathbf{A}| = s^n + a_1 s^{n-1} + \cdots + a_{n-1} s + a_n = 0$$

(Since we assumed that the system is completely observable, the inverse of matrix $\mathbf{WN'}$ exists.)

Define a new state vector (n-vector) $\boldsymbol{\xi}$ by

$$\mathbf{x} = \mathbf{Q}\boldsymbol{\xi} \tag{2-69}$$

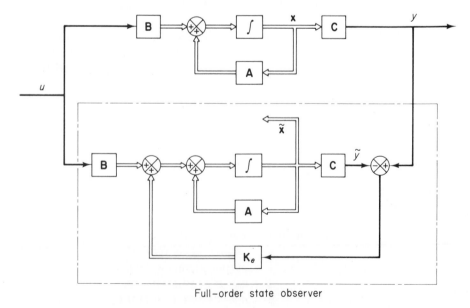

Full-order state observer

Figure 2-18

Then Eqs. (2-65) and (2-66) become

$$\dot{\xi} = Q^{-1}AQ\xi + Q^{-1}Bu \qquad (2\text{-}70)$$

$$y = CQ\xi \qquad (2\text{-}71)$$

where

$$Q^{-1}AQ = \begin{bmatrix} 0 & 0 & \cdots & 0 & -a_n \\ 1 & 0 & \cdots & 0 & -a_{n-1} \\ 0 & 1 & \cdots & 0 & -a_{n-2} \\ \vdots & \vdots & & \vdots & \vdots \\ 0 & 0 & \cdots & 1 & -a_1 \end{bmatrix} \qquad (2\text{-}72)$$

$$Q^{-1}B = \begin{bmatrix} b_n - a_n b_0 \\ b_{n-1} - a_{n-1} b_0 \\ \vdots \\ b_1 - a_1 b_0 \end{bmatrix} \qquad (2\text{-}73)$$

$$CQ = \begin{bmatrix} 0 & 0 & \cdots & 0 & 1 \end{bmatrix} \qquad (2\text{-}74)$$

Equations (2-70) and (2-71) are in the observable canonical form. Thus, given a state equation and output equation, they can be transformed into the observable canonical form if the system is completely observable and if the original state vector $\mathbf{x}$ is transformed into a new state vector ξ by use of the transformation given by Eq. (2-69). Note that if matrix $\mathbf{A}$ is already in the observable canonical form then $\mathbf{Q} = \mathbf{I}$.

From Figure 2-18, the state observer dynamics is given by

$$\dot{\tilde{x}} = A\tilde{x} + Bu + K_e(y - C\tilde{x})$$

$$= (A - K_e C)\tilde{x} + Bu + K_e Cx \qquad (2\text{-}75)$$

Now define

$$\tilde{x} = Q\tilde{\xi} \qquad (2\text{-}76)$$

By substituting Eq. (2-76) into Eq. (2-75), we get

$$\dot{\tilde{\xi}} = Q^{-1}(A - K_e C)Q\tilde{\xi} + Q^{-1}Bu + Q^{-1}K_e CQ\xi \qquad (2\text{-}77)$$

Subtracting Eq. (2-77) from Eq. (2-70), we obtain

$$\dot{\xi} - \dot{\tilde{\xi}} = Q^{-1}(A - K_e C)Q(\xi - \tilde{\xi}) \qquad (2\text{-}78)$$

Define

$$\epsilon = \xi - \tilde{\xi}$$

Then Eq. (2-78) becomes

$$\dot{\epsilon} = Q^{-1}(A - K_e C)Q\epsilon \qquad (2\text{-}79)$$

We require the error dynamics to be asymptotically stable and $\epsilon(t)$ to reach zero with sufficient speed. The procedure for determining matrix K_e is first to select the desired observer poles (the eigenvalues of $\mathbf{A} - \mathbf{K}_e \mathbf{C}$) and then to determine matrix $\mathbf{K}_e$ so that it will give the desired observer poles. Noting that $\mathbf{Q}^{-1} = \mathbf{W}\mathbf{N}'$, we have

$$\mathbf{Q}^{-1}\mathbf{K}_e = \begin{bmatrix} a_{n-1} & a_{n-2} & \cdots & a_1 & 1 \\ a_{n-2} & a_{n-3} & \cdots & 1 & 0 \\ \vdots & \vdots & & \vdots & \vdots \\ a_1 & 1 & \cdots & 0 & 0 \\ 1 & 0 & \cdots & 0 & 0 \end{bmatrix} \begin{bmatrix} \mathbf{C} \\ \mathbf{CA} \\ \vdots \\ \mathbf{CA}^{n-2} \\ \mathbf{CA}^{n-1} \end{bmatrix} \begin{bmatrix} k_1 \\ k_2 \\ \vdots \\ k_{n-1} \\ k_n \end{bmatrix}$$

where

$$\mathbf{K}_e = \begin{bmatrix} k_1 \\ k_2 \\ \vdots \\ k_n \end{bmatrix}$$

Since $\mathbf{Q}^{-1}\mathbf{K}_e$ is an n-vector, let us write

$$\mathbf{Q}^{-1}\mathbf{K}_e = \begin{bmatrix} \delta_n \\ \delta_{n-1} \\ \vdots \\ \delta_1 \end{bmatrix} \tag{2-80}$$

Then, referring to Eq. (2-74), we have

$$\mathbf{Q}^{-1}\mathbf{K}_e\,\mathbf{CQ} = \begin{bmatrix} \delta_n \\ \delta_{n-1} \\ \vdots \\ \delta_1 \end{bmatrix} \begin{bmatrix} 0 & 0 & \cdots & 1 \end{bmatrix} = \begin{bmatrix} 0 & 0 & \cdots & 0 & \delta_n \\ 0 & 0 & \cdots & 0 & \delta_{n-1} \\ \vdots & \vdots & & \vdots & \vdots \\ 0 & 0 & \cdots & 0 & \delta_1 \end{bmatrix}$$

and

$$\mathbf{Q}^{-1}(\mathbf{A} - \mathbf{K}_e\,\mathbf{C})\mathbf{Q} = \mathbf{Q}^{-1}\mathbf{A}\mathbf{Q} - \mathbf{Q}^{-1}\mathbf{K}_e\,\mathbf{CQ}$$

$$= \begin{bmatrix} 0 & 0 & \cdots & 0 & -a_n - \delta_n \\ 1 & 0 & \cdots & 0 & -a_{n-1} - \delta_{n-1} \\ 0 & 1 & \cdots & 0 & -a_{n-2} - \delta_{n-2} \\ \vdots & \vdots & & \vdots & \vdots \\ 0 & 0 & \cdots & 1 & -a_1 - \delta_1 \end{bmatrix}$$

The characteristic equation

$$|s\mathbf{I} - \mathbf{Q}^{-1}(\mathbf{A} - \mathbf{K}_e\,\mathbf{C})\mathbf{Q}| = 0$$

becomes

$$\begin{bmatrix} s & 0 & 0 & \cdots & 0 & a_n + \delta_n \\ -1 & s & 0 & \cdots & 0 & a_{n-1} + \delta_{n-1} \\ 0 & -1 & s & \cdots & 0 & a_{n-2} + \delta_{n-2} \\ \vdots & \vdots & \vdots & & \vdots & \vdots \\ 0 & 0 & 0 & \cdots & -1 & s + a_1 + \delta_1 \end{bmatrix} = 0$$

or

$$s^n + (a_1 + \delta_1)s^{n-1} + (a_2 + \delta_2)s^{n-2} + \cdots + (a_n + \delta_n) = 0 \tag{2-81}$$

It can be seen that each of $\delta_n, \delta_{n-1}, \ldots, \delta_1$ is associated with only one of the coefficients of the characteristic equation.

Suppose that the desired characteristic equation for the error dynamics is

$$(s - \mu_1)(s - \mu_2) \cdots (s - \mu_n)$$
$$= s^n + \alpha_1 s^{n-1} + \alpha_2 s^{n-2} + \cdots + \alpha_{n-1} s + \alpha_n = 0 \qquad (2\text{-}82)$$

(Note that the desired eigenvalues μ_i's determine how fast the observed state converges to the actual state of the plant.) Comparing the coefficients of terms of like powers of s in Eqs. (2-81) and (2-82), we obtain

$$a_1 + \delta_1 = \alpha_1$$
$$a_2 + \delta_2 = \alpha_2$$
$$\vdots$$
$$a_n + \delta_n = \alpha_n$$

from which we get

$$\delta_1 = \alpha_1 - a_1$$
$$\delta_2 = \alpha_2 - a_2$$
$$\vdots$$
$$\delta_n = \alpha_n - a_n$$

Then, from Eq. (2-80), we have

$$\mathbf{Q}^{-1}\mathbf{K}_e = \begin{bmatrix} \delta_n \\ \delta_{n-1} \\ \vdots \\ \delta_1 \end{bmatrix} = \begin{bmatrix} \alpha_n - a_n \\ \alpha_{n-1} - a_{n-1} \\ \vdots \\ \alpha_1 - a_1 \end{bmatrix}$$

Hence

$$\mathbf{K}_e = \mathbf{Q} \begin{bmatrix} \alpha_n - a_n \\ \alpha_{n-1} - a_{n-1} \\ \vdots \\ \alpha_1 - a_1 \end{bmatrix} = (\mathbf{WN'})^{-1} \begin{bmatrix} \alpha_n - a_n \\ \alpha_{n-1} - a_{n-1} \\ \vdots \\ \alpha_1 - a_1 \end{bmatrix} \qquad (2\text{-}83)$$

Equation (2-83) specifies the necessary state observer gain matrix $\mathbf{K}_e$.

Obtaining the state observer gain matrix $\mathbf{K}_e$ from the state feedback gain matrix K for the dual system

It is a well-known fact that Eq. (2-83) can also be obtained from Eq. (2-13) by considering the dual problem. That is, consider the pole-placement problem for the dual system and obtain the state feedback gain matrix **K** for the dual system. Then the state observer gain matrix $\mathbf{K}_e$ can be given by $\mathbf{K'}$.

Ackermann's formula

Consider the system defined by

$$\dot{\mathbf{x}} = \mathbf{Ax} + \mathbf{B}u \qquad (2\text{-}84)$$

$$y = \mathbf{Cx} \qquad (2\text{-}85)$$

In Section 2-2 we derived Ackermann's formula for pole placement for the system defined by Eq. (2-84). The result was given by Eq. (2-18), rewritten thus:

$$\mathbf{K} = [0 \quad 0 \quad \cdots \quad 0 \quad 1][\mathbf{B} \vdots \mathbf{AB} \vdots \cdots \vdots \mathbf{A}^{n-1}\mathbf{B}]^{-1}\phi(\mathbf{A})$$

For the dual of the system defined by Eqs. (2-84) and (2-85),

$$\dot{\mathbf{z}} = \mathbf{A}'\mathbf{z} + \mathbf{C}'v$$

$$n = \mathbf{B}'\mathbf{z}$$

the preceding Ackermann's formula for pole placement is modified to

$$\mathbf{K} = [0 \quad 0 \quad \cdots \quad 0 \quad 1][\mathbf{C}' \vdots \mathbf{A}'\mathbf{C}' \vdots \cdots \vdots (\mathbf{A}')^{n-1}\mathbf{C}']^{-1}\phi(\mathbf{A}') \qquad (2\text{-}86)$$

As stated earlier, the state observer gain matrix $\mathbf{K}_e$ is given by $\mathbf{K}'$, where $\mathbf{K}$ is given by Eq. (2-86). Thus

$$\mathbf{K}_e = \mathbf{K}' = \phi(\mathbf{A}')' \begin{bmatrix} \mathbf{C} \\ \mathbf{CA} \\ \vdots \\ \mathbf{CA}^{n-2} \\ \mathbf{CA}^{n-1} \end{bmatrix}^{-1} \begin{bmatrix} 0 \\ 0 \\ \vdots \\ 0 \\ 1 \end{bmatrix} = \phi(\mathbf{A}) \begin{bmatrix} \mathbf{C} \\ \mathbf{CA} \\ \vdots \\ \mathbf{CA}^{n-2} \\ \mathbf{CA}^{n-1} \end{bmatrix}^{-1} \begin{bmatrix} 0 \\ 0 \\ \vdots \\ 0 \\ 1 \end{bmatrix} \qquad (2\text{-}87)$$

where $\phi(s)$ is the desired characteristic polynomial for the state observer, or

$$\phi(s) = (s - \mu_1)(s - \mu_2) \cdots (s - \mu_n)$$

where $\mu_1, \mu_2, \ldots, \mu_n$ are the desired eigenvalues. Equation (2-87) is called Ackermann's formula for the determination of the observer gain matrix $\mathbf{K}_e$.

Comments on selecting the best $\mathbf{K}_e$

Remember that the observer gain matrix $\mathbf{K}_e$ depends on the desired characteristic equation

$$(s - \mu_1)(s - \mu_2) \cdots (s - \mu_n) = 0$$

The choice of a set of $\mu_1, \mu_2, \ldots, \mu_n$ is, in many instances, not unique. The desired eigenvalues or characteristic equation should be chosen so that the state observer responds at least two to five times faster than the closed-loop system considered.

If several possible observer gain matrices $\mathbf{K}_e$ are determined based on several different desired characteristic equations, then for each of these matrices $\mathbf{K}_e$ simulation tests must be run to evaluate the resulting system performance. Then we select the best $\mathbf{K}_e$ from the viewpoint of overall system performance. In many practical cases, the selection of the best matrix $\mathbf{K}_e$ boils down to a compromise between speedy response and sensitivity to disturbances and noises.

EXAMPLE 2-4

Consider the system

$$\dot{\mathbf{x}} = \mathbf{Ax} + \mathbf{B}u$$

$$y = \mathbf{Cx}$$

where

$$\mathbf{A} = \begin{bmatrix} 0 & 1 & 0 \\ 0 & 0 & 1 \\ -6 & -11 & -6 \end{bmatrix}, \quad \mathbf{B} = \begin{bmatrix} 0 \\ 0 \\ 1 \end{bmatrix}, \quad \mathbf{C} = [1 \quad 0 \quad 0]$$

Design a full-order state observer, assuming that the system configuration is identical to that shown in Figure 2-18. Assume that the desired eigenvalues of the observer matrix are

$$\mu_1 = -2 + j2\sqrt{3}, \qquad \mu_2 = -2 - j2\sqrt{3}, \qquad \mu_3 = -5$$

Let us examine the observability matrix. The rank of

$$\mathbf{N} = [\mathbf{C}' \vdots \mathbf{A}'\mathbf{C}' \vdots (\mathbf{A}')^2 \mathbf{C}'] = \begin{bmatrix} 1 & 0 & 0 \\ 0 & 1 & 0 \\ 0 & 0 & 1 \end{bmatrix}$$

is 3. Hence, the system is completely observable and the determination of the observer gain matrix $\mathbf{K}_e$ is possible.

Since the characteristic equation of the given system is

$$|s\mathbf{I} - \mathbf{A}| = \begin{vmatrix} s & -1 & 0 \\ 0 & s & -1 \\ 6 & 11 & s+6 \end{vmatrix}$$

$$= s^3 + 6s^2 + 11s + 6$$

$$= s^3 + a_1 s^2 + a_2 s + a_3 = 0$$

we have

$$a_1 = 6, \qquad a_2 = 11, \qquad a_3 = 6$$

The desired characteristic equation is

$$(s - \mu_1)(s - \mu_2)(s - \mu_3) = (s + 2 - j2\sqrt{3})(s + 2 + j2\sqrt{3})(s + 5)$$

$$= s^3 + 9s^2 + 36s + 80$$

$$= s^3 + \alpha_1 s^2 + \alpha_2 s + \alpha_3 = 0$$

Hence

$$\alpha_1 = 9, \qquad \alpha_2 = 36, \qquad \alpha_3 = 80$$

1. We shall solve this problem by using Eq. (2-83):

$$\mathbf{K}_e = (\mathbf{W}\mathbf{N}')^{-1} \begin{bmatrix} \alpha_3 - a_3 \\ \alpha_2 - a_2 \\ \alpha_1 - a_1 \end{bmatrix}$$

Noting that

$$\mathbf{N}' = \begin{bmatrix} 1 & 0 & 0 \\ 0 & 1 & 0 \\ 0 & 0 & 1 \end{bmatrix}, \quad \mathbf{W} = \begin{bmatrix} 11 & 6 & 1 \\ 6 & 1 & 0 \\ 1 & 0 & 0 \end{bmatrix}$$

we have

$$(\mathbf{WN'})^{-1} = \left\{ \begin{bmatrix} 11 & 6 & 1 \\ 6 & 1 & 0 \\ 1 & 0 & 0 \end{bmatrix} \begin{bmatrix} 1 & 0 & 0 \\ 0 & 1 & 0 \\ 0 & 0 & 1 \end{bmatrix} \right\}^{-1} = \begin{bmatrix} 0 & 0 & 1 \\ 0 & 1 & -6 \\ 1 & -6 & 25 \end{bmatrix}$$

Hence

$$\mathbf{K}_e = \begin{bmatrix} 0 & 0 & 1 \\ 0 & 1 & -6 \\ 1 & -6 & 25 \end{bmatrix} \begin{bmatrix} 80 - 6 \\ 36 - 11 \\ 9 - 6 \end{bmatrix} = \begin{bmatrix} 3 \\ 7 \\ -1 \end{bmatrix}$$

2. Next we shall obtain the observer gain matrix $\mathbf{K}_e$ by use of Ackermann's formula. Referring to Eq. (2-87), we have

$$\mathbf{K}_e = \phi(\mathbf{A}) \begin{bmatrix} \mathbf{C} \\ \mathbf{CA} \\ \mathbf{CA}^2 \end{bmatrix}^{-1} \begin{bmatrix} 0 \\ 0 \\ 1 \end{bmatrix}$$

Since the desired characteristic polynomial is

$$\phi(s) = s^3 + 9s^2 + 36s + 80$$

we have

$$\phi(\mathbf{A}) = \mathbf{A}^3 + 9\mathbf{A}^2 + 36\mathbf{A} + 80\mathbf{I}$$

$$= \begin{bmatrix} 0 & 1 & 0 \\ 0 & 0 & 1 \\ -6 & -11 & -6 \end{bmatrix}^3 + 9 \begin{bmatrix} 0 & 1 & 0 \\ 0 & 0 & 1 \\ -6 & -11 & -6 \end{bmatrix}^2$$

$$+ 36 \begin{bmatrix} 0 & 1 & 0 \\ 0 & 0 & 1 \\ -6 & -11 & -6 \end{bmatrix} + 80 \begin{bmatrix} 1 & 0 & 0 \\ 0 & 1 & 0 \\ 0 & 0 & 1 \end{bmatrix}$$

$$= \begin{bmatrix} 74 & 25 & 3 \\ -18 & 41 & 7 \\ -42 & -95 & -1 \end{bmatrix}$$

Also,

$$\begin{bmatrix} \mathbf{C} \\ \mathbf{CA} \\ \mathbf{CA}^2 \end{bmatrix}^{-1} = \begin{bmatrix} 1 & 0 & 0 \\ 0 & 1 & 0 \\ 0 & 0 & 1 \end{bmatrix}^{-1} = \begin{bmatrix} 1 & 0 & 0 \\ 0 & 1 & 0 \\ 0 & 0 & 1 \end{bmatrix}$$

Hence

$$\mathbf{K}_e = \begin{bmatrix} 74 & 25 & 3 \\ -18 & 41 & 7 \\ -42 & -95 & -1 \end{bmatrix} \begin{bmatrix} 1 & 0 & 0 \\ 0 & 1 & 0 \\ 0 & 0 & 1 \end{bmatrix} \begin{bmatrix} 0 \\ 0 \\ 1 \end{bmatrix} = \begin{bmatrix} 3 \\ 7 \\ -1 \end{bmatrix}$$

A MATLAB program for designing the observer gain matrix $\mathbf{K}_e$ using the transformation matrix $\mathbf{Q}$ is given as MATLAB Program 2-7. A program based on Ackermann's formula is given as MATLAB Program 2-8.

MATLAB Program 2–7

```
% ---------- Design of full-order state observer ----------

% ***** This program determines observer gain matrix Ke by use
% of transformation matrix Q *****

% ***** Enter matrices A and C *****

A = [0    1    0
     0    0    1
    -6  -11   -6];
C = [1   0   0];

% ***** Enter the observability matrix N and check its rank *****

N = [C'  A'*C'  (A')^2*C'];
rank(N)

ans =

     3

% ***** Since the rank of the observability matrix is 3, design
% of observer is possible *****

% ***** Determine a1, a2, a3 of the characteristic equation by
% entering statement poly(A) *****

p = poly(A)

p =

   1.0000    6.0000    11.0000    6.0000

a1 = p(2); a2 = p(3); a3 = p(4);

% ***** Enter the desired characteristic polynomial by defining
% the following matrix J and entering statement poly(J) *****

J = [-2+2*sqrt(3)*i   0   0
      0    -2-2*sqrt(3)*i   0
      0                0   -5];

JJ = poly(J)

JJ =

   1.0000    9.0000    36.0000    80.0000

aa1 = JJ(2); aa2 = JJ(3); aa3 = JJ(4);

% ***** Compute matrix W *****
```

```
W = [a2  a1  1;a1  1  0;1  0  0];

% ***** The observer gain matrix Ke is obtained from *****

Ke = inv(W*N')*[aa3-a3;aa2-a2;aa1-a1]

Ke =

    3.0000
    7.0000
   -1.0000
```

```
MATLAB Program 2–8

% ---------- Design of full-order state observer ----------

% ***** This program determines observer gain matrix Ke
% based on Ackermann's formula *****

% ***** Enter matrices A and C *****

A = [0    1    0
     0    0    1
    -6  -11   -6];
C = [1   0   0];

% ***** Enter the observability matrix N and check its rank *****

N = [C'  A'*C'  (A')^2*C'];
rank(N)

ans =

     3

% ***** Since the rank of the observability matrix is 3, design
% of observer is possible *****

% ***** Enter the desired characteristic polynomial by defining
% the following matrix J and entering statement poly(J) *****

J = [-2+2*sqrt(3)*i     0   0
        0      -2-2*sqrt(3)*i   0
        0                 0  -5];

JJ = poly(J)

JJ =

    1.0000    9.0000    36.0000    80.0000

% ***** Enter characteristic polynomial Phi *****
```

Phi = polyvalm(poly(J),A);

% ***** The observer gain matrix Ke is obtained from *****

Ke = Phi*(inv(N'))*[0;0;1]

Ke =

    3.0000
    7.0000
   -1.0000

EXAMPLE 2-5

Consider the design of a regulator system for the following plant:

$$\dot{\mathbf{x}} = \mathbf{A}\mathbf{x} + \mathbf{B}u \tag{2-88}$$

$$y = \mathbf{C}\mathbf{x} \tag{2-89}$$

where

$$\mathbf{A} = \begin{bmatrix} 0 & 1 \\ 20.6 & 0 \end{bmatrix}, \qquad \mathbf{B} = \begin{bmatrix} 0 \\ 1 \end{bmatrix}, \qquad \mathbf{C} = \begin{bmatrix} 1 & 0 \end{bmatrix}$$

Suppose that we use the pole-placement approach to the design of the system and that the desired closed-loop poles for this system are at $s = \mu_i\,(i = 1, 2)$, where $\mu_1 = -1.8 + j2.4$ and $\mu_2 = -1.8 - j2.4$. The state feedback gain matrix $\mathbf{K}$ for this case can be obtained as follows:

$$\mathbf{K} = \begin{bmatrix} 29.6 & 3.6 \end{bmatrix}$$

Using this state feedback gain matrix $\mathbf{K}$, the control signal u is given by

$$u = -\mathbf{K}\mathbf{x} = -\begin{bmatrix} 29.6 & 3.6 \end{bmatrix}\begin{bmatrix} x_1 \\ x_2 \end{bmatrix}$$

Suppose that we use the observed-state feedback control instead of actual-state feedback control, or

$$u = -\mathbf{K}\tilde{\mathbf{x}} = -\begin{bmatrix} 29.6 & 3.6 \end{bmatrix}\begin{bmatrix} \tilde{x}_1 \\ \tilde{x}_2 \end{bmatrix}$$

where we choose the eigenvalues of the observer gain matrix to be

$$\mu_1 = \mu_2 = -8$$

Obtain the observer gain matrix $\mathbf{K}_e$ and draw a block diagram for the observed-state feedback control system.

For the system defined by Eq. (2-88), the characteristic polynomial is

$$|s\mathbf{I} - \mathbf{A}| = \begin{vmatrix} s & -1 \\ -20.6 & s \end{vmatrix} = s^2 - 20.6 = s^2 + a_1 s + a_2$$

Thus

$$a_1 = 0, \qquad a_2 = -20.6$$

The desired characteristic polynomial for the observer is

$$(s - \mu_1)(s - \mu_2) = (s + 8)(s + 8) = s^2 + 16s + 64$$
$$= s^2 + \alpha_1 s + \alpha_2$$

Hence

$$\alpha_1 = 16, \qquad \alpha_2 = 64$$

For the determination of the observer gain matrix, we may use Eq. (2-83), or

$$\mathbf{K}_e = (\mathbf{W}\mathbf{N}')^{-1} \begin{bmatrix} \alpha_2 - a_2 \\ \alpha_1 - a_1 \end{bmatrix}$$

where

$$\mathbf{N} = [\mathbf{C}' \vdots \mathbf{A}'\mathbf{C}'] = \begin{bmatrix} 1 & 0 \\ 0 & 1 \end{bmatrix}$$

$$\mathbf{W} = \begin{bmatrix} a_1 & 1 \\ 1 & 0 \end{bmatrix} = \begin{bmatrix} 0 & 1 \\ 1 & 0 \end{bmatrix}$$

Hence

$$\mathbf{K}_e = \left\{ \begin{bmatrix} 0 & 1 \\ 1 & 0 \end{bmatrix} \begin{bmatrix} 1 & 0 \\ 0 & 1 \end{bmatrix} \right\}^{-1} \begin{bmatrix} 64 + 20.6 \\ 16 - 0 \end{bmatrix}$$

$$= \begin{bmatrix} 0 & 1 \\ 1 & 0 \end{bmatrix} \begin{bmatrix} 84.6 \\ 16 \end{bmatrix} = \begin{bmatrix} 16 \\ 84.6 \end{bmatrix} \qquad (2\text{-}90)$$

If we use Ackermann's formula, Eq. (2-87), we obtain

$$\mathbf{K}_e = \phi(\mathbf{A}) \begin{bmatrix} \mathbf{C} \\ \mathbf{C}\mathbf{A} \end{bmatrix}^{-1} \begin{bmatrix} 0 \\ 1 \end{bmatrix}$$

$$= [\mathbf{A}^2 + 16\mathbf{A} + 64\mathbf{I}] \begin{bmatrix} 1 & 0 \\ 0 & 1 \end{bmatrix}^{-1} \begin{bmatrix} 0 \\ 1 \end{bmatrix}$$

$$= \begin{bmatrix} 16 \\ 84.6 \end{bmatrix} \qquad (2\text{-}91)$$

Equation (2-90) or (2-91) gives the observer gain matrix $\mathbf{K}_e$. Referring to Eq. (2-75), the observer equation can be given by

$$\dot{\tilde{\mathbf{x}}} = (\mathbf{A} - \mathbf{K}_e \mathbf{C})\tilde{\mathbf{x}} + \mathbf{B}u + \mathbf{K}_e y \qquad (2\text{-}92)$$

Since

$$u = -\mathbf{K}\tilde{\mathbf{x}}$$

Equation (2-92) becomes

$$\dot{\tilde{\mathbf{x}}} = (\mathbf{A} - \mathbf{K}_e \mathbf{C} - \mathbf{B}\mathbf{K})\tilde{\mathbf{x}} + \mathbf{K}_e y$$

or

$$\begin{bmatrix} \dot{\tilde{x}}_1 \\ \dot{\tilde{x}}_2 \end{bmatrix} = \left\{ \begin{bmatrix} 0 & 1 \\ 20.6 & 0 \end{bmatrix} - \begin{bmatrix} 16 \\ 84.6 \end{bmatrix} [1 \quad 0] - \begin{bmatrix} 0 \\ 1 \end{bmatrix} [29.6 \quad 3.6] \right\} \begin{bmatrix} \tilde{x}_1 \\ \tilde{x}_2 \end{bmatrix} + \begin{bmatrix} 16 \\ 84.6 \end{bmatrix} y$$

$$= \begin{bmatrix} -16 & 1 \\ -93.6 & -3.6 \end{bmatrix} \begin{bmatrix} \tilde{x}_1 \\ \tilde{x}_2 \end{bmatrix} + \begin{bmatrix} 16 \\ 84.6 \end{bmatrix} y$$

The block diagram of the system with observed-state feedback is shown in Figure 2-19.

The dynamics of the observed-state feedback control system just designed can be described by the following equations: For the plant,

$$\begin{bmatrix} \dot{x}_1 \\ \dot{x}_2 \end{bmatrix} = \begin{bmatrix} 0 & 1 \\ 20.6 & 0 \end{bmatrix} \begin{bmatrix} x_1 \\ x_2 \end{bmatrix} + \begin{bmatrix} 0 \\ 1 \end{bmatrix} u$$

$$y = [1 \quad 0] \begin{bmatrix} x_1 \\ x_2 \end{bmatrix}$$

$$u = -[29.6 \quad 3.6] \begin{bmatrix} \tilde{x}_1 \\ \tilde{x}_2 \end{bmatrix}$$

For the observer,

$$\begin{bmatrix} \dot{\tilde{x}}_1 \\ \dot{\tilde{x}}_2 \end{bmatrix} = \begin{bmatrix} -16 & 1 \\ -93.6 & -3.6 \end{bmatrix} \begin{bmatrix} \tilde{x}_1 \\ \tilde{x}_2 \end{bmatrix} + \begin{bmatrix} 16 \\ 84.6 \end{bmatrix} y$$

The system, as a whole, is of fourth order. The characteristic equation for the system is

$$|s\mathbf{I} - \mathbf{A} + \mathbf{BK}||s\mathbf{I} - \mathbf{A} + \mathbf{K}_e \mathbf{C}| = (s^2 + 3.6s + 9)(s^2 + 16s + 64)$$

$$= s^4 + 19.6s^3 + 130.6s^2 + 374.4s + 576 = 0$$

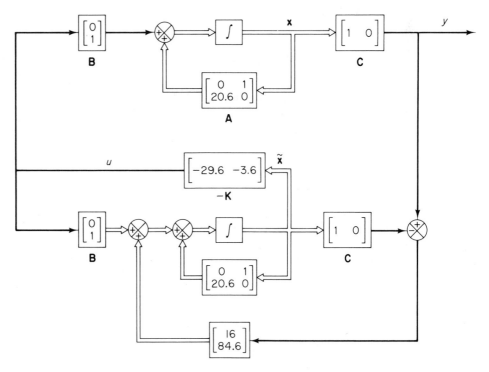

Figure 2-19

(For the derivation of the characteristic equation for the observed-state feedback system, see, for example, Reference 4 listed at the end of the book.)

MATLAB Program 2-9 may be used to determine the state feedback gain matrix **K** and the observer gain matrix $\mathbf{K}_e$ for the system considered. The characteristic polynomial for the designed system may be obtained from MATLAB Program 2-10.

MATLAB Program 2–9

```
% ---------- Pole placement and design of observer ----------

% ***** Design of a control system using pole-placement
% technique and state observer. First solve pole-placement
% problem *****

% ***** Enter matrices A, B, C, and D *****

A = [0   1;20.6   0];
B = [0;1];
C = [1   0];
D = [0];

% ***** Check the rank of the controllability matrix M *****

M = [B   A*B];
rank(M)

ans =

        2

% ***** Since the rank of the controllability matrix M is 2,
% arbitrary pole placement is possible *****

% ***** Enter the desired characteristic polynomial by
% defining the following matrix J and computing poly(J) *****

J = [-1.8+2.4*i   0;0   -1.8-2.4*i];

poly(J)

ans =

     1.0000      3.6000      9.0000

% ***** Enter characteristic polynomial Phi *****

Phi = polyvalm(poly(J),A);

% ***** State feedback gain matrix K can be given by *****

K = [0   1]*inv(M)*Phi
```

```
K =

    29.6000    3.6000

% ***** The following program determines the observer matrix Ke *****

% ***** Enter the observability matrix N and check its rank *****

N = [C'  A'*C'];
rank(N)

ans =

        2

% ***** Since the rank of the observability matrix is 2, design of
% the observer is possible *****

% ***** Enter the desired characteristic polynomial by defining
% the following matrix J0 and entering statement poly(J0) *****

J0 = [-8   0;0   -8];
poly(J0)

ans =

        1    16    64

% ***** Enter characteristic polynomial Ph *****

Ph = polyvalm(poly(J0),A);

% ***** The observer gain matrix Ke is obtained from *****

Ke = Ph*(inv(N'))*[0;1]

Ke =

    16.0000
    84.6000
```

```
MATLAB Program 2–10

% ---------- Characteristic polynomial ----------

% ***** The characteristic polynomial for the designed system
% is given by |sI - A + BK||sI - A + KeC| *****

% ***** This characteristic polynomial can be obtained by use of
% eigenvalues of A-BK and A-KeC as follows *****
```

```
X  = [eig(A-B*K);eig(A-Ke*C)]

X  =

   -1.8000 + 2.4000i
   -1.8000 - 2.4000i
   -8.0000
   -8.0000

poly(X)

ans =

    1.0000    19.6000   130.6000   374.4000   576.0000
```

2-5 DESIGN OF MINIMUM-ORDER STATE OBSERVERS

Minimum-order state observer

The observers discussed thus far are designed to reconstruct all the state variables. In practice, some state variables may be accurately measured. Such accurately measurable state variables need not be estimated. An observer that estimates fewer than n state variables, where n is the dimension of the state vector, is called a reduced-order state observer or, simply, a reduced-order observer. If the order of the reduced-order observer is the minimum possible, the observer is called a minimum-order state observer or minimum-order observer.

Suppose the state vector $\mathbf{x}$ is an n-vector and the output vector $\mathbf{y}$ is an m-vector that can be measured. Since m output variables are linear combinations of the state variables, m state variables need not be estimated. We need to estimate only $n - m$ state variables. Then the reduced-order observer becomes an $(n - m)$th-order observer. Such an $(n - m)$th-order observer is the minimum-order observer. Figure 2-20 shows the block diagram of a system with a minimum-order observer.

It is important to note, however, that, if the measurement of output variables involves significant noises and is relatively inaccurate, then the use of the full-order observer may result in a better system performance.

To present the basic idea of the minimum-order observer, without undue mathematical complications, we shall present the case where the output is a scalar (that is, $m = 1$) and derive the state equation for the minimum-order observer. Consider the system

$$\dot{\mathbf{x}} = \mathbf{Ax} + \mathbf{B}u$$

$$y = \mathbf{Cx}$$

where the state vector $\mathbf{x}$ can be partitioned into two parts x_a (a scalar) and $\mathbf{x}_b$ [an $(n - 1)$-vector]. Here the state variable x_a is equal to the output y and thus can be

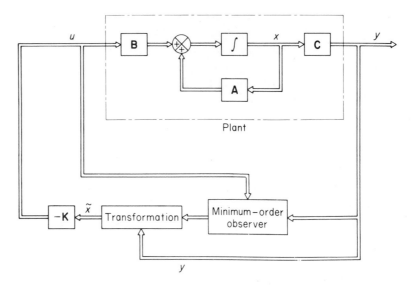

Plant

Figure 2-20

directly measured, and $\mathbf{x}_b$ is the unmeasurable portion of the state vector. Then the partitioned state and output equations become

$$\begin{bmatrix} \dot{x}_a \\ \hline \dot{\mathbf{x}}_b \end{bmatrix} = \begin{bmatrix} A_{aa} & \vdots & \mathbf{A}_{ab} \\ \hline \mathbf{A}_{ba} & \vdots & \mathbf{A}_{bb} \end{bmatrix} \begin{bmatrix} x_a \\ \hline \mathbf{x}_b \end{bmatrix} + \begin{bmatrix} B_a \\ \hline \mathbf{B}_b \end{bmatrix} u \tag{2-93}$$

$$y = [1 \vdots \mathbf{0}] \begin{bmatrix} x_a \\ \hline \mathbf{x}_b \end{bmatrix} \tag{2-94}$$

where A_{aa} = scalar

$\mathbf{A}_{ab} = 1 \times (n-1)$ matrix

$\mathbf{A}_{ba} = (n-1) \times 1$ matrix

$\mathbf{A}_{bb} = (n-1) \times (n-1)$ matrix

B_a = scalar

$\mathbf{B}_b = (n-1) \times 1$ matrix

From Eq. (2-93), the equation for the measured portion of the state becomes

$$\dot{x}_a = A_{aa} x_a + \mathbf{A}_{ab} \mathbf{x}_b + B_a u$$

or

$$\dot{x}_a - A_{aa} x_a - B_a u = \mathbf{A}_{ab} \mathbf{x}_b \tag{2-95}$$

The terms on the left side of Eq. (2-95) can be measured. Equation (2-95) acts as the output equation. In designing the minimum-order observer, we consider the left side of Eq. (2-95) to be known quantities. Thus Eq. (2-95) relates the measurable quantities and unmeasurable quantities of the state.

From Eq. (2-93), the equation for the unmeasured portion of the state becomes

$$\dot{\mathbf{x}}_b = \mathbf{A}_{ba} x_a + \mathbf{A}_{bb} \mathbf{x}_b + \mathbf{B}_b u \tag{2-96}$$

Noting that terms $\mathbf{A}_{ba} x_a$ and $\mathbf{B}_b u$ are known quantities, Eq. (2-96) describes the dynamics of the unmeasured portion of the state.

In what follows we shall present a method for designing a minimum-order observer. The design procedure can be simplified if we utilize the design technique developed for the full-order state observer.

Let us compare the state equation for the full-order observer with that for the minimum-order observer. The state equation for the full-order observer is

$$\dot{\mathbf{x}} = \mathbf{A}\mathbf{x} + \mathbf{B}u$$

and the "state equation" for the minimum-order observer is

$$\dot{\mathbf{x}}_b = \mathbf{A}_{bb}\,\mathbf{x}_b + \mathbf{A}_{ba}x_a + \mathbf{B}_b u$$

The output equation for the full-order observer is

$$y = \mathbf{C}\mathbf{x}$$

and the "output equation" for the minimum-order observer is

$$\dot{x}_a - A_{aa}x_a - B_a u = \mathbf{A}_{ab}\,\mathbf{x}_b$$

The design of the minimum-order observer can be carried out as follows: Referring to Eq. (2-75), the observer equation for the full-order observer can be given by

$$\dot{\tilde{\mathbf{x}}} = (\mathbf{A} - \mathbf{K}_e\,\mathbf{C})\tilde{\mathbf{x}} + \mathbf{B}u + \mathbf{K}_e y \tag{2-97}$$

Then, making substitutions from Table 2-1 into Eq. (2-97), we obtain

$$\dot{\tilde{\mathbf{x}}}_b = (\mathbf{A}_{bb} - \mathbf{K}_e\,\mathbf{A}_{ab})\tilde{\mathbf{x}}_b + \mathbf{A}_{ba}x_a + \mathbf{B}_b u + \mathbf{K}_e(\dot{x}_a - A_{aa}x_a - B_a u) \tag{2-98}$$

where the state observer gain matrix $\mathbf{K}_e$ is an $(n - 1) \times 1$ matrix. In Eq. (2-98), notice that in order to estimate $\tilde{\mathbf{x}}_b$ we need the derivative of x_a. This is undesirable, and so we need to modify Eq. (2-98).

Let us rewrite Eq. (2-98) as follows. Noting that $x_a = y$, we have

$$\begin{aligned}
\dot{\tilde{\mathbf{x}}}_b - \mathbf{K}_e\dot{x}_a &= (\mathbf{A}_{bb} - \mathbf{K}_e\,\mathbf{A}_{ab})\tilde{\mathbf{x}}_b + (\mathbf{A}_{ba} - \mathbf{K}_e A_{aa})y + (\mathbf{B}_b - \mathbf{K}_e B_a)u \\
&= (\mathbf{A}_{bb} - \mathbf{K}_e\,\mathbf{A}_{ab})(\tilde{\mathbf{x}}_b - \mathbf{K}_e y) \\
&\quad + [(\mathbf{A}_{bb} - \mathbf{K}_e\,\mathbf{A}_{ab})\mathbf{K}_e + \mathbf{A}_{ba} - \mathbf{K}_e A_{aa}]y \\
&\quad + (\mathbf{B}_b - \mathbf{K}_e B_a)u
\end{aligned} \tag{2-99}$$

Table 2-1 LIST OF NECESSARY SUBSTITUTIONS FOR WRITING THE OBSERVER EQUATION FOR THE MINIMUM-ORDER STATE OBSERVER

Full-order state observer	Minimum-order state observer
$\tilde{\mathbf{x}}$	$\tilde{\mathbf{x}}_b$
$\mathbf{A}$	$\mathbf{A}_{bb}$
$\mathbf{B}u$	$\mathbf{A}_{ba}x_a + \mathbf{B}_b u$
y	$\dot{x}_a - A_{aa}x_a - B_a u$
$\mathbf{C}$	$\mathbf{A}_{ab}$
$\mathbf{K}_e$ ($n \times 1$ matrix)	$\mathbf{K}_e$ [$(n - 1) \times 1$ matrix]

Define

$$\mathbf{x}_b - \mathbf{K}_e y = \mathbf{x}_b - \mathbf{K}_e x_a = \boldsymbol{\eta}$$

and

$$\tilde{\mathbf{x}}_b - \mathbf{K}_e y = \tilde{\mathbf{x}}_b - \mathbf{K}_e x_a = \tilde{\boldsymbol{\eta}} \tag{2-100}$$

Then Eq. (2-99) becomes

$$\dot{\tilde{\boldsymbol{\eta}}} = (\mathbf{A}_{bb} - \mathbf{K}_e \mathbf{A}_{ab})\tilde{\boldsymbol{\eta}} + [(\mathbf{A}_{bb} - \mathbf{K}_e \mathbf{A}_{ab})\mathbf{K}_e$$
$$+ \mathbf{A}_{ba} - \mathbf{K}_e A_{aa}]y + (\mathbf{B}_b - \mathbf{K}_e B_a)u \tag{2-101}$$

Equation (2-101) together with Eq. (2-100) defines the minimum-order observer.

Next we shall derive the observer error equation. Using Eq. (2-95), Eq. (2-98) can be modified to

$$\dot{\tilde{\mathbf{x}}}_b = (\mathbf{A}_{bb} - \mathbf{K}_e \mathbf{A}_{ab})\tilde{\mathbf{x}}_b + \mathbf{A}_{ba} x_a + \mathbf{B}_b u + \mathbf{K}_e \mathbf{A}_{ab} \mathbf{x}_b \tag{2-102}$$

By subtracting Eq. (2-102) from Eq. (2-96), we obtain

$$\dot{\mathbf{x}}_b - \dot{\tilde{\mathbf{x}}}_b = (\mathbf{A}_{bb} - \mathbf{K}_e \mathbf{A}_{ab})(\mathbf{x}_b - \tilde{\mathbf{x}}_b) \tag{2-103}$$

Define

$$\mathbf{e} = \mathbf{x}_b - \tilde{\mathbf{x}}_b = \boldsymbol{\eta} - \tilde{\boldsymbol{\eta}}$$

Then Eq. (2-103) becomes

$$\dot{\mathbf{e}} = (\mathbf{A}_{bb} - \mathbf{K}_e \mathbf{A}_{ab})\mathbf{e} \tag{2-104}$$

This is the error equation for the minimum-order observer. Note that $\mathbf{e}$ is an $(n - 1)$-vector.

The error dynamics can be chosen as desired by following the technique developed for the full-order observer, provided that the rank of matrix

$$\begin{bmatrix} \mathbf{A}_{ab} \\ \mathbf{A}_{ab} \mathbf{A}_{bb} \\ \vdots \\ \mathbf{A}_{ab} \mathbf{A}_{bb}^{n-2} \end{bmatrix}$$

is $n - 1$. (This is the complete observability condition applicable to the minimum-order observer.)

The characteristic equation for the minimum-order observer is obtained from Eq. (2-104) as follows:

$$|s\mathbf{I} - \mathbf{A}_{bb} + \mathbf{K}_e \mathbf{A}_{ab}| = (s - \mu_1)(s - \mu_2) \cdots (s - \mu_{n-1})$$
$$= s^{n-1} + \hat{\alpha}_1 s^{n-2} + \cdots + \hat{\alpha}_{n-2} s + \hat{\alpha}_{n-1} = 0 \tag{2-105}$$

where $\mu_1, \mu_2, \ldots, \mu_{n-1}$ are desired eigenvalues for the minimum-order observer. The observer gain matrix $\mathbf{K}_e$ can be determined by first choosing the desired eigenvalues for the minimum-order observer [that is, by placing the roots of the characteristic equation, Eq. (2-105), at the desired locations] and then using the procedure developed for the full-order observer with appropriate modifications. For example, if the formula for determining matrix $\mathbf{K}_e$ given by Eq. (2-83) is to be used, it should be modified to

$$\mathbf{K}_e = \hat{\mathbf{Q}} \begin{bmatrix} \hat{\alpha}_{n-1} - \hat{a}_{n-1} \\ \hat{\alpha}_{n-2} - \hat{a}_{n-2} \\ \vdots \\ \hat{\alpha}_1 - \hat{a}_1 \end{bmatrix} = (\hat{\mathbf{W}}\hat{\mathbf{N}}')^{-1} \begin{bmatrix} \hat{\alpha}_{n-1} - \hat{a}_{n-1} \\ \hat{\alpha}_{n-2} - \hat{a}_{n-2} \\ \vdots \\ \hat{\alpha}_1 - \hat{a}_1 \end{bmatrix} \qquad (2\text{-}106)$$

where $\mathbf{K}_e$ is an $(n - 1) \times 1$ matrix and

$$\hat{\mathbf{N}} = [\mathbf{A}'_{ab} \vdots \mathbf{A}'_{bb}\mathbf{A}'_{ab} \vdots \cdots \vdots (\mathbf{A}'_{bb})^{n-2}\mathbf{A}'_{ab}] = (n - 1) \times (n - 1) \text{ matrix}$$

$$\hat{\mathbf{W}} = \begin{bmatrix} \hat{a}_{n-2} & \hat{a}_{n-3} & \cdots & \hat{a}_1 & 1 \\ \hat{a}_{n-3} & \hat{a}_{n-4} & \cdots & 1 & 0 \\ \vdots & \vdots & & \vdots & \vdots \\ \hat{a}_1 & 1 & \cdots & 0 & 0 \\ 1 & 0 & \cdots & 0 & 0 \end{bmatrix} = (n - 1) \times (n - 1) \text{ matrix}$$

Note that $\hat{a}_1, \hat{a}_2, \ldots, \hat{a}_{n-2}$ are coefficients in the characteristic equation for the state equation

$$|s\mathbf{I} - \mathbf{A}_{bb}| = s^{n-1} + \hat{a}_1 s^{n-2} + \cdots + \hat{a}_{n-2}s + \hat{a}_{n-1} = 0$$

Also, if Ackermann's formula given by Eq. (2-87) is to be used, then it should be modified to

$$\mathbf{K}_e = \phi(\mathbf{A}_{bb}) \begin{bmatrix} \mathbf{A}_{ab} \\ \mathbf{A}_{ab}\mathbf{A}_{bb} \\ \vdots \\ \mathbf{A}_{ab}\mathbf{A}_{bb}^{n-3} \\ \mathbf{A}_{ab}\mathbf{A}_{bb}^{n-2} \end{bmatrix}^{-1} \begin{bmatrix} 0 \\ 0 \\ \vdots \\ 0 \\ 1 \end{bmatrix} \qquad (2\text{-}107)$$

where

$$\phi(\mathbf{A}_{bb}) = \mathbf{A}_{bb}^{n-1} + \hat{\alpha}_1 \mathbf{A}_{bb}^{n-2} + \cdots + \hat{\alpha}_{n-2}\mathbf{A}_{bb} + \hat{\alpha}_{n-1}\mathbf{I}$$

EXAMPLE 2-6

Consider the system defined by

$$\dot{\mathbf{x}} = \mathbf{A}\mathbf{x} + \mathbf{B}u$$

$$y = \mathbf{C}\mathbf{x}$$

where

$$\mathbf{A} = \begin{bmatrix} 0 & 1 & 0 \\ \hline 0 & 0 & 1 \\ -6 & -11 & -6 \end{bmatrix}, \qquad \mathbf{B} = \begin{bmatrix} 0 \\ 0 \\ 1 \end{bmatrix}, \qquad \mathbf{C} = [1 \vdots 0 \quad 0]$$

Suppose that the state variable x_1 (which is equal to y) is measurable and need not be observed. Determine the observer gain matrix $\mathbf{K}_e$ for the minimum-order observer. The desired eigenvalues are

$$\mu_1 = -2 + j2\sqrt{3}, \qquad \mu_2 = -2 - j2\sqrt{3}$$

From the partitioned matrix, we have

$$A_{aa} = 0, \qquad \mathbf{A}_{ab} = [1 \quad 0]$$

$$\mathbf{A}_{ba} = \begin{bmatrix} 0 \\ -6 \end{bmatrix}, \qquad \mathbf{A}_{bb} = \begin{bmatrix} 0 & 1 \\ -11 & -6 \end{bmatrix}$$

$$B_a = 0, \qquad \mathbf{B}_b = \begin{bmatrix} 0 \\ 1 \end{bmatrix}$$

The characteristic polynomial for the unobserved portion of the system is

$$|s\mathbf{I} - \mathbf{A}_{bb}| = \begin{vmatrix} s & -1 \\ 11 & s+6 \end{vmatrix} = s^2 + 6s + 11 = s^2 + \hat{a}_1 s + \hat{a}_2$$

Hence

$$\hat{a}_1 = 6, \qquad \hat{a}_2 = 11$$

Notice that

$$\hat{\mathbf{N}} = [\mathbf{A}'_{ab} \vdots \mathbf{A}'_{bb}\mathbf{A}'_{ab}] = \begin{bmatrix} 1 & 0 \\ 0 & 1 \end{bmatrix}$$

$$\hat{\mathbf{W}} = \begin{bmatrix} \hat{a}_1 & 1 \\ 1 & 0 \end{bmatrix} = \begin{bmatrix} 6 & 1 \\ 1 & 0 \end{bmatrix}$$

Therefore,

$$\hat{\mathbf{Q}} = (\hat{\mathbf{W}}\hat{\mathbf{N}}')^{-1} = \begin{bmatrix} 6 & 1 \\ 1 & 0 \end{bmatrix}^{-1} = \begin{bmatrix} 0 & 1 \\ 1 & -6 \end{bmatrix}$$

The desired characteristic polynomial for the minimum-order observer is

$$|s\mathbf{I} - \mathbf{A}_{bb} + \mathbf{K}_e\mathbf{A}_{ab}| = (s - \mu_1)(s - \mu_2)$$
$$= (s + 2 - j2\sqrt{3})(s + 2 + j2\sqrt{3})$$
$$= s^2 + 4s + 16$$

Hence

$$\hat{\alpha}_1 = 4, \qquad \hat{\alpha}_2 = 16$$

Referring to Eq. (2-106), we have

$$\mathbf{K}_e = \hat{\mathbf{Q}}\begin{bmatrix} \hat{\alpha}_2 - \hat{a}_2 \\ \hat{\alpha}_1 - \hat{a}_1 \end{bmatrix} = \begin{bmatrix} 0 & 1 \\ 1 & -6 \end{bmatrix}\begin{bmatrix} 16-11 \\ 4-6 \end{bmatrix} = \begin{bmatrix} 0 & 1 \\ 1 & -6 \end{bmatrix}\begin{bmatrix} 5 \\ -2 \end{bmatrix} = \begin{bmatrix} -2 \\ 17 \end{bmatrix}$$

In what follows, we shall solve the same problem by using Ackermann's formula. Referring to Eq. (2-107), we have

$$\mathbf{K}_e = \phi(\mathbf{A}_{bb}) \left[\begin{array}{c} \mathbf{A}_{ab} \\ \hline \mathbf{A}_{ab}\,\mathbf{A}_{bb} \end{array} \right]^{-1} \left[\begin{array}{c} 0 \\ 1 \end{array} \right]$$ (2-108)

where

$$\phi(\mathbf{A}_{bb}) = \mathbf{A}_{bb}^2 + \hat{\alpha}_1 \mathbf{A}_{bb} + \hat{\alpha}_2 \mathbf{I} = \mathbf{A}_{bb}^2 + 4\mathbf{A}_{bb} + 16\mathbf{I}$$

Since

$$\mathbf{x} = \left[\begin{array}{c} x_a \\ \hline \mathbf{x}_b \end{array} \right] = \left[\begin{array}{c} x_1 \\ x_2 \\ x_3 \end{array} \right], \qquad \mathbf{A} = \left[\begin{array}{ccc} 0 & 1 & 0 \\ \hline 0 & 0 & 1 \\ -6 & -11 & -6 \end{array} \right], \qquad \mathbf{B} = \left[\begin{array}{c} 0 \\ \hline 0 \\ 1 \end{array} \right]$$

we have

$$A_{aa} = 0, \qquad \mathbf{A}_{ab} = [1 \quad 0], \qquad \mathbf{A}_{ba} = \left[\begin{array}{c} 0 \\ -6 \end{array} \right]$$

$$\mathbf{A}_{bb} = \left[\begin{array}{cc} 0 & 1 \\ -11 & -6 \end{array} \right], \qquad B_a = 0, \qquad \mathbf{B}_b = \left[\begin{array}{c} 0 \\ 1 \end{array} \right]$$

Equation (2-108) now becomes

$$\mathbf{K}_e = \left\{ \left[\begin{array}{cc} 0 & 1 \\ -11 & -6 \end{array} \right]^2 + 4 \left[\begin{array}{cc} 0 & 1 \\ -11 & -6 \end{array} \right] + 16 \left[\begin{array}{cc} 1 & 0 \\ 0 & 1 \end{array} \right] \right\} \left[\begin{array}{cc} 1 & 0 \\ 0 & 1 \end{array} \right]^{-1} \left[\begin{array}{c} 0 \\ 1 \end{array} \right]$$

$$= \left[\begin{array}{cc} 5 & -2 \\ 22 & 17 \end{array} \right] \left[\begin{array}{c} 0 \\ 1 \end{array} \right] = \left[\begin{array}{c} -2 \\ 17 \end{array} \right]$$

Next, we shall derive the equation for the minimum-order observer. Referring to Eqs. (2-100) and (2-101), we obtain

$$\dot{\tilde{\boldsymbol{\eta}}} = (\mathbf{A}_{bb} - \mathbf{K}_e\,\mathbf{A}_{ab})\tilde{\boldsymbol{\eta}} + [(\mathbf{A}_{bb} - \mathbf{K}_e\,\mathbf{A}_{ab})\mathbf{K}_e + \mathbf{A}_{ba} - \mathbf{K}_e A_{aa}]y + (\mathbf{B}_b - \mathbf{K}_e B_a)u$$ (2-109)

where

$$\tilde{\boldsymbol{\eta}} = \tilde{\mathbf{x}}_b - \mathbf{K}_e y = \tilde{\mathbf{x}}_b - \mathbf{K}_e x_a$$

Noting that

$$\mathbf{A}_{bb} - \mathbf{K}_e\,\mathbf{A}_{ab} = \left[\begin{array}{cc} 0 & 1 \\ -11 & -6 \end{array} \right] - \left[\begin{array}{c} -2 \\ 17 \end{array} \right] [1 \quad 0] = \left[\begin{array}{cc} 2 & 1 \\ -28 & -6 \end{array} \right]$$

the equation for the minimum-order observer, Eq. (2-109), becomes

$$\left[\begin{array}{c} \dot{\tilde{\eta}}_2 \\ \dot{\tilde{\eta}}_3 \end{array} \right] = \left[\begin{array}{cc} 2 & 1 \\ -28 & -6 \end{array} \right] \left[\begin{array}{c} \tilde{\eta}_2 \\ \tilde{\eta}_3 \end{array} \right] + \left\{ \left[\begin{array}{cc} 2 & 1 \\ -28 & -6 \end{array} \right] \left[\begin{array}{c} -2 \\ 17 \end{array} \right] \right.$$

$$\left. + \left[\begin{array}{c} 0 \\ -6 \end{array} \right] - \left[\begin{array}{c} -2 \\ 17 \end{array} \right] 0 \right\} y + \left\{ \left[\begin{array}{c} 0 \\ 1 \end{array} \right] - \left[\begin{array}{c} -2 \\ 17 \end{array} \right] 0 \right\} u$$

or

$$\begin{bmatrix} \dot{\tilde{\eta}}_2 \\ \dot{\tilde{\eta}}_3 \end{bmatrix} = \begin{bmatrix} 2 & 1 \\ -28 & -6 \end{bmatrix} \begin{bmatrix} \tilde{\eta}_2 \\ \tilde{\eta}_3 \end{bmatrix} + \begin{bmatrix} 13 \\ -52 \end{bmatrix} y + \begin{bmatrix} 0 \\ 1 \end{bmatrix} u$$

This is the equation for the minimum-order observer.

Examples of MATLAB programs for the design of a minimum-order observer

We present next two programs for the design of minimum-order observers, one using the transformation matrix **Q** (MATLAB Program 2-11) and the other using Ackermann's formula (MATLAB Program 2-12).

```
MATLAB Program 2–11

% ---------- Design of minimum-order observer ----------

% ***** This program uses transformation matrix Q *****

% ***** Enter matrices Aaa, Aab, Aba, Abb, Ba, and Bb *****

Aaa = [0]; Aab = [1  0]; Aba = [0;-6]; Abb = [0  1;-11  -6];
Ba = [0]; Bb = [0;1];

% ***** Note that state matrix A and control matrix B are *****

A = [Aaa   Aab;Aba   Abb], B = [Ba;Bb]

A =

     0    1    0
     0    0    1
    -6  -11   -6

B =

     0
     0
     1

% ***** Determine a1 and a2 of the characteristic polynomial
% for the unobserved portion of the system *****

p = poly(Abb)

p =

     1    6    11

a1 = p(2); a2 = p(3);
```

```
% ***** Enter the reduced observablity matrix NN *****

NN = [Aab'  Abb'*Aab'];

% ***** Enter matrix WW *****

WW = [a1   1;1   0];

% ***** Enter the desired characteristic polynomial by defining
% the following matrix J and entering statement poly(J) *****

J = [-2+2*sqrt(3)*i      0
        0    -2-2*sqrt(3)*i];

JJ = poly(J)

JJ =

    1.0000    4.0000    16.0000

% ***** Determine aa1 and aa2 of the desired characteristic
% polynomial *****

aa1 = JJ(2); aa2 = JJ(3);

% ***** Observer gain matrix Ke for the minimum-order
% observer is given by *****

Ke = inv(WW*NN')*[aa2-a2;aa1-a1]

Ke =

    -2
    17
```

```
MATLAB Program 2–12

% ---------- Design of minimum-order observer ----------

% ***** This program is based on Ackermann's formula *****

% ***** Enter matrices Aaa, Aab, Aba, Abb, Ba, and Bb *****

Aaa = [0]; Aab = [1   0]; Aba = [0;-6]; Abb = [0   1;-11   -6];
Ba = [0]; Bb = [0;1];

% ***** Enter the reduced observablity matrix NN *****

NN = [Aab'  Abb'*Aab'];

% ***** Enter the desired characteristic polynomial by defining
% the following matrix J and entering statement poly(J) *****
```

```
J = [-2+2*sqrt(3)*i    0
      0    -2-2*sqrt(3)*i];

JJ = poly(J)

JJ =

    1.0000      4.0000      16.0000

% ***** Enter characteristic polynomial Phi *****

Phi = polyvalm(poly(J),Abb);

% ***** Observer gain matrix Ke for the minimum-order observer
% is given by *****

Ke = Phi*inv(NN')*[0;1]

Ke =

    -2
    17
```

Chapter 3 Pole Placement and Design of Observers for Discrete-Time Systems

3-1 INTRODUCTION

This chapter presents pole-placement techniques and the design of state observers for discrete-time control systems. The techniques of pole placement and the design of state observers are basically the same for the continuous-time and discrete-time control systems. The equations for the determination of state feedback gain matrix $\mathbf{K}$ and observer gain matrix $\mathbf{K}_e$ are virtually the same for both continuous-time and discrete-time control systems.

Outline of the chapter

To begin this chapter, we shall discuss in this section the discretization of continuous-time state-space equations and the computation of the matrix exponential. Then, in Section 3-2, we discuss pole-placement techniques for discrete-time control systems. Section 3-3 presents a case study of a pole-placement problem. Finally, Section 3-4 treats the design of state observers for discrete-time control systems.

Obtaining a discrete-time state-space equation from a continuous-time state-space equation

To obtain a discrete-time state-space equation from a continuous-time state-space equation, use the following command:

$$[G,H] = c2d(A,B,T)$$

where T is the sampling period of the discrete-time system. T should be specified in seconds.

If good accuracy is needed in obtaining $\mathbf{G}$ and $\mathbf{H}$, use *format long*. If only four decimal places are needed, use *format short*. If no format statement is included in the program, MATLAB will produce $\mathbf{G}$ and $\mathbf{H}$ in *format short*.

Consider the following example: If the continuous-time system is given by

$$\begin{bmatrix} \dot{x}_1 \\ \dot{x}_2 \end{bmatrix} = \begin{bmatrix} 0 & 1 \\ -25 & -4 \end{bmatrix} \begin{bmatrix} x_1 \\ x_2 \end{bmatrix} + \begin{bmatrix} 0 \\ 1 \end{bmatrix} u \tag{3-1}$$

then, assuming the sampling period to be 0.05 sec and using *format long*, we obtain **G** and **H** as follows:

```
A = [0   1;−25   −4];
B = [0;1];
format long;
[G,H] = c2d(A,B,0.05)

G =

      0.97088325381929     0.04484704238264
     −1.12117605956599     0.79149508428874


H =

      0.00116466984723
      0.04484704238264
```

If we use *format short*, then we get **G** and **H** as follows:

```
A = [0   1;−25   −4];
B = [0;1];
format short;
[G,H] = c2d(A,B,0.05)

G =

      0.9709     0.0448
     −1.1212     0.7915


H =

      0.0012
      0.0448
```

If we do not specify the format, we get format short, as follows:

```
A = [0   1;−25   −4];
B = [0;1];
[G,H] = c2d(A,B,0.05)

G =

      0.9709     0.0448
     −1.1212     0.7915


H =
      0.0012
      0.0448
```

Note that the state matrix **G** and control matrix **H** of the discrete-time state-space equation

$$\mathbf{x}(k + 1) = \mathbf{G}\mathbf{x}(k) + \mathbf{H}u(k)$$

depend on the sampling period T. For example, consider discretization of the continuous-time system given by Eq. (3-1) with three different sampling periods: $T = 0.01$ sec, $T = 0.2$ sec, and $T = 1$ sec. As seen in the following MATLAB outputs, a set of matrices **G** and **H** differs for a different sampling period T.

```
A = [0   1;−25   −4];
B = [0;1];
[G,H] = c2d(A,B,0.01)

G =

        0.9988      0.0098
       −0.2450      0.9596


H =

        0.0000
        0.0098
```

```
A = [0   1;−25   −4];
B = [0;1];
[G,H] = c2d(A,B,0.2)

G =

        0.6401      0.1161
       −2.9017      0.1758


H =

        0.0144
        0.1161
```

```
A = [0   1;−25   −4];
B = [0;1];
[G,H] = c2d(A,B,1)

G =

       −0.0761     −0.0293
        0.7321      0.0410


H =

        0.0430
       −0.0293
```

As another example, consider the following system:

$$\dot{\mathbf{x}} = \mathbf{A}\mathbf{x} + \mathbf{B}u$$

where

$$\mathbf{A} = \begin{bmatrix} 0 & 1 & 0 & 0 \\ 20.601 & 0 & 0 & 0 \\ 0 & 0 & 0 & 1 \\ -0.4905 & 0 & 0 & 0 \end{bmatrix}, \quad \mathbf{B} = \begin{bmatrix} 0 \\ -1 \\ 0 \\ 0.5 \end{bmatrix}$$

Assuming that the sampling period T is 0.05 sec and without specifying the format, we get the following discrete-time state equation:

$$\mathbf{x}(k + 1) = \mathbf{G}\mathbf{x}(k) + \mathbf{H}u(k)$$

where matrices $\mathbf{G}$ and $\mathbf{H}$ can be found in the following computer output:

```
A = [0          1  0  0
     20.601     0  0  0
     0          0  0  1
     -0.4905    0  0  0];
B = [0;-1;0;0.5];
[G,H] = c2d(A,B,0.05)

G =

      1.0259    0.0504        0        0
      1.0389    1.0259        0        0
     -0.0006   -0.0000   1.0000   0.0500
     -0.0247   -0.0006        0   1.0000


H =

     -0.0013
     -0.0504
      0.0006
      0.0250
```

Matrix exponential

In analyzing or designing control systems (both continuous and discrete time), we frequently require the computation of the matrix exponential. Discretization of continuous-time control systems involves computations of the matrix exponential. The command [G,H] = c2d(A,B,T) performs a series of matrix computations including matrix exponentials. In what follows, we shall discuss how to get the matrix exponential of a square matrix if it is needed in certain situations.

The matrix exponential of a square matrix $\mathbf{A}$ can be obtained easily by use of the following command:

expm(A)

Consider the following matrix **A**:

$$\mathbf{A} = \begin{bmatrix} 0 & 1 \\ -25 & -4 \end{bmatrix}$$

The command

format long, expm(A)

will give the matrix exponential as follows:

```
A = [0   1;−25   −4];
format long, expm(A)

ans =

   −0.07608720775055   −0.02928409524696
    0.73210238117404    0.04104917323730
```

The command

format short, expm(A)

will produce the following output:

```
A = [0   1;−25   −4];
format short, expm(A)

ans =

   −0.0761   −0.0293
    0.7321    0.0410
```

Simply giving the command

expm(A)

will produce the output in format short, as follows:

```
A = [0   1;−25   −4];
expm(A)

ans =

   −0.0761   −0.0293
    0.7321    0.0410
```

3-2 POLE PLACEMENT

In this section we shall discuss the design of discrete-time control systems using the pole-placement technique. We assume that all state variables are measurable and are available for feedback. If the system considered is completely state controllable, then poles of the closed-loop system may be placed at any desired locations by means of state feedback through an appropriate state feedback gain matrix. (For the proof of this statement, see, for example, Reference 3 listed at the end of the book.)

The present design technique begins with a determination of the desired closed-loop poles based on transient-response and/or frequency-response requirements. Let us assume that we decide that the desired closed-loop poles are to be at $z = \mu_1, z = \mu_2, \ldots, z = \mu_n$. (In choosing the sampling period, care must be exercised so that the desired system will not require unusually large control signals. Otherwise, saturation phenomena will occur in the system. If saturation takes place in the system, the system will become nonlinear, and the design method presented here will no longer apply, since the method is applicable only to linear time-invariant systems.) Then, by choosing an appropriate gain matrix for state feedback, it is possible to force the system to have closed-loop poles at the desired locations, provided that the original system is completely state controllable.

Consider the open-loop control system shown in Figure 3-1(a). The state equation is

$$\mathbf{x}(k + 1) = \mathbf{G}\mathbf{x}(k) + \mathbf{H}u(k) \tag{3-2}$$

where $\mathbf{x}(k)$ = state vector (n-vector) at kth sampling instant
     $u(k)$ = control signal (scalar) at kth sampling instant
      $\mathbf{G} = n \times n$ matrix
      $\mathbf{H} = n \times 1$ matrix

We assume that the magnitude of the control signal $u(k)$ is unbounded. If the control signal $u(k)$ is chosen as

$$u(k) = -\mathbf{K}\mathbf{x}(k)$$

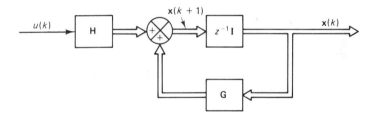

(a)

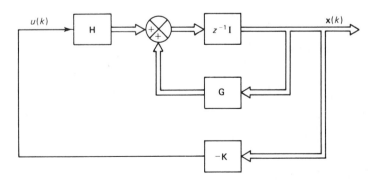

(b)

Figure 3-1

where $\mathbf{K}$ is the state feedback gain matrix (a $1 \times n$ matrix), then the system becomes a closed-loop control system as shown in Figure 3-1(b) and its state equation becomes

$$\mathbf{x}(k + 1) = (\mathbf{G} - \mathbf{HK})\mathbf{x}(k) \tag{3-3}$$

Note that the eigenvalues of $\mathbf{G} - \mathbf{HK}$ are the desired closed-loop poles $\mu_1, \mu_2, \ldots, \mu_n$. A necessary and sufficient condition for arbitrary pole placement is that the system be completely state controllable.

The methods for determining the state feedback gain matrix $\mathbf{K}$ are the same for the continuous-time and discrete-time control systems. In what follows we shall give two methods for the determination of matrix $\mathbf{K}$. The two methods, which are the same as those we presented for continuous-time control systems, are summarized next.

1. As discussed in Section 2-2, the state feedback gain matrix $\mathbf{K}$ may be given by

$$\mathbf{K} = [\alpha_n - a_n \vdots \alpha_{n-1} - a_{n-1} \vdots \cdots \vdots \alpha_1 - a_1]\mathbf{T}^{-1} \tag{3-4}$$

where the a_i's are the coefficients of the original system characteristic equation

$$|z\mathbf{I} - \mathbf{G}| = z^n + a_1 z^{n-1} + \cdots + a_{n-1} z + a_n = 0$$

and the α_i's are the coefficients of the desired characteristic equation for the state feedback control system; that is,

$$|z\mathbf{I} - \mathbf{G} + \mathbf{HK}| = \phi(z) = z^n + \alpha_1 z^{n-1} + \cdots + \alpha_{n-1} z + \alpha_n = 0$$

Matrix $\mathbf{T}$ is given by

$$\mathbf{T} = \mathbf{MW} \tag{3-5}$$

where $\mathbf{M}$ and $\mathbf{W}$ are given by

$$\mathbf{M} = [\mathbf{H} \vdots \mathbf{GH} \vdots \cdots \vdots \mathbf{G}^{n-1}\mathbf{H}]$$

and

$$\mathbf{W} = \begin{bmatrix} a_{n-1} & a_{n-2} & \cdots & a_1 & 1 \\ a_{n-2} & a_{n-3} & \cdots & 1 & 0 \\ \vdots & \vdots & & \vdots & \vdots \\ a_1 & 1 & \cdots & 0 & 0 \\ 1 & 0 & \cdots & 0 & 0 \end{bmatrix}$$

If the system state equation is already in the controllable canonical form, the determination of the state feedback gain matrix $\mathbf{K}$ can be made simple, because the transformation matrix $\mathbf{T}$ becomes the identity matrix. In this case the desired matrix $\mathbf{K}$ is simply given as follows:

$$\mathbf{K} = [\alpha_n - a_n \vdots \alpha_{n-1} - a_{n-1} \vdots \cdots \vdots \alpha_1 - a_1] \qquad \text{when } \mathbf{T} = \mathbf{I} \tag{3-6}$$

2. The desired state feedback gain matrix $\mathbf{K}$ can be given by Ackermann's formula:

$$\mathbf{K} = [0 \quad 0 \quad \cdots \quad 0 \quad 1][\mathbf{H} \vdots \mathbf{GH} \vdots \cdots \vdots \mathbf{G}^{n-1}\mathbf{H}]^{-1}\phi(\mathbf{G})$$
$$= [0 \quad 0 \quad \cdots \quad 0 \quad 1]\mathbf{M}^{-1}\phi(\mathbf{G}) \tag{3-7}$$

where

$$\mathbf{M} = [\mathbf{H} \vdots \mathbf{GH} \vdots \cdots \vdots \mathbf{G}^{n-1}\mathbf{H}]$$

and

$$\phi(\mathbf{G}) = \mathbf{G}^n + \alpha_1 \mathbf{G}^{n-1} + \cdots + \alpha_{n-1}\mathbf{G} + \alpha_n \mathbf{I}$$

Note that the desired characteristic polynomial is

$$\phi(z) = z^n + \alpha_1 z^{n-1} + \cdots + \alpha_{n-1}z + \alpha_n$$

For the derivation of Eqs. (3-4) and (3-7), respectively, refer to Section 2-2. The derivations of these equations are identical to those for continuous-time control systems, except that s is replaced by z.

Comments

The state feedback gain matrix $\mathbf{K}$ is determined in such a way that the error (caused by disturbances) will reduce to zero with sufficient speed. Note that the matrix $\mathbf{K}$ is not unique for a given system, but depends on the desired closed-loop pole locations (which determine the speed of response) selected. The selection of the desired closed-loop poles or the desired characteristic equation is a compromise between the rapidity of the response of the error vector and the sensitivity to disturbances and measurement noises. That is, if we increase the speed of error response, then the adverse effects of disturbances and measurement noises generally increase. In determining the state feedback gain matrix $\mathbf{K}$ for a given system, it is desirable to examine several matrices $\mathbf{K}$ based on several different desired characteristic equations and to choose the one that gives the best overall system performance.

Deadbeat response

Consider the system defined by

$$\mathbf{x}(k + 1) = \mathbf{Gx}(k) + \mathbf{H}u(k)$$

With state feedback $u(k) = -\mathbf{Kx}(k)$, the state equation becomes

$$\mathbf{x}(k + 1) = (\mathbf{G} - \mathbf{HK})\mathbf{x}(k)$$

Note that the solution of this last equation is given by

$$\mathbf{x}(k) = (\mathbf{G} - \mathbf{HK})^k \mathbf{x}(0) \tag{3-8}$$

If the eigenvalues μ_i of matrix $\mathbf{G} - \mathbf{HK}$ lie inside the unit circle, then the system is asymptotically stable.

In what follows, we shall show that by choosing all eigenvalues of $\mathbf{G} - \mathbf{HK}$ to be zero it is possible to get the deadbeat response, or

$$\mathbf{x}(k) = \mathbf{0}, \qquad \text{for } k \geq q \qquad (q \leq n)$$

In discussing deadbeat response, the nilpotent matrix

$$\mathbf{N} = \begin{bmatrix} 0 & 1 & 0 & \cdots & 0 \\ 0 & 0 & 1 & \cdots & 0 \\ \vdots & \vdots & \vdots & & \vdots \\ 0 & 0 & 0 & \cdots & 1 \\ 0 & 0 & 0 & \cdots & 0 \end{bmatrix}$$

plays an important role. Consider, for example, a 4×4 nilpotent matrix:

$$\mathbf{N} = \begin{bmatrix} 0 & 1 & 0 & 0 \\ 0 & 0 & 1 & 0 \\ 0 & 0 & 0 & 1 \\ 0 & 0 & 0 & 0 \end{bmatrix}$$

Notice that

$$\mathbf{N}^2 = \begin{bmatrix} 0 & 0 & 1 & 0 \\ 0 & 0 & 0 & 1 \\ 0 & 0 & 0 & 0 \\ 0 & 0 & 0 & 0 \end{bmatrix}, \quad \mathbf{N}^3 = \begin{bmatrix} 0 & 0 & 0 & 1 \\ 0 & 0 & 0 & 0 \\ 0 & 0 & 0 & 0 \\ 0 & 0 & 0 & 0 \end{bmatrix}, \quad \mathbf{N}^4 = \begin{bmatrix} 0 & 0 & 0 & 0 \\ 0 & 0 & 0 & 0 \\ 0 & 0 & 0 & 0 \\ 0 & 0 & 0 & 0 \end{bmatrix}$$

Similarly, for an $n \times n$ nilpotent matrix $\mathbf{N}$, we have

$$\mathbf{N}^n = \mathbf{0}$$

Now consider the completely state controllable system given by

$$\mathbf{x}(k + 1) = \mathbf{G}\mathbf{x}(k) + \mathbf{H}u(k) \tag{3-9}$$

Let us choose the desired pole locations to be at the origin, or choose the desired eigenvalues to be zero: $\mu_1 = \mu_2 = \cdots = \mu_n = 0$. Then we shall show that the response to any initial state $\mathbf{x}(0)$ is deadbeat. Since the characteristic polynomial with the desired eigenvalues can be given by

$$|z\mathbf{I} - \mathbf{G} + \mathbf{H}\mathbf{K}| = (z - \mu_1)(z - \mu_2)\cdots(z - \mu_n)$$

$$= z^n + \alpha_1 z^{n-1} + \cdots + \alpha_{n-1} z + \alpha_n = z^n$$

we obtain

$$\alpha_1 = \alpha_2 = \cdots = \alpha_n = 0$$

and matrix $\mathbf{K}$ given by Eq. (3-4) can be simplified to the following:

$$\mathbf{K} = [\alpha_n - a_n \vdots \alpha_{n-1} - a_{n-1} \vdots \cdots \vdots \alpha_1 - a_1]\mathbf{T}^{-1}$$

$$= [-a_n \quad -a_{n-1} \quad \cdots \quad -a_1]\mathbf{T}^{-1} \tag{3-10}$$

By using the transformation matrix $\mathbf{T}$ given by Eq. (3-5), define

$$\mathbf{x}(k) = \mathbf{T}\hat{\mathbf{x}}(k)$$

Define also

$$\mathbf{T}^{-1}\mathbf{GT} = \hat{\mathbf{G}}, \qquad \mathbf{T}^{-1}\mathbf{H} = \hat{\mathbf{H}}$$

Then Eq. (3-9) can be written as

$$\hat{\mathbf{x}}(k+1) = \mathbf{T}^{-1}\mathbf{GT}\hat{\mathbf{x}}(k) + \mathbf{T}^{-1}\mathbf{H}u(k) = \hat{\mathbf{G}}\hat{\mathbf{x}}(k) + \hat{\mathbf{H}}u(k)$$

If we use the state feedback $u(k) = -\mathbf{K}\mathbf{x}(k) = -\mathbf{KT}\hat{\mathbf{x}}(k)$, then this last equation becomes

$$\hat{\mathbf{x}}(k+1) = (\hat{\mathbf{G}} - \hat{\mathbf{H}}\mathbf{KT})\hat{\mathbf{x}}(k)$$

Referring to Eq. (3-10), we have

$$\hat{\mathbf{G}} - \hat{\mathbf{H}}\mathbf{KT} = \hat{\mathbf{G}} - \hat{\mathbf{H}}[-a_n \quad -a_{n-1} \quad \cdots \quad -a_1]$$

$$= \begin{bmatrix} 0 & 1 & 0 & \cdots & 0 \\ 0 & 0 & 1 & \cdots & 0 \\ \vdots & \vdots & \vdots & & \vdots \\ 0 & 0 & 0 & \cdots & 1 \\ -a_n & -a_{n-1} & -a_{n-2} & \cdots & -a_1 \end{bmatrix} - \begin{bmatrix} 0 \\ 0 \\ \vdots \\ 0 \\ 1 \end{bmatrix} [-a_n \quad -a_{n-1} \quad \cdots \quad -a_1]$$

$$= \begin{bmatrix} 0 & 1 & 0 & \cdots & 0 \\ 0 & 0 & 1 & \cdots & 0 \\ \vdots & \vdots & \vdots & & \vdots \\ 0 & 0 & 0 & \cdots & 1 \\ -a_n & -a_{n-1} & -a_{n-2} & \cdots & -a_1 \end{bmatrix} - \begin{bmatrix} 0 & 0 & 0 & \cdots & 0 \\ 0 & 0 & 0 & \cdots & 0 \\ \vdots & \vdots & \vdots & & \vdots \\ 0 & 0 & 0 & \cdots & 0 \\ -a_n & -a_{n-1} & -a_{n-2} & \cdots & -a_1 \end{bmatrix}$$

$$= \begin{bmatrix} 0 & 1 & 0 & \cdots & 0 \\ 0 & 0 & 1 & \cdots & 0 \\ \vdots & \vdots & \vdots & & \vdots \\ 0 & 0 & 0 & \cdots & 1 \\ 0 & 0 & 0 & \cdots & 0 \end{bmatrix}$$

Thus $\hat{\mathbf{G}} - \hat{\mathbf{H}}\mathbf{KT}$ is a nilpotent matrix. Therefore, we have

$$(\hat{\mathbf{G}} - \hat{\mathbf{H}}\mathbf{KT})^n = \mathbf{0}$$

In terms of the original state $\mathbf{x}(n)$, we have

$$\mathbf{x}(n) = (\mathbf{G} - \mathbf{HK})^n\mathbf{x}(0) = (\mathbf{T}\hat{\mathbf{G}}\mathbf{T}^{-1} - \mathbf{T}\hat{\mathbf{H}}\mathbf{K})^n\mathbf{x}(0) = [\mathbf{T}(\hat{\mathbf{G}} - \hat{\mathbf{H}}\mathbf{KT})\mathbf{T}^{-1}]^n\mathbf{x}(0)$$

$$= \mathbf{T}(\hat{\mathbf{G}} - \hat{\mathbf{H}}\mathbf{KT})^n\mathbf{T}^{-1}\mathbf{x}(0) = \mathbf{0}$$

Thus we have shown that, if the desired eigenvalues are all zeros, then any initial state $\mathbf{x}(0)$ can be brought to the origin in at most n sampling periods, and the response is deadbeat, provided the control signal $u(k)$ is unbounded.

Comments on deadbeat control

The concept of deadbeat response is unique to discrete-time control systems. There is no such thing as deadbeat response in continuous-time control systems. In deadbeat control, any nonzero error vector will be driven to zero in at most n sampling periods if the magnitude of the scalar control $u(k)$ is unbounded. The settling time depends on the sampling period, since the response settles down in at most n sampling periods. If the sampling period T is chosen very small, the settling time will also be very small, which implies that the control signal must have an extremely large magnitude. Otherwise, it will not be possible to bring the error response to zero in a short time period.

In deadbeat control, the sampling period is the only design parameter. Thus, if the deadbeat response is desired, the designer must choose the sampling period carefully so that an extremely large control magnitude is not required in normal operation of the system. Note that it is not physically possible to increase the magnitude of the control signal without bound. If the magnitude is increased sufficiently, the saturation phenomenon always takes place. If saturation occurs in the magnitude of the control signal, then the response can no longer be deadbeat, and the settling time will be more than n sampling periods. In the actual design of deadbeat control systems, the designer must be aware of the trade-off that must be made between the magnitude of the control signal and the response speed.

EXAMPLE 3-1

Consider the system

$$\mathbf{x}(k + 1) = \mathbf{G}\mathbf{x}(k) + \mathbf{H}u(k)$$

where

$$\mathbf{G} = \begin{bmatrix} 0 & 1 \\ -0.16 & -1 \end{bmatrix}, \quad \mathbf{H} = \begin{bmatrix} 0 \\ 1 \end{bmatrix}$$

Note that

$$|z\mathbf{I} - \mathbf{G}| = \begin{vmatrix} z & -1 \\ 0.16 & z + 1 \end{vmatrix} = z^2 + z + 0.16 = z^2 + a_1 z + a_2$$

Hence

$$a_1 = 1, \quad a_2 = 0.16$$

Determine a suitable state feedback gain matrix $\mathbf{K}$ such that the system will have the closed-loop poles at

$$z = 0.5 + j0.5, \quad z = 0.5 - j0.5$$

Let us first examine the rank of the controllability matrix. The rank of

$$[\mathbf{H} \vdots \mathbf{G}\mathbf{H}] = \begin{bmatrix} 0 & 1 \\ 1 & -1 \end{bmatrix}$$

is 2. Thus the system is completely state controllable, and therefore arbitrary pole placement is possible. The characteristic equation for the desired system is

$$|z\mathbf{I} - \mathbf{G} + \mathbf{H}\mathbf{K}| = (z - 0.5 - j0.5)(z - 0.5 + j0.5) = z^2 - z + 0.5 = 0$$

Hence

$$\alpha_1 = -1, \quad \alpha_2 = 0.5$$

We shall next solve this problem by two methods.

Method 1. From Eq. (3-4), the state feedback gain matrix **K** is given by

$$\mathbf{K} = [\alpha_2 - a_2 \vdots \alpha_1 - a_1]\mathbf{T}^{-1}$$

Notice that the original system is already in the controllable canonical form, and therefore the transformation matrix **T** becomes **I**:

$$\mathbf{T} = \mathbf{MW} = [\mathbf{H} \vdots \mathbf{GH}]\begin{bmatrix} a_1 & 1 \\ 1 & 0 \end{bmatrix} = \begin{bmatrix} 0 & 1 \\ 1 & -1 \end{bmatrix}\begin{bmatrix} 1 & 1 \\ 1 & 0 \end{bmatrix} = \begin{bmatrix} 1 & 0 \\ 0 & 1 \end{bmatrix}$$

Hence

$$\mathbf{K} = [\alpha_2 - a_2 \vdots \alpha_1 - a_1] = [0.5 - 0.16 \vdots -1 - 1]$$
$$= [0.34 \quad -2]$$

Method 2. Referring to Ackermann's formula given by Eq. (3-7), we have

$$\mathbf{K} = [0 \quad 1][\mathbf{H} \vdots \mathbf{GH}]^{-1}\phi(\mathbf{G})$$

where

$$\phi(\mathbf{G}) = \mathbf{G}^2 - \mathbf{G} + 0.5\mathbf{I} = \begin{bmatrix} -0.16 & -1 \\ 0.16 & 0.84 \end{bmatrix} - \begin{bmatrix} 0 & 1 \\ -0.16 & -1 \end{bmatrix} + \begin{bmatrix} 0.5 & 0 \\ 0 & 0.5 \end{bmatrix}$$
$$= \begin{bmatrix} 0.34 & -2 \\ 0.32 & 2.34 \end{bmatrix}$$

Thus

$$\mathbf{K} = [0 \quad 1]\begin{bmatrix} 0 & 1 \\ 1 & -1 \end{bmatrix}^{-1}\begin{bmatrix} 0.34 & -2 \\ 0.32 & 2.34 \end{bmatrix}$$
$$= [0.34 \quad -2]$$

MATLAB programs for the determination of matrix **K**

MATLAB Programs 3-1 and 3-2 may be used for the determination of matrix **K**. The former uses the transformation matrix **T** and the latter is based on Ackermann's formula.

MATLAB Program 3–1

```
% ---------- Pole placement in the z plane ----------

% ***** This program determines state feedback gain matrix K
% using transformation matrix T *****

% ***** Enter state matrix G and control matrix H *****

G = [0  1;-0.16  -1];
H = [0;1];
```

```
% ***** Enter the controllability matrix M and check its
% rank *****

M = [H   G*H];
rank(M)

ans =

     2

% ***** Since the rank of controllability matrix M is 2,
% arbitrary pole placement is possible *****

% ***** Obtain the coefficients of the characteristic polynomial
% |zI - G|.  This can be done by entering statement poly(G) *****

p = poly(G)

p =

     1.0000     1.0000     0.1600

a1 = p(2); a2 = p(3);

% ***** Define matrices W and T as follows *****

W = [a1   1;1   0];
T = M*W;

% ***** Obtain the coefficients of the desired characteristic
% polynomial by defining the following matrix J and computing
% poly(J) *****

J = [0.5+0.5*i   0;0   0.5-0.5*i];

JJ = poly(J)

JJ =

     1.0000     -1.0000     0.5000

aa1 = JJ(2); aa2 = JJ(3);

% ***** State feedback gain matrix K can be determined from *****

K = [aa2-a2   aa1-a1]*(inv(T))

K =

     0.3400     -2.0000

% ***** Hence k1 and k2 are given by *****

k1 = K(1), k2 = K(2)
```

```
K1 =

    0.3400


K2 =

   -2
```

MATLAB Program 3–2

```
% ---------- Pole placement in the z plane ----------

% ***** This program determines state feedback gain matrix K
% based on Ackermann's formula *****

% ***** Enter state matrix G and control matrix H *****

G = [0   1;-0.16  -1];
H = [0;1];

% ***** Enter the controllability matrix M and check its
% rank *****

M = [H   G*H];
rank(M)

ans =

     2

% ***** Since the rank of controllability matrix M is 2,
% arbitrary pole placement is possible *****

% ***** Enter the desired characteristic polynomial by
% defining the following matrix J and computing poly(J) *****

J = [0.5+0.5*i   0;0   0.5-0.5*i];

JJ = poly(J)

JJ =

    1.0000    -1.0000     0.5000

% ***** Enter characteristic polynomial Phi *****

Phi = polyvalm(poly(J),G);

% ***** State feedback gain matrix K can be given by *****

K = [0   1]*inv(M)*Phi
```

K =

    0.3400   -2.0000

k1 = K(1), k2 = K(2)

k1 =

    0.3400

k2 =

    -2

EXAMPLE 3-2

Consider the system given by

$$\begin{bmatrix} x_1(k+1) \\ x_2(k+1) \end{bmatrix} = \begin{bmatrix} 0 & 1 \\ -0.16 & -1 \end{bmatrix} \begin{bmatrix} x_1(k) \\ x_2(k) \end{bmatrix} + \begin{bmatrix} 0 \\ 1 \end{bmatrix} u(k)$$

Determine the state feedback gain matrix **K** such that when the control signal is given by

$$u(k) = -\mathbf{K}\mathbf{x}(k)$$

the closed-loop system (regulator system) exhibits the deadbeat response to an initial state $\mathbf{x}(0)$. Assume that the control signal $u(k)$ is unbounded.

For the deadbeat response, the desired characteristic equation is

$$|z\mathbf{I} - \mathbf{G} + \mathbf{HK}| = z^2 + \alpha_1 z + \alpha_2 = z^2$$

where $\alpha_1 = 0$ and $\alpha_2 = 0$. Referring to Eq. (3-7), for the deadbeat response, the state feedback gain matrix **K** can be given by

$$\mathbf{K} = [0 \quad 1][\mathbf{H} \quad \mathbf{GH}]^{-1}\phi(\mathbf{G})$$

where

$$\phi(\mathbf{G}) = \mathbf{G}^2$$

A MATLAB program for the determination of state feedback gain matrix **K** is given in MATLAB Program 3-3.

MATLAB Program 3–3

% ---------- Pole placement (Deadbeat response) ----------

% ***** This program determines state feedback gain matrix
% K for deadbeat response using Ackermann's formula *****

% ***** Enter matrices G and H *****

```
G = [0   1;-0.16   -1];
H = [0;1];

% ***** Enter the controllability matrix M and check its
% rank *****

M = [H   G*H];
rank(M)

ans =

      2

% ***** Since the rank of M is 2, the system is completely
% state controllable and thus arbitrary pole placement is
% possible *****

% ***** For deadbeat response, the desired characteristic
% polynomial becomes Phi = G^2 *****

Phi = G^2;

% ***** State feedback gain matrix K can be given by *****

K = [0   1]*inv(M)*Phi

K =

     -0.1600      -1.0000

k1 = K(1), k2 = K(2)

k1 =

     -0.1600

k2 =

      -1
```

3-3 CASE STUDY

In this section we shall consider the design of a digital controller for a type 0 plant. The digital controller will involve state feedback and integral control. We shall first derive the equations for the system shown in Figure 3-2, where the plant does not involve an integrator. Then we shall give detailed discussions of a design of a digital controller for the inverted pendulum system.

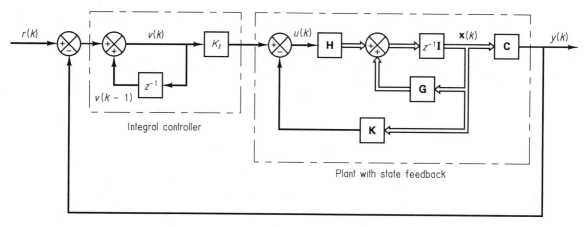

Figure 3-2

Design of a servo system in which the plant does not involve an integrator

Consider the servo system shown in Figure 3-2 in which the plant does not involve an integrator. This system uses state feedback and integral control.

Basic approach to the design of servo systems

From Figure 3-2 the plant state equation and output equation are

$$\mathbf{x}(k + 1) = \mathbf{G}\mathbf{x}(k) + \mathbf{H}u(k)$$
$$y(k) = \mathbf{C}\mathbf{x}(k)$$

The equation for the integrator is

$$v(k) = v(k - 1) + r(k) - y(k)$$

Since

$$u(k) = -\mathbf{K}\mathbf{x}(k) + K_I v(k)$$

we have

$$v(k + 1) = v(k) + r(k + 1) - y(k + 1)$$
$$= v(k) + r(k + 1) - \mathbf{C}[\mathbf{G}\mathbf{x}(k) + \mathbf{H}u(k)]$$
$$= (1 - \mathbf{C}\mathbf{H}K_I)v(k) + (-\mathbf{C}\mathbf{G} + \mathbf{C}\mathbf{H}\mathbf{K})\mathbf{x}(k) + r(k + 1)$$

Noting that

$$\mathbf{x}(k + 1) = \mathbf{G}\mathbf{x}(k) + \mathbf{H}[-\mathbf{K}\mathbf{x}(k) + K_I v(k)]$$
$$= (\mathbf{G} - \mathbf{H}\mathbf{K})\mathbf{x}(k) + \mathbf{H}K_I v(k)$$

we obtain the following state equation and output equation for the entire closed-loop system:

$$\begin{bmatrix} \mathbf{x}(k+1) \\ v(k+1) \end{bmatrix} = \begin{bmatrix} \mathbf{G} - \mathbf{HK} & \mathbf{H}K_I \\ -\mathbf{CG} + \mathbf{CHK} & 1 - \mathbf{CH}K_I \end{bmatrix} \begin{bmatrix} \mathbf{x}(k) \\ v(k) \end{bmatrix} + \begin{bmatrix} \mathbf{0} \\ 1 \end{bmatrix} r(k+1)$$

$$y(k) = \begin{bmatrix} \mathbf{C} & 0 \end{bmatrix} \begin{bmatrix} \mathbf{x}(k) \\ v(k) \end{bmatrix}$$

For a step input $r(k) = r$,

$$\begin{bmatrix} \mathbf{x}(k+1) \\ v(k+1) \end{bmatrix} = \begin{bmatrix} \mathbf{G} - \mathbf{HK} & \mathbf{H}K_I \\ -\mathbf{CG} + \mathbf{CHK} & 1 - \mathbf{CH}K_I \end{bmatrix} \begin{bmatrix} \mathbf{x}(k) \\ v(k) \end{bmatrix} + \begin{bmatrix} \mathbf{0} \\ r \end{bmatrix} \tag{3-11}$$

For a step input, as k approaches infinity, $\mathbf{x}(k)$, $u(k)$, and $v(k)$ approach constant values $\mathbf{x}(\infty)$, $u(\infty)$, and $v(\infty)$, respectively. Also,

$$v(\infty) = v(\infty) + r(\infty) - y(\infty)$$

or

$$y(\infty) = r(\infty) = r$$

There is no steady-state error. By substituting $k = \infty$ into Eq. (3-11), we obtain

$$\begin{bmatrix} \mathbf{x}(\infty) \\ v(\infty) \end{bmatrix} = \begin{bmatrix} \mathbf{G} - \mathbf{HK} & \mathbf{H}K_I \\ -\mathbf{CG} + \mathbf{CHK} & 1 - \mathbf{CH}K_I \end{bmatrix} \begin{bmatrix} \mathbf{x}(\infty) \\ v(\infty) \end{bmatrix} + \begin{bmatrix} \mathbf{0} \\ r \end{bmatrix}$$

Define

$$\mathbf{x}_e(k) = \mathbf{x}(k) - \mathbf{x}(\infty)$$

$$v_e(k) = v(k) - v(\infty)$$

Then we have

$$\begin{bmatrix} \mathbf{x}_e(k+1) \\ v_e(k+1) \end{bmatrix} = \begin{bmatrix} \mathbf{G} - \mathbf{HK} & \mathbf{H}K_I \\ -\mathbf{CG} + \mathbf{CHK} & 1 - \mathbf{CH}K_I \end{bmatrix} \begin{bmatrix} \mathbf{x}_e(k) \\ v_e(k) \end{bmatrix}$$

$$= \begin{bmatrix} \mathbf{G} & \mathbf{0} \\ -\mathbf{CG} & 1 \end{bmatrix} \begin{bmatrix} \mathbf{x}_e(k) \\ v_e(k) \end{bmatrix} + \begin{bmatrix} \mathbf{H} \\ -\mathbf{CH} \end{bmatrix} \begin{bmatrix} -\mathbf{K} & K_I \end{bmatrix} \begin{bmatrix} \mathbf{x}_e(k) \\ v_e(k) \end{bmatrix} \tag{3-12}$$

Define

$$w(k) = \begin{bmatrix} -\mathbf{K} & K_I \end{bmatrix} \begin{bmatrix} \mathbf{x}_e(k) \\ v_e(k) \end{bmatrix} \tag{3-13}$$

Then Eq. (3-12) becomes

$$\begin{bmatrix} \mathbf{x}_e(k+1) \\ v_e(k+1) \end{bmatrix} = \begin{bmatrix} \mathbf{G} & \mathbf{0} \\ -\mathbf{CG} & 1 \end{bmatrix} \begin{bmatrix} \mathbf{x}_e(k) \\ v_e(k) \end{bmatrix} + \begin{bmatrix} \mathbf{H} \\ -\mathbf{CH} \end{bmatrix} w(k) \tag{3-14}$$

Equations (3-14) and (3-13) can be rewritten, respectively, as

$$\xi(k + 1) = \hat{\mathbf{G}}\xi(k) + \hat{\mathbf{H}}w(k) \tag{3-15}$$

$$w(k) = -\hat{\mathbf{K}}\xi(k) \tag{3-16}$$

where

$$\xi(k) = \begin{bmatrix} \mathbf{x}_e(k) \\ v_e(k) \end{bmatrix}, \quad \hat{\mathbf{G}} = \begin{bmatrix} \mathbf{G} & \mathbf{0} \\ -\mathbf{CG} & 1 \end{bmatrix}, \quad \hat{\mathbf{H}} = \begin{bmatrix} \mathbf{H} \\ -\mathbf{CH} \end{bmatrix}$$

$$\hat{\mathbf{K}} = [\mathbf{K} \quad -K_I]$$

Equations (3-15) and (3-16) represent standard state-space equations. Matrix $\hat{\mathbf{K}}$ can then be determined by using the pole-placement approach, provided the system represented by Eqs. (3-15) and (3-16) is completely state controllable.

EXAMPLE 3-3: Design of an Inverted Pendulum Control System

Consider the inverted pendulum system shown in Figure 3-3, where an inverted pendulum is mounted on a motor-driven cart. Here we consider only the two-dimensional problem in which the pendulum moves only in the plane of the paper. The inverted pendulum is unstable in that it may fall over anytime unless a suitable control force is applied. Assume that the pendulum mass is concentrated at the end of the rod as shown in the figure. (We assume that the rod is massless.) The control force u is applied to the cart.

In the diagram, θ is the angle of the rod from the vertical line. We assume that angle θ is small so that we may approximate $\sin\theta$ by θ, $\cos\theta$ by 1, and also assume that $\dot{\theta}$ is small so that $\theta\dot{\theta}^2 \doteq 0$. (Under these conditions, the system's nonlinear equations can be linearized.)

It is desired to keep the pendulum upright in response to step changes in the cart position. (The control force u is the force applied to the cart.) This pendulum system is the same as that considered in Section 2-3. Design a digital controller for the inverted pendulum system.

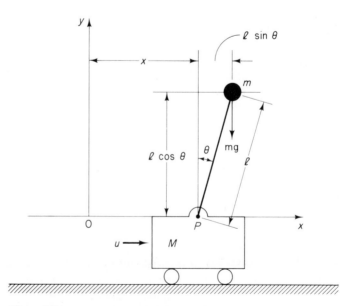

Figure 3-3

Since the plant (inverted pendulum system) does not involve an integrator, we need to include an integral controller. If we implement this system as a servo system, the block diagram for the system may take the form shown in Figure 3-2. (This means that the controller to be designed will include state feedback and an integrator in the closed loop.)

As was done in Section 2-3, define state variables x_1, x_2, x_3, and x_4 by

$$x_1 = \theta$$

$$x_2 = \dot{\theta}$$

$$x_3 = x$$

$$x_4 = \dot{x}$$

Assume the same numerical values for M, m, and l as we did in Section 2-3. That is, we assume that

$$M = 2 \text{ kg}, \qquad m = 0.1 \text{ kg}, \qquad l = 0.5 \text{ m}$$

In this system we would like to keep angle θ as small as possible when the cart is moved in the step fashion. We consider the displacement of the cart as the output of the system. Thus the output equation becomes

$$y = [0 \quad 0 \quad 1 \quad 0] \begin{bmatrix} x_1 \\ x_2 \\ x_3 \\ x_4 \end{bmatrix}$$

Then the state equation and output equation for the inverted pendulum with cart become as follows:

$$\dot{\mathbf{x}} = \mathbf{A}\mathbf{x} + \mathbf{B}u \qquad (3\text{-}17)$$

$$y = \mathbf{C}\mathbf{x} + Du \qquad (3\text{-}18)$$

where

$$\mathbf{A} = \begin{bmatrix} 0 & 1 & 0 & 0 \\ 20.601 & 0 & 0 & 0 \\ 0 & 0 & 0 & 1 \\ -0.4905 & 0 & 0 & 0 \end{bmatrix}, \qquad \mathbf{B} = \begin{bmatrix} 0 \\ -1 \\ 0 \\ 0.5 \end{bmatrix}, \qquad \mathbf{C} = [0 \quad 0 \quad 1 \quad 0], \qquad D = 0$$

We shall use the state feedback control scheme

$$u = -\mathbf{K}\mathbf{x}$$

Since we are required to design a digital control system, we shall first discretize the state equation, Eq. (3-17). The discretization can be accomplished by using the following MATLAB command:

$$[G,H] = c2d(A,B,T)$$

where T is the sampling period involved in the discrete-time control system. In this problem we assume that T = 0.1 sec. Then the command

$$[G,H] = c2d(A,B,0.1)$$

will transform the continuous-time state-space equations into discrete-time state-space equations. See the following MATLAB command and output:

```
A = [0          1  0  0
     20.601     0  0  0
     0          0  0  1
     −0.4905    0  0  0];
B = [0;−1;0;0.5];

[G,H] = c2d(A,B,0.1)

G =

        1.1048     0.1035       0        0
        2.1316     1.1048       0        0
       −0.0025    −0.0001   1.0000   0.1000
       −0.0508    −0.0025        0   1.0000


H =

       −0.0051
       −0.1035
        0.0025
        0.0501
```

The state-space representation for the plant (inverted pendulum with cart) is now given by

$$\mathbf{x}(k + 1) = \mathbf{G}\mathbf{x}(k) + \mathbf{H}u(k)$$

$$y(k) = \mathbf{C}\mathbf{x}(k) + Du(k)$$

$$v(k) = v(k − 1) + r(k) − y(k)$$

$$u(k) = −\mathbf{K}\mathbf{x}(k) + K_I v(k)$$

For the entire control system, the state equation and output equation can be given by

$$\boldsymbol{\xi}(k + 1) = \hat{\mathbf{G}}\boldsymbol{\xi}(k) + \hat{\mathbf{H}}w(k)$$

$$w(k) = −\hat{\mathbf{K}}\boldsymbol{\xi}(k)$$

where

$$\boldsymbol{\xi}(k) = \begin{bmatrix} x_1(k) \\ x_2(k) \\ x_3(k) \\ x_4(k) \\ x_5(k) \end{bmatrix}, \qquad \hat{\mathbf{G}} = \mathbf{G1} = \begin{bmatrix} \mathbf{G} & \mathbf{0} \\ -\mathbf{CG} & 1 \end{bmatrix}, \qquad \hat{\mathbf{H}} = \mathbf{H1} = \begin{bmatrix} \mathbf{H} \\ -\mathbf{CH} \end{bmatrix}$$

$$\hat{\mathbf{K}} = [\mathbf{K} \quad -K_i] = [k_1 \quad k_2 \quad k_3 \quad k_4 \quad -K_I], \qquad x_5(k) = v(k)$$

Our problem here is to determine matrix $\hat{\mathbf{K}}$. We assume that the desired closed-loop poles are located as follows:

$$\mu_1 = 0.9 + j0.25, \qquad \mu_2 = 0.9 - j0.25, \qquad \mu_3 = 0, \qquad \mu_4 = 0, \qquad \mu_5 = 0$$

Note that matrices **G1** and **H1** are, respectively, 5×5 and 5×1 matrices as shown next.

```
G1 = [G  zeros(4,1);−C*G  1]

G1 =

      1.1048    0.1035        0        0        0
      2.1316    1.1048        0        0        0
     −0.0025   −0.0001   1.0000   0.1000        0
     −0.0508   −0.0025        0   1.0000        0
      0.0025    0.0001  −1.0000  −0.1000   1.0000

H1 = [H;−C*H]

H1 =

     −0.0051
     −0.1035
      0.0025
      0.0501
     −0.0025
```

The controllability matrix for the entire system is

```
M = [H1   G1*H1   G1^2*H1   G1^3*H1   G1^4*H1]

M =

     −0.0051   −0.0163   −0.0310   −0.0521   −0.0842
     −0.1035   −0.1252   −0.1731   −0.2572   −0.3953
      0.0025    0.0075    0.0126    0.0179    0.0234
      0.0501    0.0506    0.0517    0.0537    0.0570
     −0.0025   −0.0100   −0.0227   −0.0406   −0.0640
```

The rank of **M** is found to be 5. Hence arbitrary pole placement is possible.

Next we present MATLAB Program 3-4 for the determination of matrix $\hat{\mathbf{K}}$ using Ackermann's formula. In MATLAB Program 3-4, we use notation KK for $\hat{\mathbf{K}}$.

```
MATLAB Program 3–4

% ---------- Design of a digital controller ----------

% ***** Design of a digital controller for the inverted pendulum
% with cart system *****

% ***** This is a program to compute KK (K'hat') matrix.  It is
% a 1 x 5 matrix where the first four columns are the state
% feedback gain matrix and the fifth column is the integral
% gain constant.  Ackermann's formula is utilized to solve
% for the KK matrix *****

% ***** Enter matrices G, H, C, and D *****
```

```
G = [1.1048     0.1035   0    0
      2.1316     1.1048   0    0
     -0.0025    -0.0001   1    0.1
     -0.0508    -0.0025   0     1];
H = [-0.0051;-0.1035;0.0025;0.0501];
C = [0   0   1   0];
D = [0];

% ***** Enter matrices G1 and H1 *****

G1 = [G  zeros(4,1);-C*G   1];
H1 = [H;-C*H];

% ***** Enter the controllability matrix M *****

M = [H1   G1*H1   G1^2*H1   G1^3*H1   G1^4*H1];

% ***** Check the rank of M *****

rank(M)

ans =

     5

% ***** Since the rank of M is 5, arbitrary pole placement
% is possible *****

% ***** Determine the desired characteristic polynomial by
% entering the following matrix J and computing poly(J) *****

J = [0.9+0.25*i  0   0   0   0
      0  0.9-0.25*i   0   0   0
      0           0   0   0   0
      0           0   0   0   0
      0           0   0   0   0];

JJ = poly(J)

JJ =

     1.0000     -1.8000     0.8725        0        0        0

% ***** Enter characteristic polynomial Phi *****

Phi = polyvalm(poly(J),G1);

% ***** Matrix KK can be given by the following equation *****

KK = [0   0   0   0   1]*(inv(M))*Phi

KK =

  -371.1822   -103.7521   -236.7336   -168.5108      72.6484
```

```
k1 = KK(1), k2 = KK(2), k3 = KK(3), k4 = KK(4), kI = -KK(5)

k1 =

  -371.1822


k2 =

  -103.7521


k3 =

  -236.7336


k4 =

  -168.5108


KI =

  -72.6484
```

Step response of the designed system. Next we shall obtain the step response of the designed system. Referring to Eq. (3-11), the unit-step response is obtained from the following equations:

$$\begin{bmatrix} \mathbf{x}(k+1) \\ v(k+1) \end{bmatrix} = \begin{bmatrix} \mathbf{G} - \mathbf{HK} & \mathbf{H}K_I \\ -\mathbf{CG} + \mathbf{CHK} & 1 - \mathbf{CH}K_I \end{bmatrix} \begin{bmatrix} \mathbf{x}(k) \\ v(k) \end{bmatrix} + \begin{bmatrix} \mathbf{0} \\ 1 \end{bmatrix} r \qquad (3\text{-}19)$$

$$y(k) = [\mathbf{C} \quad 0] \begin{bmatrix} \mathbf{x}(k) \\ v(k) \end{bmatrix} \qquad (3\text{-}20)$$

Define

$$\mathbf{GG} = \begin{bmatrix} \mathbf{G} - \mathbf{HK} & \mathbf{H}K_I \\ -\mathbf{CG} + \mathbf{CHK} & 1 - \mathbf{CH}K_I \end{bmatrix}, \qquad \mathbf{HH} = \begin{bmatrix} \mathbf{0} \\ 1 \end{bmatrix}$$

$$\mathbf{CC} = [\mathbf{C} \quad 0], \qquad DD = [D]$$

MATLAB outputs for **GG**, **HH**, **CC**, and *DD* are shown next.

```
GG = [G−H∗K   H∗KI;−C∗G+C∗H∗K   1−C∗H∗KI]

GG =

         −0.7832    −0.4243    −1.2041    −0.8571     0.3695
        −36.2743    −9.6303   −24.4946   −17.4357     7.5169
          0.9262     0.2595     1.5923     0.5216    −0.1818
         18.5390     5.1937    11.8562     9.4395    −3.6384
         −0.9262    −0.2595    −1.5923    −0.5216     1.1818
```

```
  HH = [0;0;0;0;1]

  HH =

          0
          0
          0
          0
          1

  CC = [C   0]

  CC =

          0   0   1   0   0

  DD = [0]

  DD =

          0
```

To obtain the unit-step response $y(k)$ versus k, we may first transform the state-space equations [Eqs. (3-19) and (3-20)] into the pulse transfer function $Y(z)/R(z)$ by use of the following command:

$$[\text{num,den}] = \text{ss2tf(GG,HH,CC,DD)}$$

The computer output follows:

```
  [num,den] = ss2tf(GG,HH,CC,DD)

  num =

          0   −0.0000   −0.1818   0.2180   0.2180   −0.1818

  den =

      1.0000   −1.8000   0.8725   0.0000   −0.0000   0.0000
```

Then use the command filter as follows:

$$y = \text{filter (num,den,u)}$$

where u is the unit-step input.

To obtain the response $x_1(k)$, use the following fictitious output equation:

$$x_1(k) = [1 \quad 0 \quad 0 \quad 0 \quad 0] \begin{bmatrix} x_1(k) \\ x_2(k) \\ x_3(k) \\ x_4(k) \\ x_5(k) \end{bmatrix} = \mathbf{FF} \begin{bmatrix} \mathbf{x}(k) \\ v(k) \end{bmatrix} \qquad (3\text{-}21)$$

where

$$\mathbf{FF} = [1 \quad 0 \quad 0 \quad 0 \quad 0]$$

Then convert the state-space equations [Eqs. (3-19) and (3-21)] into the pulse transfer function $X_1(z)/R(z)$ by use of the command

$$[\text{num1,den1}] = \text{ss2tf(GG,HH,FF,DD)}$$

and use the filter command:

$$\text{x1} = \text{filter(num1,den1,u)}$$

To obtain the response $x_2(k)$, we use the following fictitious output equation:

$$x_2(k) = [0 \quad 1 \quad 0 \quad 0 \quad 0] \begin{bmatrix} x_1(k) \\ x_2(k) \\ x_3(k) \\ x_4(k) \\ x_5(k) \end{bmatrix} = \mathbf{JJ} \begin{bmatrix} \mathbf{x}(k) \\ v(k) \end{bmatrix} \tag{3-22}$$

where

$$\mathbf{JJ} = [0 \quad 1 \quad 0 \quad 0 \quad 0]$$

Then convert the state-space equations [Eqs. (3-19) and (3-22)] into the pulse transfer function $X_2(z)/R(z)$ by use of the command

$$[\text{num2,den2}] = \text{ss2tf(GG,HH,JJ,DD)}$$

and then use the filter command to obtain the unit-step response.

$$\text{x2} = \text{filter(num2,den2,u)}$$

Similarly, to obtain the responses $x_4(k)$ and $x_5(k)$, use the following commands:

$$[\text{num4,den4}] = \text{ss2tf(GG,HH,LL,DD)}$$
$$\text{x4} = \text{filter(num4,den4,u)}$$

and

$$[\text{num5,den5}] = \text{ss2tf(GG,HH,MM,DD)}$$
$$\text{x5} = \text{filter(num5,den5,u)}$$

where

$$\mathbf{LL} = [0 \quad 0 \quad 0 \quad 1 \quad 0]$$
$$\mathbf{MM} = [0 \quad 0 \quad 0 \quad 0 \quad 1]$$

Using MATLAB Program 3-5, we can obtain the responses $y(k)$, $x_1(k)$, $x_2(k)$, $x_4(k)$, and $x_5(k)$ to the unit-step input, $r = 1$.

MATLAB Program 3–5

```
% ---------- Step response of the designed system ----------

% ***** This program calculates the response of the system when
% subjected to a unit-step input.  The values that are used for
% K and KI are computed in another program (MATLAB Program 3-4).
% The step response is obtained using the method to convert the
% discrete-time state-space equations into transfer-function form.
% The step response is then found with the conventional 'filter'
% command *****

% ***** Enter matrices K, KI, GG, HH, CC, FF, JJ, LL, MM, DD *****

K = [KK(1)  KK(2)  KK(3)  KK(4)];
KI = -KK(5);
GG = [G-H*K  H*KI;-C*G+C*H*K  1-C*H*KI];
HH = [0;0;0;0;1];
CC = [0  0  1  0  0];
FF  = [1  0  0  0  0];
JJ  = [0  1  0  0  0];
LL  = [0  0  0  1  0];
MM = [0  0  0  0  1];
DD = [0];

[num,den] = ss2tf(GG,HH,CC,DD);

% ***** Enter command to obtain unit-step response *****

r = ones(1,101);
axis([0  100  -0.5  2]);
k = 0:100;
y = filter(num,den,r);
plot(k,y,'o',k,y,'-')
grid
title('Position of Cart : y(k) = x3(k)')
xlabel('k')
ylabel('y(k) = x3(k)')

% ***** To obtain x1(k) convert state-space equations into pulse
% transfer function X1(z)/R(z) *****

[num1,den1] = ss2tf(GG,HH,FF,DD);

% ***** Enter command to obtain unit-step response *****

axis([0  100  -1  1]);
x1 = filter(num1,den1,r);
plot(k,x1,'o',k,x1,'-')
grid
title('Angular Displacement Theta : x1(k)')
xlabel('k')
```

```
ylabel('x1(k)')

% ***** To obtain x2(k) convert state-space equations into pulse
% transfer function X2(z)/R(z) *****

[num2,den2] = ss2tf(GG,HH,JJ,DD);

% ***** Enter command to obtain unit-step response *****

axis([0   100   -5   10]);
x2 = filter(num2,den2,r);
plot(k,x2,'o',k,x2,'-')
grid
title('Angular Velocity Theta Dot : x2(k)')
xlabel('k')
ylabel('x2(k)')

% ***** To obtain x4(k) convert state-space equations into pulse
% transfer function X4(z)/R(z) *****

[num4,den4] = ss2tf(GG,HH,LL,DD);

% ***** Enter command to obtain unit-step response *****

axis([0   100   -5   5]);
x4 = filter(num4,den4,r);
plot(k,x4,'o',k,x4,'-')
grid
title('Velocity of Cart : x4(k)')
xlabel('k')
ylabel('x4(k)')

% ***** To obtain x5(k) convert state-space equations into pulse
% transfer function X5(z)/R(z) *****

[num5,den5] = ss2tf(GG,HH,MM,DD);

% ***** Enter command to obtain unit-step response *****

axis([0   100   -2   8]);
x5 = filter(num5,den5,r);
plot(k,x5,'o',k,x5,'-')
grid
title('Output of Integrator : x5(k) = v(k)')
xlabel('k')
ylabel('x5(k) = v(k)')
```

Figure 3-4 shows the position of the cart $y(k)$ when the system is subjected to a unit-step input. From this figure it can be seen that, when a unit-step input is given, the cart first moves in the opposite direction to the input for a short period (approximately 0.4 sec or so) and then moves in the direction of the input. Such a response is a typical response behavior of the nonminimum-phase system. The fact that this system is nonminimum-phase can be seen from the following analysis.

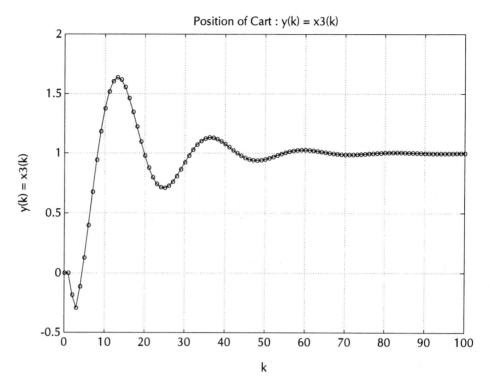

Figure 3-4

Earlier, we obtained the numerator and denominator of the transfer function as follows:

$$\frac{\text{num}}{\text{den}} = \frac{-0.1818z^3 + 0.2180z^2 + 0.2180z - 0.1818}{z^5 - 1.8z^4 + 0.8725z^3}$$

$$= \frac{-0.1818z^{-2} + 0.2180z^{-3} + 0.2180z^{-4} - 0.1818z^{-5}}{1 - 1.8z^{-1} + 0.8725z^{-2}}$$

Since the coefficient of the z^{-2} term in the numerator is negative, the unit-step response starts from 0 to -0.1818 in three steps, as follows:

$$y(0) = 0$$
$$y(1) = 0$$
$$y(2) = -0.1818$$

The output $y(\infty)$ in the unit-step response approaches unity, because the final value $y(\infty)$ can be obtained as

$$y(\infty) = \lim_{z \to 1} (1 - z^{-1}) \frac{-0.1818z^{-2} + 0.2180z^{-3} + 0.2180z^{-4} - 0.1818z^{-5}}{(1 - 1.8z^{-1} + 0.8725z^{-2})(1 - z^{-1})}$$

$$= 1$$

Thus, although the response starts in the negative direction and stays in the negative region for a short period, the response comes back to the positive region and eventually approaches unity. This is a typical step response of the nonminimum-phase system.

Figure 3-5 shows the angular displacement of the pendulum [$x1(k)$ versus k]. Figure 3-6 depicts the angular velocity of the pendulum [$x2(k)$ versus k]. Figure 3-7 shows the velocity

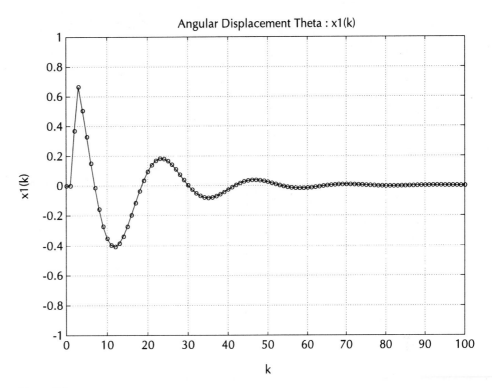

Figure 3-5

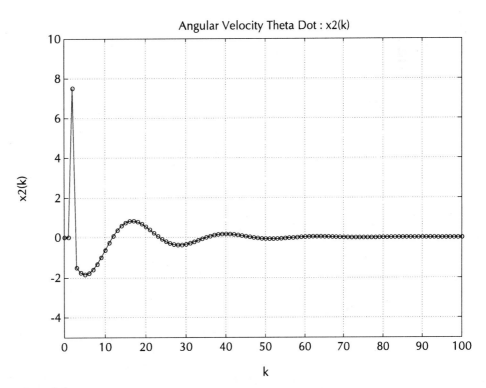

Figure 3-6

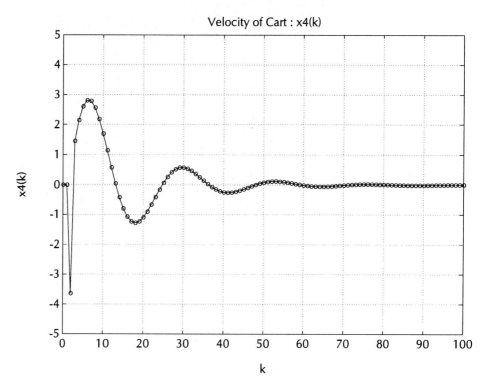

Figure 3-7

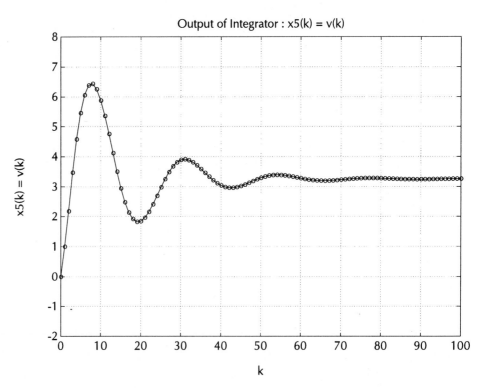

Figure 3-8

of the cart [$x4(k)$ versus k]. The output of the integrator [$v(k)$ versus k] is shown in Figure 3-8.

From Figures 3-4 through 3-8, it can be seen that the state variables almost reach steady state for $k > 70$. Since the sampling period T is 0.1 sec, the steady state is reached in approximately 7 sec.

3-4 DESIGN OF STATE OBSERVERS

In this section we shall first discuss the full-order state observer and then the minimum-order state observer.

Full-order state observer

The order of the state observer that will be discussed here is the same as that of the system. As stated earlier, such a state observer is called a full-order state observer or simply a full-order observer.

In the following analysis we assume that the actual state $\mathbf{x}(k)$ cannot be measured directly. If the state $\mathbf{x}(k)$ is to be estimated, it is desirable that the observed state or estimated state $\tilde{\mathbf{x}}(k)$ be as close to the actual state $\mathbf{x}(k)$ as possible. Although it is not necessary, it is convenient if the state observer has the same $\mathbf{G}$ and $\mathbf{H}$ matrices as the original system.

It is important to note that, in the present analysis, state $\mathbf{x}(k)$ is not available for direct measurement, and consequently the observed state $\tilde{\mathbf{x}}(k)$ cannot be compared with the actual state $\mathbf{x}(k)$. Since the output $\mathbf{y}(k) = \mathbf{Cx}(k)$ can be measured, however, it is possible to compare $\tilde{\mathbf{y}}(k) = \mathbf{C\tilde{x}}(k)$ with $\mathbf{y}(k)$. The performance of the dynamic model can be improved if the difference between the measured output $\mathbf{y}(k)$ and the estimated output $\mathbf{C\tilde{x}}(k)$ is used to monitor the state $\tilde{\mathbf{x}}(k)$.

Consider the state feedback control system shown in Figure 3-9. The system equations are

$$\mathbf{x}(k + 1) = \mathbf{Gx}(k) + \mathbf{Hu}(k) \qquad (3\text{-}23)$$

$$\mathbf{y}(k) = \mathbf{Cx}(k) \qquad (3\text{-}24)$$

$$\mathbf{u}(k) = -\mathbf{Kx}(k)$$

where $\mathbf{x}(k)$ = state vector (n-vector)
$\quad\ \mathbf{u}(k)$ = control vector (r-vector)
$\quad\ \mathbf{y}(k)$ = output vector (m-vector)

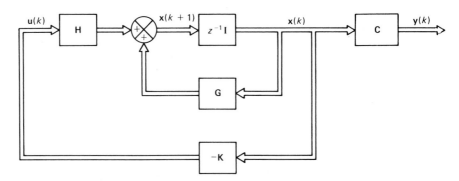

Figure 3-9

$\mathbf{G} = n \times n$ nonsingular matrix
$\mathbf{H} = n \times r$ matrix
$\mathbf{C} = m \times n$ matrix
$\mathbf{K} =$ state feedback gain matrix ($n \times r$ matrix)

We assume that the system is completely observable and, as stated earlier, $\mathbf{x}(k)$ is not available for direct measurement. Figure 3-10 shows a state observer incorporated into the system of Figure 3-9. The observed state $\tilde{\mathbf{x}}(k)$ is used to form the control vector $\mathbf{u}(k)$, or

$$\mathbf{u}(k) = -\mathbf{K}\tilde{\mathbf{x}}(k) \tag{3-25}$$

From Figure 3-10 we have

$$\tilde{\mathbf{x}}(k + 1) = \mathbf{G}\tilde{\mathbf{x}}(k) + \mathbf{H}\mathbf{u}(k) + \mathbf{K}_e[\mathbf{y}(k) - \tilde{\mathbf{y}}(k)] \tag{3-26}$$

where $\mathbf{K}_e$ is the observer feedback gain matrix (an $n \times m$ matrix). This last equation can be modified to read

$$\tilde{\mathbf{x}}(k + 1) = (\mathbf{G} - \mathbf{K}_e\mathbf{C})\tilde{\mathbf{x}}(k) + \mathbf{H}\mathbf{u}(k) + \mathbf{K}_e\mathbf{y}(k) \tag{3-27}$$

The state observer given by Eq. (3-27) is called a *prediction observer*, since the estimate $\tilde{\mathbf{x}}(k + 1)$ is one sampling period ahead of the measurement $\mathbf{y}(k)$. The eigenvalues of $\mathbf{G} - \mathbf{K}_e\mathbf{C}$ are commonly called the *observer poles*.

To obtain the observer error equation, let us subtract Eq. (3-27) from Eq. (3-23):

$$\mathbf{x}(k + 1) - \tilde{\mathbf{x}}(k + 1) = (\mathbf{G} - \mathbf{K}_e\mathbf{C})[\mathbf{x}(k) - \tilde{\mathbf{x}}(k)] \tag{3-28}$$

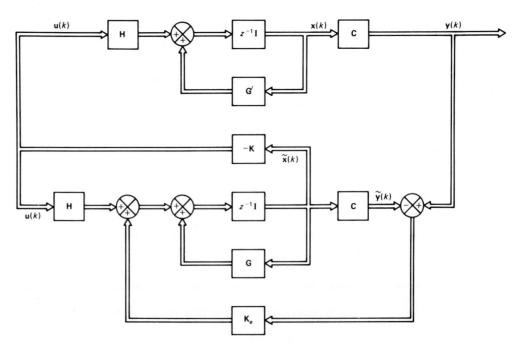

Figure 3-10

Now let us define the difference between $\mathbf{x}(k)$ and $\tilde{\mathbf{x}}(k)$ as the error $\mathbf{e}(k)$:

$$\mathbf{e}(k) = \mathbf{x}(k) - \tilde{\mathbf{x}}(k)$$

Then Eq. (3-28) becomes

$$\mathbf{e}(k + 1) = (\mathbf{G} - \mathbf{K}_e \mathbf{C})\mathbf{e}(k) \tag{3-29}$$

From Eq. (3-29) we see that the dynamic behavior of the error signal is determined by the eigenvalues of $\mathbf{G} - \mathbf{K}_e \mathbf{C}$. If matrix $\mathbf{G} - \mathbf{K}_e \mathbf{C}$ is a stable matrix, the error vector will converge to zero for any initial error $\mathbf{e}(0)$. That is, $\tilde{\mathbf{x}}(k)$ will converge to $\mathbf{x}(k)$ regardless of the values of $\mathbf{x}(0)$ and $\tilde{\mathbf{x}}(0)$. If the eigenvalues of $\mathbf{G} - \mathbf{K}_e \mathbf{C}$ are located in such a way that the dynamic behavior of the error vector is adequately fast, then any error will tend to zero with adequate speed. One way to obtain fast response is to use deadbeat response. This can be achieved if all eigenvalues of $\mathbf{G} - \mathbf{K}_e \mathbf{C}$ are chosen to be zero.

Equations for observer gain matrix $\mathbf{K}_e$

By using the same approaches as we did in Section 2-4, the equations for the determination of the observer gain matrix can be derived. Here we shall give only the result.

The observer gain matrix $\mathbf{K}_e$ can be given by

$$\mathbf{K}_e = \mathbf{Q} \begin{bmatrix} \alpha_n - a_n \\ \alpha_{n-1} - a_{n-1} \\ \vdots \\ \alpha_1 - a_1 \end{bmatrix} = (\mathbf{W}\mathbf{N}')^{-1} \begin{bmatrix} \alpha_n - a_n \\ \alpha_{n-1} - a_{n-1} \\ \vdots \\ \alpha_1 - a_1 \end{bmatrix} \tag{3-30}$$

where matrices $\mathbf{N}$ and $\mathbf{W}$ are defined by

$$\mathbf{N} = [\mathbf{C}' \vdots \mathbf{G}'\mathbf{C}' \vdots \cdots \vdots (\mathbf{G}')^{n-1}\mathbf{C}'] \tag{3-31}$$

$$\mathbf{W} = \begin{bmatrix} a_{n-1} & a_{n-2} & \cdots & a_1 & 1 \\ a_{n-2} & a_{n-3} & \cdots & 1 & 0 \\ \vdots & \vdots & & \vdots & \vdots \\ a_1 & 1 & \cdots & 0 & 0 \\ 1 & 0 & \cdots & 0 & 0 \end{bmatrix} \tag{3-32}$$

and

$$\mathbf{Q} = (\mathbf{W}\mathbf{N}')^{-1} \tag{3-33}$$

The α_i's are the coefficients of the desired characteristic equation

$$z^n + \alpha_1 z^{n-1} + \cdots + \alpha_{n-1} z + \alpha_n = 0$$

and the a_i's are coefficients of the characteristic equation of the original state equation

$$|z\mathbf{I} - \mathbf{G}| = z^n + a_1 z^{n-1} + \cdots + a_{n-1} z + a_n = 0$$

Note that, if the system is already in an observable canonical form, then the matrix $\mathbf{K}_e$ can be determined easily, because matrix $\mathbf{WN}'$ becomes an identity matrix and thus $(\mathbf{WN}')^{-1} = \mathbf{I}$.

Since for deadbeat response all α's are zero, the equation for $\mathbf{K}_e$ can be simplified as follows:

$$\mathbf{K}_e = \begin{bmatrix} k_1 \\ k_2 \\ \vdots \\ k_n \end{bmatrix} = \mathbf{Q} \begin{bmatrix} \delta_n \\ \delta_{n-1} \\ \vdots \\ \delta_1 \end{bmatrix} = (\mathbf{WN}')^{-1} \begin{bmatrix} -a_n \\ -a_{n-1} \\ \vdots \\ -a_1 \end{bmatrix} \quad \text{(for the deadbeat response)} \quad (3\text{-}34)$$

Ackermann's formula for the observer gain matrix becomes

$$\mathbf{K}_e = \phi(\mathbf{G}) \begin{bmatrix} \mathbf{C} \\ \mathbf{CG} \\ \vdots \\ \mathbf{CG}^{n-1} \end{bmatrix}^{-1} \begin{bmatrix} 0 \\ 0 \\ \vdots \\ 1 \end{bmatrix} \quad (3\text{-}35)$$

where

$$\phi(\mathbf{G}) = \mathbf{G}^n + \alpha_1 \mathbf{G}^{n-1} + \cdots + \alpha_{n-1} \mathbf{G} + \alpha_n \mathbf{I}$$

For the deadbeat response, $\phi(\mathbf{G})$ becomes

$$\phi(\mathbf{G}) = \mathbf{G}^n$$

EXAMPLE 3-4

Consider the system

$$\mathbf{x}(k + 1) = \mathbf{Gx}(k) + \mathbf{H}u(k)$$
$$y(k) = \mathbf{Cx}(k)$$

where

$$\mathbf{G} = \begin{bmatrix} 0 & -0.16 \\ 1 & -1 \end{bmatrix}, \quad \mathbf{H} = \begin{bmatrix} 0 \\ 1 \end{bmatrix}, \quad \mathbf{C} = [0 \quad 1]$$

Design a full-order state observer, assuming that the system configuration is identical to that shown in Figure 3-10. The desired eigenvalues of the observer matrix are

$$z = 0.5 + j0.5, \quad z = 0.5 - j0.5$$

and so the desired characteristic equation is

$$(z - 0.5 - j0.5)(z - 0.5 + j0.5) = z^2 - z + 0.5 = 0$$

Since the configuration of the state observer is specified as shown in Figure 3-10, the design of the state observer reduces to the determination of an appropriate observer feedback gain matrix $\mathbf{K}_e$. Before we proceed further, let us examine the observability matrix. The rank of

$$[\mathbf{C}' \vdots \mathbf{G}'\mathbf{C}'] = \begin{bmatrix} 0 & 1 \\ 1 & -1 \end{bmatrix}$$

is 2. Hence the system is completely observable, and determination of the desired observer feedback gain matrix is possible.

Referring to Eq. (3-29),

$$\mathbf{e}(k + 1) = (\mathbf{G} - \mathbf{K}_e\mathbf{C})\mathbf{e}(k)$$

where

$$\mathbf{e}(k) = \mathbf{x}(k) - \tilde{\mathbf{x}}(k)$$

the characteristic equation of the observer becomes

$$|z\mathbf{I} - \mathbf{G} + \mathbf{K}_e\mathbf{C}| = 0$$

Let us denote the observer feedback gain matrix $\mathbf{K}_e$ as follows:

$$\mathbf{K}_e = \begin{bmatrix} k_1 \\ k_2 \end{bmatrix}$$

Then the characteristic equation becomes

$$\left| z\begin{bmatrix} 1 & 0 \\ 0 & 1 \end{bmatrix} - \begin{bmatrix} 0 & -0.16 \\ 1 & -1 \end{bmatrix} + \begin{bmatrix} k_1 \\ k_2 \end{bmatrix}\begin{bmatrix} 0 & 1 \end{bmatrix} \right| = \left| \begin{matrix} z & 0.16 + k_1 \\ -1 & z + 1 + k_2 \end{matrix} \right| = 0$$

which reduces to

$$z^2 + (1 + k_2)z + k_1 + 0.16 = 0 \tag{3-36}$$

Since the desired characteristic equation is

$$z^2 - z + 0.5 = 0$$

by comparing Eq. (3-36) with this last equation, we obtain

$$k_1 = 0.34, \qquad k_2 = -2$$

or

$$\mathbf{K}_e = \begin{bmatrix} 0.34 \\ -2 \end{bmatrix}$$

MATLAB Program 3-6 solves this example problem.

MATLAB Program 3–6

```
% ---------- Design of state observer ----------

% ***** This program determines state observer gain matrix Ke
% by use of Ackermann's formula *****

% ***** Enter matrices G and C *****

G = [0  -0.16;1  -1];
C = [0  1];
```

```
% ***** Enter the observability matrix N and check its rank *****

N = [C'  G'*C'];
rank(N)

ans =

     2

% ***** Since the rank of the observability matrix is 2, design
% of observer is possible *****

% ***** Enter the desired characteristic polynomial by defining
% the following matrix J and entering statement poly(J) *****

J = [0.5+0.5*i    0
        0     0.5-0.5*i];

JJ = poly(J)

JJ =

    1.0000    -1.0000     0.5000

% ***** Enter characteristic polynomial Phi *****

Phi = polyvalm(poly(J),G);

% ***** The observer gain matrix Ke is obtained from *****

Ke = Phi*inv(N')*[0;1]

Ke =

     0.3400
    -2.0000
```

Minimum-order state observer

The observers discussed thus far are designed to reconstruct all state variables. In practice, some of the state variables may be accurately measured. Such accurately measurable state variables need not be estimated. An observer that estimates fewer than n state variables, where n is the dimension of the state vector, is a reduced-order state observer (or simply a reduced-order observer). If the order of the reduced-order observer is the minimum possible, the observer is a minimum-order state observer (or a minimum-order observer).

Suppose the state vector $\mathbf{x}(k)$ is an n-vector and the output vector $\mathbf{y}(k)$ is an m-vector that can be measured. Since m output variables are linear combinations of the state variables, m state variables need not be estimated. We need to estimate only $n - m$ state variables. Then the reduced-order observer becomes an $(n - m)$th-order observer. Such an $(n - m)$th-order observer is the minimum-order observer. Figure 3-11 shows the block diagram of a system with a minimum-order observer.

It is important to note, however, that, if the measurement of output variables involves significant noises and is relatively inaccurate, then the use of the full-order observer may result in better system performance.

The minimum-order observer can be designed by first partitioning the state vector $\mathbf{x}(k)$ into two parts, as follows:

$$\mathbf{x}(k) = \left[\begin{array}{c} \mathbf{x}_a(k) \\ \hline \mathbf{x}_b(k) \end{array}\right]$$

where $\mathbf{x}_a(k)$ is that portion of the state vector that can be directly measured [thus $\mathbf{x}_a(k)$ is an m-vector] and $\mathbf{x}_b(k)$ is the unmeasurable portion of the state vector [thus $\mathbf{x}_b(k)$ is an $(n - m)$-vector]. Then the partitioned state equations become as follows:

$$\left[\begin{array}{c} \mathbf{x}_a(k + 1) \\ \hline \mathbf{x}_b(k + 1) \end{array}\right] = \left[\begin{array}{c|c} \mathbf{G}_{aa} & \mathbf{G}_{ab} \\ \hline \mathbf{G}_{ba} & \mathbf{G}_{bb} \end{array}\right]\left[\begin{array}{c} \mathbf{x}_a(k) \\ \hline \mathbf{x}_b(k) \end{array}\right] + \left[\begin{array}{c} \mathbf{H}_a \\ \hline \mathbf{H}_b \end{array}\right]\mathbf{u}(k) \tag{3-37}$$

$$\mathbf{y}(k) = [\mathbf{I} \vdots \mathbf{0}]\left[\begin{array}{c} \mathbf{x}_a(k) \\ \mathbf{x}_b(k) \end{array}\right] \tag{3-38}$$

where $\mathbf{G}_{aa} = m \times m$ matrix
$\mathbf{G}_{ab} = m \times (n - m)$ matrix
$\mathbf{G}_{ba} = (n - m) \times m$ matrix
$\mathbf{G}_{bb} = (n - m) \times (n - m)$ matrix
$\mathbf{H}_a = m \times r$ matrix
$\mathbf{H}_b = (n - m) \times r$ matrix

By rewriting Eq. (3-37), the equation for the measured portion of the state becomes

$$\mathbf{x}_a(k + 1) = \mathbf{G}_{aa}\mathbf{x}_a(k) + \mathbf{G}_{ab}\mathbf{x}_b(k) + \mathbf{H}_a\mathbf{u}(k)$$

or

$$\mathbf{x}_a(k + 1) - \mathbf{G}_{aa}\mathbf{x}_a(k) - \mathbf{H}_a\mathbf{u}(k) = \mathbf{G}_{ab}\mathbf{x}_b(k) \tag{3-39}$$

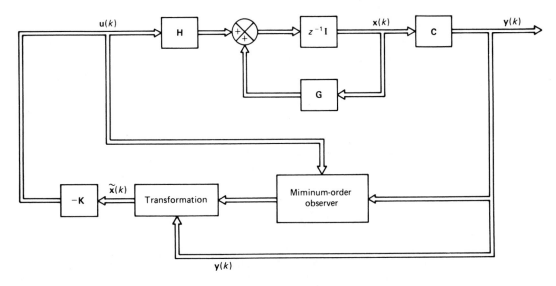

Figure 3-11

where the terms on the left side of the equation can be measured. Equation (3-39) acts as the output equation. In designing the minimum-order observer, we consider the left side of Eq. (3-39) to be known quantities. In fact, Eq. (3-39) relates the measurable quantities and the unmeasurable quantities of the state.

From Eq. (3-37) the equation for the unmeasured portion of the state becomes

$$\mathbf{x}_b(k + 1) = \mathbf{G}_{ba}\,\mathbf{x}_a(k) + \mathbf{G}_{bb}\,\mathbf{x}_b(k) + \mathbf{H}_b\,\mathbf{u}(k) \tag{3-40}$$

Equation (3-40) describes the dynamics of the unmeasured portion of the state. Notice that the terms $\mathbf{G}_{ba}\,\mathbf{x}_a(k)$ and $\mathbf{H}_b\,\mathbf{u}(k)$ are known quantities.

The design of the minimum-order observer can be facilitated if we utilize the design technique developed for the full-order observer. Let us now compare the state equation for the full-order observer with that for the minimum-order observer. The state equation for the full-order observer is

$$\mathbf{x}(k + 1) = \mathbf{Gx}(k) + \mathbf{Hu}(k)$$

and the "state equation" for the minimum-order observer is

$$\mathbf{x}_b(k + 1) = \mathbf{G}_{bb}\,\mathbf{x}_b(k) + [\mathbf{G}_{ba}\,\mathbf{x}_a(k) + \mathbf{H}_b\,\mathbf{u}(k)]$$

The output equation for the full-order observer is

$$\mathbf{y}(k) = \mathbf{Cx}(k)$$

and the "output equation" for the minimum-order observer is

$$\mathbf{x}_a(k + 1) - \mathbf{G}_{aa}\,\mathbf{x}_a(k) - \mathbf{H}_a\,\mathbf{u}(k) = \mathbf{G}_{ab}\,\mathbf{x}_b(k)$$

The design of the minimum-order observer can be carried out by making the substitutions given in Table 3-1 in the observer equation for the full-order observer given by Eq. (3-27), which we repeat here:

$$\tilde{\mathbf{x}}(k + 1) = (\mathbf{G} - \mathbf{K}_e\,\mathbf{C})\tilde{\mathbf{x}}(k) + \mathbf{Hu}(k) + \mathbf{K}_e\,\mathbf{y}(k) \tag{3-41}$$

Making the substitutions from Table 3-1 in Eq. (3-41), we obtain

$$\tilde{\mathbf{x}}_b(k + 1) = (\mathbf{G}_{bb} - \mathbf{K}_e\,\mathbf{G}_{ab})\tilde{\mathbf{x}}_b(k) + \mathbf{G}_{ba}\,\mathbf{x}_a(k) + \mathbf{H}_b\,\mathbf{u}(k)$$
$$+ \mathbf{K}_e[\mathbf{x}_a(k + 1) - \mathbf{G}_{aa}\,\mathbf{x}_a(k) - \mathbf{H}_a\,\mathbf{u}(k)] \tag{3-42}$$

Table 3-1 LIST OF NECESSARY SUBSTITUTIONS FOR WRITING THE OBSERVER EQUATION FOR THE MINIMUM-ORDER STATE OBSERVER

Full-order state observer	Minimum-order state observer
$\tilde{\mathbf{x}}(k)$	$\tilde{\mathbf{x}}_b(k)$
$\mathbf{G}$	$\mathbf{G}_{bb}$
$\mathbf{Hu}(k)$	$\mathbf{G}_{ba}\,\mathbf{x}_a(k) + \mathbf{H}_b\,\mathbf{u}(k)$
$\mathbf{y}(k)$	$\mathbf{x}_a(k + 1) - \mathbf{G}_{aa}\,\mathbf{x}_a(k) - \mathbf{H}_a\,\mathbf{u}(k)$
$\mathbf{C}$	$\mathbf{G}_{ab}$
$\mathbf{K}_e$ ($n \times m$ matrix)	$\mathbf{K}_e[(n - m) \times m$ matrix]

where the observer feedback gain matrix $\mathbf{K}_e$ is an $(n - m) \times m$ matrix. Equation (3-42) defines the minimum-order observer.

Referring to Eq. (3-38), we have

$$\mathbf{y}(k) = \mathbf{x}_a(k) \tag{3-43}$$

Substituting Eq. (3-43) into Eq. (3-42), we obtain

$$\tilde{\mathbf{x}}_b(k + 1) = (\mathbf{G}_{bb} - \mathbf{K}_e\,\mathbf{G}_{ab})\tilde{\mathbf{x}}_b(k) + \mathbf{K}_e\,\mathbf{y}(k + 1)$$
$$+ (\mathbf{G}_{ba} - \mathbf{K}_e\,\mathbf{G}_{aa})\mathbf{y}(k) + (\mathbf{H}_b - \mathbf{K}_e\,\mathbf{H}_a)\mathbf{u}(k) \tag{3-44}$$

Notice that in order to estimate $\tilde{\mathbf{x}}_b(k + 1)$ we need the measured value of $\mathbf{y}(k + 1)$. This is inconvenient, and so we may desire some modifications. [In the case of the full-order observer, $\tilde{\mathbf{x}}(k + 1)$ can be estimated by use of measurement $\mathbf{y}(k)$ and does not require measurement of $\mathbf{y}(k + 1)$. See Eq. (3-27).] Let us rewrite Eq. (3-44) as follows:

$$\tilde{\mathbf{x}}_b(k + 1) - \mathbf{K}_e\,\mathbf{y}(k + 1) = (\mathbf{G}_{bb} - \mathbf{K}_e\,\mathbf{G}_{ab})\tilde{\mathbf{x}}_b(k) + (\mathbf{G}_{ba} - \mathbf{K}_e\,\mathbf{G}_{aa})\mathbf{y}(k)$$
$$+ (\mathbf{H}_b - \mathbf{K}_e\,\mathbf{H}_a)\mathbf{u}(k)$$
$$= (\mathbf{G}_{bb} - \mathbf{K}_e\,\mathbf{G}_{ab})[\tilde{\mathbf{x}}_b(k) - \mathbf{K}_e\,\mathbf{y}(k)]$$
$$+ (\mathbf{G}_{bb} - \mathbf{K}_e\,\mathbf{G}_{ab})\mathbf{K}_e\,\mathbf{y}(k)$$
$$+ (\mathbf{G}_{ba} - \mathbf{K}_e\,\mathbf{G}_{aa})\mathbf{y}(k) + (\mathbf{H}_b - \mathbf{K}_e\,\mathbf{H}_a)\mathbf{u}(k)$$
$$= (\mathbf{G}_{bb} - \mathbf{K}_e\,\mathbf{G}_{ab})[\tilde{\mathbf{x}}_b(k) - \mathbf{K}_e\,\mathbf{y}(k)]$$
$$+ [(\mathbf{G}_{bb} - \mathbf{K}_e\,\mathbf{G}_{ab})\mathbf{K}_e$$
$$+ \mathbf{G}_{ba} - \mathbf{K}_e\,\mathbf{G}_{aa}]\mathbf{y}(k) + (\mathbf{H}_b - \mathbf{K}_e\,\mathbf{H}_a)\mathbf{u}(k) \tag{3-45}$$

Define

$$\mathbf{x}_b(k) - \mathbf{K}_e\,\mathbf{y}(k) = \mathbf{x}_b(k) - \mathbf{K}_e\,\mathbf{x}_a(k) = \boldsymbol{\eta}(k) \tag{3-46}$$

and

$$\tilde{\mathbf{x}}_b(k) - \mathbf{K}_e\,\mathbf{y}(k) = \tilde{\mathbf{x}}_b(k) - \mathbf{K}_e\,\mathbf{x}_a(k) = \tilde{\boldsymbol{\eta}}(k) \tag{3-47}$$

Then Eq. (3-45) can be written as follows:

$$\tilde{\boldsymbol{\eta}}(k + 1) = (\mathbf{G}_{bb} - \mathbf{K}_e\,\mathbf{G}_{ab})\tilde{\boldsymbol{\eta}}(k) + [(\mathbf{G}_{bb} - \mathbf{K}_e\,\mathbf{G}_{ab})\mathbf{K}_e + \mathbf{G}_{ba}$$
$$- \mathbf{K}_e\,\mathbf{G}_{aa}]\mathbf{y}(k) + (\mathbf{H}_b - \mathbf{K}_e\,\mathbf{H}_a)\mathbf{u}(k) \tag{3-48}$$

Equations (3-47) and (3-48) define the dynamics of the minimum-order observer. Notice that in order to obtain $\tilde{\boldsymbol{\eta}}(k + 1)$ we do not need the measured value of $\mathbf{y}(k + 1)$.

Let us next obtain the observer error equation. Define

$$\mathbf{e}(k) = \boldsymbol{\eta}(k) - \tilde{\boldsymbol{\eta}}(k) = \mathbf{x}_b(k) - \tilde{\mathbf{x}}_b(k) \tag{3-49}$$

Subtracting Eq. (3-42) from Eq. (3-40), we obtain

$$\mathbf{x}_b(k+1) - \tilde{\mathbf{x}}_b(k+1) = \mathbf{G}_{bb}[\mathbf{x}_b(k) - \tilde{\mathbf{x}}_b(k)] + \mathbf{K}_e\,\mathbf{G}_{ab}\,\tilde{\mathbf{x}}_b(k)$$
$$- \mathbf{K}_e[\mathbf{x}_a(k+1) - \mathbf{G}_{aa}\,\mathbf{x}_a(k) - \mathbf{H}_a\,\mathbf{u}(k)]$$

By substituting Eq. (3-39) into this last equation, we obtain

$$\mathbf{x}_b(k+1) - \tilde{\mathbf{x}}_b(k+1) = \mathbf{G}_{bb}[\mathbf{x}_b(k) - \tilde{\mathbf{x}}_b(k)] + \mathbf{K}_e\,\mathbf{G}_{ab}\,\tilde{\mathbf{x}}_b(k) - \mathbf{K}_e\,\mathbf{G}_{ab}\,\mathbf{x}_b(k)$$
$$= (\mathbf{G}_{bb} - \mathbf{K}_e\,\mathbf{G}_{ab})[\mathbf{x}_b(k) - \tilde{\mathbf{x}}_b(k)]$$

Referring to Eq. (3-49) this last equation can be written in the form

$$\mathbf{e}(k+1) = (\mathbf{G}_{bb} - \mathbf{K}_e\,\mathbf{G}_{ab})\mathbf{e}(k) \tag{3-50}$$

This is the observer error equation. Note that $\mathbf{e}(k)$ is an $(n-m)$-vector. The error dynamics can be determined as desired by following the technique developed for the full-order observer, provided that the rank of matrix

$$\begin{bmatrix} \mathbf{G}_{ab} \\ \mathbf{G}_{ab}\,\mathbf{G}_{bb} \\ \vdots \\ \mathbf{G}_{ab}\,\mathbf{G}_{bb}^{n-m-1} \end{bmatrix}$$

is $n-m$. (This is the complete observability condition applicable to the minimum-order observer.)

The characteristic equation for the minimum-order observer is obtained from Eq. (3-50) as follows:

$$|z\mathbf{I} - \mathbf{G}_{bb} + \mathbf{K}_e\,\mathbf{G}_{ab}| = 0 \tag{3-51}$$

The observer feedback gain matrix $\mathbf{K}_e$ can be determined from Eq. (3-51) by first choosing the desired closed-loop pole locations for the minimum-order observer [that is, by placing the roots of the characteristic equation, Eq. (3-51), at the desired locations] and then using the procedure developed for the full-order prediction observer.

If, for example, the output $y(k)$ is a scalar, then $x_a(k)$ is a scalar, $\mathbf{G}_{ab}$ is a $1 \times (n-1)$ matrix, and $\mathbf{G}_{bb}$ is an $(n-1) \times (n-1)$ matrix. For this case, Acker-mann's formula as given by Eq. (3-35) may be modified to read

$$\mathbf{K}_e = \phi(\mathbf{G}_{bb}) \begin{bmatrix} \mathbf{G}_{ab} \\ \mathbf{G}_{ab}\,\mathbf{G}_{bb} \\ \vdots \\ \mathbf{G}_{ab}\,\mathbf{G}_{bb}^{n-3} \\ \mathbf{G}_{ab}\,\mathbf{G}_{bb}^{n-2} \end{bmatrix}^{-1} \begin{bmatrix} 0 \\ 0 \\ \vdots \\ 0 \\ 1 \end{bmatrix} \tag{3-52}$$

where

$$\phi(\mathbf{G}_{bb}) = \mathbf{G}_{bb}^{n-1} + \alpha_1\,\mathbf{G}_{bb}^{n-2} + \cdots + \alpha_{n-2}\,\mathbf{G}_{bb} + \alpha_{n-1}\,\mathbf{I} \tag{3-53}$$

EXAMPLE 3-5

Consider the system

$$\mathbf{x}(k + 1) = \mathbf{G}\mathbf{x}(k) + \mathbf{H}u(k)$$

$$y(k) = \mathbf{C}\mathbf{x}(k)$$

where $\mathbf{x}(k)$ = state vector (3-vector)
   $u(k)$ = control signal (scalar)
   $y(k)$ = output signal (scalar)

and

$$\mathbf{G} = \begin{bmatrix} 0 & 0 & -0.25 \\ 1 & 0 & 0 \\ 0 & 1 & 0.5 \end{bmatrix}, \qquad \mathbf{H} = \begin{bmatrix} 1 \\ 0 \\ 1 \end{bmatrix}, \qquad \mathbf{C} = [1 \quad 0 \quad 0]$$

Assuming that the output $y(k)$ is measurable, design a minimum-order observer such that the response to the initial observer error is deadbeat.

For this system,

$$G_{aa} = 0, \qquad \mathbf{G}_{ab} = [0 \quad -0.25], \qquad \mathbf{G}_{ba} = \begin{bmatrix} 1 \\ 0 \end{bmatrix}, \qquad \mathbf{G}_{bb} = \begin{bmatrix} 0 & 0 \\ 1 & 0.5 \end{bmatrix}$$

$$H_a = [1], \qquad \mathbf{H}_b = \begin{bmatrix} 0 \\ 1 \end{bmatrix}$$

The reduced-order observability matrix $\mathbf{N}$ is

$$\mathbf{N} = [\mathbf{G}_{ab}' \vdots \mathbf{G}_{bb}' \, \mathbf{G}_{ab}'] = \begin{bmatrix} 0 & -0.25 \\ -0.25 & -0.125 \end{bmatrix}$$

The rank of matrix $\mathbf{N}$ is 2. Hence the minimum-order observer can be designed.
The desired characteristic equation for deadbeat response is

$$\phi(\mathbf{G}_{bb}) = \mathbf{G}_{bb}^2$$

The gain matrix $\mathbf{K}_e$ for the minimum-order observer is obtained as

$$\mathbf{K}_e = \phi(\mathbf{G}_{bb}) \begin{bmatrix} \mathbf{G}_{ab} \\ \mathbf{G}_{ab} \, \mathbf{G}_{bb} \end{bmatrix}^{-1} \begin{bmatrix} 0 \\ 1 \end{bmatrix} = (\mathbf{G}_{bb}^2)(\mathbf{N}')^{-1} \begin{bmatrix} 0 \\ 1 \end{bmatrix} = \begin{bmatrix} 0 \\ -2 \end{bmatrix}$$

MATLAB Program 3-7 is a program to design the minimum-order observer discussed in this example.

MATLAB Program 3–7

% ---------- Design of minimum-order observer ----------

% ***** A minimum-order observer is designed by use of Ackermann's
% formula *****

% ***** Enter matrices Gaa, Gab, Gba, Gbb, Ha, and Hb *****

```
Gaa = [0]; Gab = [0   -0.25]; Gba = [1;0];
Gbb = [0   0;1   0.5]; Ha = [1]; Hb = [0;1];

% ***** Enter the reduced-order observability matrix N and check
% the rank of matrix N *****

N = [Gab'   Gbb'*Gab'];
rank(N)

ans =

     2

% ***** Since the rank of N is 2, the minimum-order (second-order)
% observer can be designed *****

% ***** The desired characteristic equation for the deadbeat
% response is Phi = Gbb^2 *****

Phi = Gbb^2;

% ***** The minimum-order observer gain matrix Ke can be determined
% from *****

Ke = Phi*inv(N')*[0;1]

Ke =

     0
    -2
```

EXAMPLE 3-6

Consider the system

$$\mathbf{x}(k + 1) = \mathbf{G}\mathbf{x}(k) + \mathbf{H}u(k)$$

$$y(k) = \mathbf{C}\mathbf{x}(k)$$

where

$$\mathbf{G} = \begin{bmatrix} 0.16 & 2.16 \\ -0.16 & -1.16 \end{bmatrix}, \qquad \mathbf{H} = \begin{bmatrix} -1 \\ 1 \end{bmatrix}, \qquad \mathbf{C} = \begin{bmatrix} 1 & 1 \end{bmatrix}$$

The output $y(k)$ can be measured. Determine the state feedback gain matrix $\mathbf{K}$ such that the closed-loop poles of the system are located at

$$z_1 = 0.6 + j0.4, \qquad z_2 = 0.6 - j0.4$$

Then design a minimum-order observer for the system. [Since $y(k)$ is a linear combination of $x_1(k)$ and $x_2(k)$, we need observe only one state variable.] For the error dynamics it is desired that the response to an initial error be deadbeat.

First, we shall examine the controllability and observability conditions for the system. The rank of each of the matrices

$$[\mathbf{H} \vdots \mathbf{GH}] = \begin{bmatrix} -1 & 2 \\ 1 & -1 \end{bmatrix}, \qquad [\mathbf{C'} \vdots \mathbf{G'C'}] = \begin{bmatrix} 1 & 0 \\ 1 & 1 \end{bmatrix}$$

is 2. Hence an arbitrary pole placement and observer design are possible.

To apply the method for designing the minimum-order observer presented in this section, we must transform matrix $\mathbf{C}$ from $[1 \quad 1]$ to $[1 \quad 0]$. To do so, define

$$\mathbf{x}(k) = \mathbf{P}\boldsymbol{\xi}(k) = \begin{bmatrix} 1 & -1 \\ 0 & 1 \end{bmatrix} \boldsymbol{\xi}(k)$$

Then the system equations become

$$\boldsymbol{\xi}(k + 1) = \mathbf{P}^{-1}\mathbf{GP}\boldsymbol{\xi}(k) + \mathbf{P}^{-1}\mathbf{H}u(k) = \hat{\mathbf{G}}\boldsymbol{\xi}(k) + \hat{\mathbf{H}}u(k)$$
$$y(k) = \mathbf{CP}\boldsymbol{\xi}(k) = \hat{\mathbf{C}}\boldsymbol{\xi}(k)$$

where

$$\hat{\mathbf{G}} = \mathbf{P}^{-1}\mathbf{GP} = \begin{bmatrix} 1 & 1 \\ 0 & 1 \end{bmatrix}\begin{bmatrix} 0.16 & 2.16 \\ -0.16 & -1.16 \end{bmatrix}\begin{bmatrix} 1 & -1 \\ 0 & 1 \end{bmatrix} = \begin{bmatrix} 0 & 1 \\ -0.16 & -1 \end{bmatrix}$$

$$\hat{\mathbf{H}} = \mathbf{P}^{-1}\mathbf{H} = \begin{bmatrix} 1 & 1 \\ 0 & 1 \end{bmatrix}\begin{bmatrix} -1 \\ 1 \end{bmatrix} = \begin{bmatrix} 0 \\ 1 \end{bmatrix}$$

$$\hat{\mathbf{C}} = \mathbf{CP} = [1 \quad 1]\begin{bmatrix} 1 & -1 \\ 0 & 1 \end{bmatrix} = [1 \quad 0]$$

Thus the system equations in the new state variables are

$$\begin{bmatrix} \xi_1(k + 1) \\ \xi_2(k + 1) \end{bmatrix} = \begin{bmatrix} 0 & 1 \\ -0.16 & -1 \end{bmatrix}\begin{bmatrix} \xi_1(k) \\ \xi_2(k) \end{bmatrix} + \begin{bmatrix} 0 \\ 1 \end{bmatrix}u(k) \qquad (3\text{-}54)$$

$$y(k) = [1 \quad 0]\begin{bmatrix} \xi_1(k) \\ \xi_2(k) \end{bmatrix} \qquad (3\text{-}55)$$

where $\xi_1(k)$ is the measurable state variable and $\xi_2(k)$ is the unmeasurable state variable that must be estimated. Notice that Eqs. (3-54) and (3-55) are in the forms of Eqs. (3-37) and (3-38), respectively.

In the following design, we shall use the state equation and the output equation given by Eqs. (3-54) and (3-55). The state feedback control is given by

$$u(k) = -\mathbf{K}\boldsymbol{\xi}(k)$$

We shall now design the state feedback gain matrix $\mathbf{K}$. Since the characteristic equation for the system of Eq. (3-54) is

$$|z\mathbf{I} - \hat{\mathbf{G}}| = \begin{vmatrix} z & -1 \\ 0.16 & z + 1 \end{vmatrix} = z^2 + z + 0.16 = z^2 + a_1 z + a_2 = 0$$

we have

$$a_1 = 1, \qquad a_2 = 0.16$$

The desired characteristic equation for the system is

$$|z\mathbf{I} - \hat{\mathbf{G}} + \hat{\mathbf{H}}\mathbf{K}| = (z - 0.6 - j0.4)(z - 0.6 + j0.4) = z^2 - 1.2z + 0.52$$
$$= z^2 + \alpha_1 z + \alpha_2 = 0$$

Hence

$$\alpha_1 = -1.2, \qquad \alpha_2 = 0.52$$

Since the system defined by Eqs. (3-54) and (3-55) is in the controllable canonical form, the required matrix $\mathbf{K}$ can be given by Eq. (3-6):

$$\mathbf{K} = [\alpha_2 - a_2 \vdots \alpha_1 - a_1] = [0.52 - 0.16 \vdots -1.2 - 1] = [0.36 \quad -2.2]$$

Next, we shall design the minimum-order observer. Since the minimum-order observer is of the first order, we know the desired deadbeat characteristic polynomial to be

$$\phi(z) = z$$

From the system equations given by Eqs. (3-54) and (3-55), we have

$$G_{aa} = 0, \quad G_{ab} = 1, \quad G_{ba} = -0.16, \quad G_{bb} = -1, \quad H_a = 0, \quad H_b = 1$$

Referring to Ackermann's formula as given by Eq. (3-52), we obtain

$$K_e = \phi(G_{bb})[G_{ab}]^{-1}[1] = (-1)(1)^{-1}(1) = -1$$

Then, referring to Eqs. (3-49) and (3-50), the observer equation becomes

$$\tilde{\xi}_2(k) = \xi_2(k) - e(k)$$
$$e(k + 1) = (G_{bb} - K_e G_{ab})e(k) = (-1 + 1)e(k) = 0e(k)$$

Thus the error becomes zero in at most one sampling period.

Next, let us obtain the equation for the minimum-order observer. In terms of $\bar{\eta}(k)$, we have, from Eq. (3-48),

$$\bar{\eta}(k + 1) = (G_{bb} - K_e G_{ab})\bar{\eta}(k) + [(G_{bb} - K_e G_{ab})K_e + G_{ba} - K_e G_{aa}]y(k)$$
$$+ (H_b - K_e H_a)u(k)$$
$$= (-1 + 1 \times 1)\bar{\eta}(k) + [(-1 + 1 \times 1)(-1) - 0.16 + 1 \times 0]y(k)$$
$$+ (1 + 1 \times 0)u(k)$$
$$= -0.16y(k) + u(k)$$

Hence the minimum-order observer equation is

$$\bar{\eta}(k) = -0.16y(k - 1) + u(k - 1)$$

The observed-state feedback control $u(k)$ is given by

$$u(k) = -\mathbf{K}\tilde{\xi}(k) = -[0.36 \quad -2.2]\begin{bmatrix} \tilde{\xi}_1(k) \\ \tilde{\xi}_2(k) \end{bmatrix}$$
$$= -0.36\tilde{\xi}_1(k) + 2.2\tilde{\xi}_2(k)$$
$$= -0.36y(k) + 2.2\tilde{\xi}_2(k)$$

MATLAB Program 3-8 computes the state feedback gain matrix $\mathbf{K}$ and the gain matrix K_e for the minimum-order observer for the system considered in the present example problem. (In the present case, K_e is a scalar.)

MATLAB Program 3–8

```
% ---------- Design of a control system ----------

% ***** In this program we shall determine the state feedback
% gain matrix K and minimum-order observer gain matrix Ke *****

% ***** We shall begin with the determination of state feedback
% gain matrix K *****

% ***** Enter matrices G, H, and C *****

G = [0.16   2.16;-0.16   -1.16];
H = [-1;1];
C = [1   1];

% ***** Enter the controllability matrix M and observability
% matrix N *****

M = [H   G*H]; N = [C'   G'*C'];

% ***** Check the ranks of M and N *****

rank(M)

ans =

     2

rank(N)

ans =

     2

% ***** Hence arbitrary pole placement and observer design are
% possible *****

% ***** In order to apply the method for designing the minimum-
% order observer presented earlier, let us tranform matrix C
% from [1   1] to [1   0] *****

% ***** This can be done by defining the state transformation
% matrix P, where *****

P = [1   -1;0   1];

% ***** Using the state transformation matrix P, state matrix G,
% control matrix H, and output matrix C are modified to GG, HH,
% and CC, respectively, where *****

GG = inv(P)*G*P, HH = inv(P)*H, CC = C*P
```

GG =

        0   1.0000
   -0.1600   -1.0000

HH =

    0
    1

CC =

    1   0

% ***** To determine state feedback gain matrix K, enter the
% desired characteristic polynomial by defining the following
% matrix J and computing poly(J) *****

J = [0.6+0.4*i   0
     0   0.6-0.4*i];

poly(J)

ans =

    1.0000   -1.2000   0.5200

% ***** Enter characteristic polynomial Phi *****

Phi = polyvalm(poly(J),GG);

% ***** For the transformed system, the controllability matrix M
% is modified to MM, where *****

MM = [HH   GG*HH];

% ***** The state feedback gain matrix can be determined by the
% following equation *****

K = [0 1]*inv(MM)*Phi

K =

    0.3600   -2.2000

% ***** Next, we shall design a minimum-order observer, which
% in this case, is a first-order observer *****

% ***** Referring to GG and HH obtained earlier, enter GGaa,
% GGab, GGba, GGbb, HHa, and HHb *****

GGaa = 0; GGab = 1; GGba = -0.16; GGbb = -1; HHa = 0; HHb = 1;

% ***** Since the deadbeat response is desired, the desired
% characteristic polynomial becomes Ph = GGbb *****

Ph = GGbb;

% ***** Minimum-order observer gain matrix Ke is given by *****

Ke = Ph*inv(GGab)*[1]

Ke =

    -1

EXAMPLE 3-7

Consider the system

$$\mathbf{x}(k + 1) = \mathbf{G}\mathbf{x}(k) + \mathbf{H}u(k)$$

$$y(k) = \mathbf{C}\mathbf{x}(k)$$

where

$$\mathbf{G} = \begin{bmatrix} 0 & 0 & 1 \\ 1 & 0 & 0 \\ -0.2 & -0.5 & 1.1 \end{bmatrix}, \quad \mathbf{H} = \begin{bmatrix} 0 \\ 0 \\ 1 \end{bmatrix}, \quad \mathbf{C} = \begin{bmatrix} 1 & 0 & 0 \end{bmatrix}$$

Assume that the system configuration is the same as that shown in Figure 3-11. That is, the system uses the state feedback and minimum-order observer. Thus the control signal is given by

$$u(k) = -\mathbf{K}\tilde{\mathbf{x}}(k)$$

Determine the state feedback gain matrix **K** such that the system will exhibit a deadbeat response to any initial state. Assuming that only the output $y(k)$ is measurable, design a minimum-order observer such that the response to the observer error is deadbeat.

    We shall solve this problem with MATLAB. MATLAB Program 3-9 computes the state feedback gain matrix **K** and the gain matrix $\mathbf{K}_e$ for the minimum-order observer for the system.

    The state feedback gain matrix **K** obtained through MATLAB Program 3-9 is

$$\mathbf{K} = \begin{bmatrix} -0.2 & -0.5 & 1.1 \end{bmatrix}$$

MATLAB Program 3–9

% ---------- Design of a control system ----------

% ***** In this program we determine the state feedback gain
% matrix K and minimum-order observer gain matrix Ke *****

% ***** We shall first determine the state feedback gain
% matrix K *****

```
% ***** Enter matrices G, H, and C *****

G = [0   0   1;1   0   0;-0.2   -0.5   1.1];
H = [0;0;1];
C = [1   0   0];

% ***** Enter the controllability matrix M *****

M = [H   G*H   G^2*H];

% ***** Check the rank of matrix M *****

rank(M)

ans =

      3

% ***** Since the rank of controllability matrix M is 3,
% arbitrary pole placement is possible *****

% ***** To determine state feedback gain matrix K, enter
% the desired characteristic polynomial Phi, which is G^3
% in this case *****

Phi = G^3;

% ***** The state feedback gain matrix K is given by *****

K = [0   0   1]*inv(M)*Phi

K =

    -0.2000      -0.5000       1.1000

% ***** Next, we shall design a minimum-order observer, which
% in this case is a second-order observer *****

% ***** Enter Gaa, Gab, Gba, Gbb, Ha, and Hb *****

Gaa = [G(1,1)];
Gab = [G(1,2)   G(1,3)];
Gba = [G(2,1);G(3,1)];
Gbb = [G(2,2)   G(2,3);G(3,2)   G(3,3)];
Ha = [H(1,1)];
Hb = [H(2,1);H(3,1)];

% ***** To be able to design a minimum-order observer, the
% rank of observability matrix N = [C'   G'*C'   (G')^2*C'] must
% be 3, or the rank of reduced-order observability matrix NN =
% [Gab'   Gbb'*Gab'] must be 2 *****

% ***** Let us check the rank of NN = [Gab'   Gbb'*Gab'] *****
```

```
NN = [Gab'   Gbb'*Gab'];
rank(NN)

ans =

    2

% ***** Since the rank of the reduced-order observability
% matrix NN is 2, design of minimum-order observer is
% possible *****

% ***** Since the deadbeat response is desired for the
% minimum-order observer, the desired characteristic
% polynomial becomes Ph = Gbb^2 *****

Ph = Gbb^2;

% ***** Minimum-order observer gain matrix Ke is given by *****

Ke = Ph*inv(NN')*[0;1]

Ke =

         0
    1.1000
```

The observer gain matrix $\mathbf{K}_e$ for the minimum-order observer is

$$\mathbf{K}_e = \begin{bmatrix} 0 \\ 1.1 \end{bmatrix}$$

Let us verify that the response of the designed system is deadbeat to all initial conditions. The equations for the state feedback control system with a minimum-order observer are given by

$$\mathbf{x}(k+1) = \mathbf{G}\mathbf{x}(k) + \mathbf{H}u(k)$$

$$y(k) = \mathbf{C}\mathbf{x}(k)$$

$$u(k) = -\mathbf{K}\tilde{\mathbf{x}}(k)$$

The state vector $\mathbf{x}(k)$ and estimated state vector $\tilde{\mathbf{x}}(k)$ can be written as

$$\mathbf{x}(k) = \begin{bmatrix} x_1(k) \\ x_2(k) \\ x_3(k) \end{bmatrix} = \begin{bmatrix} x_1(k) \\ \hline \mathbf{x}_b(k) \end{bmatrix}, \qquad \tilde{\mathbf{x}}(k) = \begin{bmatrix} x_1(k) \\ \tilde{x}_2(k) \\ \tilde{x}_3(k) \end{bmatrix} = \begin{bmatrix} x_1(k) \\ \hline \tilde{\mathbf{x}}_b(k) \end{bmatrix}$$

where

$$\mathbf{x}_b(k) = \begin{bmatrix} x_2(k) \\ x_3(k) \end{bmatrix}, \qquad \tilde{\mathbf{x}}_b(k) = \begin{bmatrix} \tilde{x}_2(k) \\ \tilde{x}_3(k) \end{bmatrix}$$

Then we have

$$\mathbf{x}(k+1) = \mathbf{G}\mathbf{x}(k) - \mathbf{H}\mathbf{K}\tilde{\mathbf{x}}(k)$$

$$= (\mathbf{G} - \mathbf{H}\mathbf{K})\mathbf{x}(k) + \mathbf{H}\mathbf{K}[\mathbf{x}(k) - \tilde{\mathbf{x}}(k)] \qquad (3\text{-}56)$$

Notice that

$$\mathbf{x}(k) - \tilde{\mathbf{x}}(k) = \left[\begin{array}{c} x_1(k) \\ \hline \mathbf{x}_b(k) \end{array}\right] - \left[\begin{array}{c} x_1(k) \\ \hline \tilde{\mathbf{x}}_b(k) \end{array}\right] = \left[\begin{array}{c} 0 \\ \hline \mathbf{x}_b(k) - \tilde{\mathbf{x}}_b(k) \end{array}\right] = \left[\begin{array}{c} 0 \\ \hline \mathbf{e}(k) \end{array}\right]$$

where

$$\mathbf{e}(k) = \mathbf{x}_b(k) - \tilde{\mathbf{x}}_b(k) = \left[\begin{array}{c} e_1(k) \\ e_2(k) \end{array}\right] \tag{3-57}$$

Define

$$\mathbf{F} = \left[\begin{array}{cc} 0 & 0 \\ 1 & 0 \\ 0 & 1 \end{array}\right]$$

Then

$$\mathbf{x}(k) - \tilde{\mathbf{x}}(k) = \mathbf{F}\mathbf{e}(k)$$

Thus Eq. (3-56) can be written as

$$\mathbf{x}(k + 1) = (\mathbf{G} - \mathbf{HK})\mathbf{x}(k) + \mathbf{HKF}\mathbf{e}(k) \tag{3-58}$$

The observer error equation is given by Eq. (3-50), rewritten as

$$\mathbf{e}(k + 1) = (\mathbf{G}_{bb} - \mathbf{K}_e \mathbf{G}_{ab})\mathbf{e}(k) \tag{3-59}$$

where $\mathbf{e}(k)$ is given by Eq. (3-57).

Combining Eqs. (3-58) and (3-59), the equation for the state feedback control system with the minimum-order observer is given by

$$\left[\begin{array}{c} \mathbf{x}(k + 1) \\ \mathbf{e}(k + 1) \end{array}\right] = \left[\begin{array}{cc} \mathbf{G} - \mathbf{HK} & \mathbf{HKF} \\ \mathbf{0} & \mathbf{G}_{bb} - \mathbf{K}_e \mathbf{G}_{ab} \end{array}\right] \left[\begin{array}{c} \mathbf{x}(k) \\ \mathbf{e}(k) \end{array}\right] = \mathbf{G}_1 \left[\begin{array}{c} \mathbf{x}(k) \\ \mathbf{e}(k) \end{array}\right] \tag{3-60}$$

where

$$\mathbf{G}_1 = \left[\begin{array}{cc} \mathbf{G} - \mathbf{HK} & \mathbf{HKF} \\ \mathbf{0} & \mathbf{G}_{bb} - \mathbf{K}_e \mathbf{G}_{ab} \end{array}\right]$$

Notice from Eq. (3-60) that we have

$$\left[\begin{array}{c} \mathbf{x}(k) \\ \mathbf{e}(k) \end{array}\right] = \mathbf{G}_1^k \left[\begin{array}{c} \mathbf{x}(0) \\ \mathbf{e}(0) \end{array}\right], \qquad k = 1, 2, 3, \ldots$$

If the designed system is indeed a deadbeat response system, then for any initial condition the settling time is at most five sampling periods. That is, at most two sampling periods are needed for the error vector to become zero and, additionally, at most three sampling periods are needed for the state vector to become zero. MATLAB Program 3-10

MATLAB Program 3–10

```
% ---------- Computation of G1^k, where k = 1, 2, 3, 4, 5 ----------

% ***** Matrices G, H, K, Gab, Gbb, and Ke are defined in MATLAB
% Program 3-9 *****
```

```
F = [0  0;1  0;0  1];
G1 = [G-H*K    H*K*F;zeros(2,3)    Gbb-Ke*Gab]

G1 =

              0        0   1.0000        0        0
         1.0000        0        0        0        0
              0        0        0  -0.5000   1.1000
              0        0        0        0        0
              0        0        0  -0.5000        0

G1^2

ans =

              0        0        0  -0.5000   1.1000
              0        0   1.0000        0        0
              0        0        0  -0.5500        0
              0        0        0        0        0
              0        0        0        0        0

G1^3

ans =

              0        0        0  -0.5500        0
              0        0        0  -0.5000   1.1000
              0        0        0        0        0
              0        0        0        0        0
              0        0        0        0        0

G1^4

ans =

              0        0        0        0        0
              0        0        0  -0.5500        0
              0        0        0        0        0
              0        0        0        0        0
              0        0        0        0        0

G1^5

ans =

         0        0        0        0        0
         0        0        0        0        0
         0        0        0        0        0
         0        0        0        0        0
         0        0        0        0        0
```

shows $\mathbf{G}_1$, $\mathbf{G}_1^2$, $\mathbf{G}_1^3$, $\mathbf{G}_1^4$, and $\mathbf{G}_1^5$. Clearly, $\mathbf{G}_1^5$ is a 5×5 zero matrix. Thus, for whatever initial condition

$$\begin{bmatrix} \mathbf{x}(0) \\ \mathbf{e}(0) \end{bmatrix}$$

the response

$$\begin{bmatrix} \mathbf{x}(k) \\ \mathbf{e}(k) \end{bmatrix}$$

becomes a zero vector in at most five sampling periods. The response is thus deadbeat, as specified in the problem statement. Thus the designed system is satisfactory.

Chapter 4 Design of Optimal Control Systems

4-1 INTRODUCTION

This chapter deals with optimal control of both continuous- and discrete-time systems. We shall first treat quadratic optimal control of continuous-time systems. Then we shall discuss quadratic optimal control of discrete-time systems, for which we consider both finite-stage and infinite-stage (steady-state) problems.

An advantage of using the quadratic optimal control scheme is that the system designed will be stable, except in very special cases. In designing control systems based on the minimization of quadratic performance indexes, we need to solve Riccati equations. MATLAB has a command lqr that gives the solution to the continuous-time Riccati equation and determines the optimal feedback gain matrix. In this chapter we design control systems using quadratic performance indexes both analytically and computationally with MATLAB.

A special case of optimal control, minimum-energy control, is also treated in this chapter. Pseudoinverses of matrices play an important role in solving minimum-energy control problems. We shall review pseudoinverses in this chapter.

Outline of the chapter

Section 4-1 has presented introductory material. Section 4-2 discusses quadratic optimal control of continuous-time systems. Section 4-3 deals with quadratic optimal control of discrete-time systems, for which the number of stages is finite, while Section 4-4 treats the steady-state quadratic optimal control when the number of stages is infinite. Section 4-5 deals with minimum-energy control of discrete-time systems. A review of pseudoinverses is included in this section.

4-2 QUADRATIC OPTIMAL CONTROL OF CONTINUOUS-TIME SYSTEMS

In this section we shall consider the design of stable control systems based on quadratic performance indexes. The control system that we shall consider here may be defined by

$$\dot{\mathbf{x}} = \mathbf{A}\mathbf{x} + \mathbf{B}\mathbf{u} \tag{4-1}$$

where $\mathbf{x}$ = state vector (n-vector)
  $\mathbf{u}$ = control vector (r-vector)
  $\mathbf{A}$ = $n \times n$ constant matrix
  $\mathbf{B}$ = $n \times r$ constant matrix

Control systems considered in this section are mostly regulator systems.

In designing control systems, we are often interested in choosing the control vector $\mathbf{u}(t)$ such that a given performance index is minimized. It can be proved that a quadratic performance index, where the limits of integration are 0 and ∞, such as

$$J = \int_0^\infty L(\mathbf{x}, \mathbf{u}) \, dt$$

where $L(\mathbf{x}, \mathbf{u})$ is a quadratic function or Hermitian function of $\mathbf{x}$ and $\mathbf{u}$, will yield linear control laws; that is,

$$\mathbf{u}(t) = -\mathbf{K}\mathbf{x}(t)$$

where $\mathbf{K}$ is an $r \times n$ matrix, or

$$\begin{bmatrix} u_1 \\ u_2 \\ \vdots \\ u_r \end{bmatrix} = - \begin{bmatrix} k_{11} & k_{12} & \cdots & k_{1n} \\ k_{21} & k_{22} & \cdots & k_{2n} \\ \vdots & \vdots & & \vdots \\ k_{r1} & k_{r2} & \cdots & k_{rn} \end{bmatrix} \begin{bmatrix} x_1 \\ x_2 \\ \vdots \\ x_n \end{bmatrix}$$

Therefore, the design of optimal control systems and optimal regulator systems based on such quadratic performance indexes boils down to the determination of the elements of the matrix $\mathbf{K}$.

In the following, we consider the problem of determining the optimal control vector $\mathbf{u}(t)$ for the system described by Eq. (4-1) and the performance index given by

$$J = \int_0^\infty (\mathbf{x}'\mathbf{Q}\mathbf{x} + \mathbf{u}'\mathbf{R}\mathbf{u}) \, dt$$

where $\mathbf{Q}$ is a positive-definite (or positive-semidefinite) Hermitian or real symmetric matrix, $\mathbf{R}$ is a positive-definite Hermitian or real symmetric matrix, and $\mathbf{u}$ is unconstrained. The optimal control system is to minimize the performance index. Among many different approaches to the solution of this type of problem, we shall present here one approach that is based on the second method of Liapunov.

Control system optimization via the second method of Liapunov

Classically, control systems are first designed and then their stability is examined. In a different approach, the conditions for stability are formulated first and then the system is designed within these limitations. If the second method of Liapunov is utilized to form the basis for the design of an optimal controller, we are assured that the system will work; that is, the system output will be continually driven toward its desired value. Thus the designed system has a configuration with inherent stability characteristics.

For a large class of control systems, a direct relationship can be shown between Liapunov functions and quadratic performance indexes used in the synthesis of optimal control systems.

Quadratic optimal control problem

We shall now consider the optimal control problem: given the system equation

$$\dot{\mathbf{x}} = \mathbf{Ax} + \mathbf{Bu} \tag{4-2}$$

determine the matrix $\mathbf{K}$ of the optimal control vector

$$\mathbf{u}(t) = -\mathbf{Kx}(t) \tag{4-3}$$

so as to minimize the performance index

$$J = \int_0^\infty (\mathbf{x'Qx} + \mathbf{u'Ru})\, dt \tag{4-4}$$

where $\mathbf{Q}$ is a positive-definite (or positive-semidefinite) Hermitian or real symmetric matrix and $\mathbf{R}$ is a positive-definite Hermitian or real symmetric matrix. Note that the second term on the right side of Eq. (4-4) accounts for the expenditure of the energy of the control signals. The matrices $\mathbf{Q}$ and $\mathbf{R}$ determine the relative importance of the error and the expenditure of this energy. In this problem, we assume that the control vector $\mathbf{u}(t)$ is unconstrained.

As will be seen later, the linear control law given by Eq. (4-3) is the optimal control law. Therefore, if the unknown elements of the matrix $\mathbf{K}$ are determined so as to minimize the performance index, then $\mathbf{u}(t) = -\mathbf{Kx}(t)$ is optimal for any initial state $\mathbf{x}(0)$. The block diagram showing the optimal configuration is shown in Figure 4-1.

Now let us solve the optimization problem. Substituting Eq. (4-3) into Eq. (4-2), we obtain

$$\dot{\mathbf{x}} = \mathbf{Ax} - \mathbf{BKx} = (\mathbf{A} - \mathbf{BK})\mathbf{x}$$

In the following derivations, we assume that the matrix $\mathbf{A} - \mathbf{BK}$ is stable or that the eigenvalues of $\mathbf{A} - \mathbf{BK}$ have negative real parts.

Substituting Eq. (4-3) into Eq. (4-4) yields

$$J = \int_0^\infty (\mathbf{x'Qx} + \mathbf{x'K'RKx})\, dt$$

$$= \int_0^\infty \mathbf{x'(Q + K'RK)x}\, dt$$

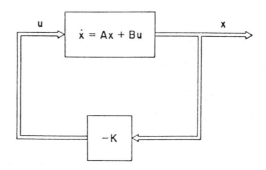

Figure 4-1

We shall use the Liapunov approach to solve this optimization problem. Let us assume that for any $\mathbf{x}$

$$\mathbf{x}'(\mathbf{Q} + \mathbf{K}'\mathbf{R}\mathbf{K})\mathbf{x} = -\frac{d}{dt}(\mathbf{x}'\mathbf{P}\mathbf{x})$$

where $\mathbf{P}$ is a positive definite Hermitian or real symmetric matrix. Then we obtain

$$\mathbf{x}'(\mathbf{Q} + \mathbf{K}'\mathbf{R}\mathbf{K})\mathbf{x} = -\dot{\mathbf{x}}'\mathbf{P}\mathbf{x} - \mathbf{x}'\mathbf{P}\dot{\mathbf{x}} = -\mathbf{x}'[(\mathbf{A} - \mathbf{B}\mathbf{K})'\mathbf{P} + \mathbf{P}(\mathbf{A} - \mathbf{B}\mathbf{K})]\mathbf{x}$$

By the second method of Liapunov, we know that, for a given positive-definite (or under certain conditions positive-semidefinite) matrix $\mathbf{Q} + \mathbf{K}'\mathbf{R}\mathbf{K}$, there exists a positive definite matrix $\mathbf{P}$, if matrix $\mathbf{A} - \mathbf{B}\mathbf{K}$ is stable, such that

$$(\mathbf{A} - \mathbf{B}\mathbf{K})'\mathbf{P} + \mathbf{P}(\mathbf{A} - \mathbf{B}\mathbf{K}) = -(\mathbf{Q} + \mathbf{K}'\mathbf{R}\mathbf{K}) \tag{4-5}$$

Hence our procedure is to determine the elements of $\mathbf{P}$ from this equation and see if it is positive definite. (Note that more than one matrix $\mathbf{P}$ may satisfy this equation. If the system is stable, there always exists one positive definite matrix $\mathbf{P}$ to satisfy this equation. This means that, if we solve this equation and find one positive-definite matrix $\mathbf{P}$, the system is stable. Other $\mathbf{P}$ matrices that satisfy this equation are not positive definite and must be discarded.)

The performance index J can be evaluated as

$$J = \int_0^\infty \mathbf{x}'(\mathbf{Q} + \mathbf{K}'\mathbf{R}\mathbf{K})\mathbf{x}\,dt = -\mathbf{x}'\mathbf{P}\mathbf{x}\Big|_0^\infty = -\mathbf{x}'(\infty)\mathbf{P}\mathbf{x}(\infty) + \mathbf{x}'(0)\mathbf{P}\mathbf{x}(0)$$

Since all eigenvalues of $\mathbf{A} - \mathbf{B}\mathbf{K}$ are assumed to have negative real parts, we have $\mathbf{x}(\infty) \to \mathbf{0}$. Therefore, we obtain

$$J = \mathbf{x}'(0)\mathbf{P}\mathbf{x}(0) \tag{4-6}$$

Thus the performance index J can be obtained in terms of the initial condition $\mathbf{x}(0)$ and $\mathbf{P}$.

Solution to quadratic optimal control problem

To obtain the solution to the quadratic optimal control problem, we proceed as follows: Since $\mathbf{R}$ has been assumed to be a positive-definite Hermitian or real symmetric matrix, we can write

$$\mathbf{R} = \mathbf{T}'\mathbf{T}$$

where $\mathbf{T}$ is a nonsingular matrix. Then Eq. (4-5) can be written as

$$(\mathbf{A}' - \mathbf{K}'\mathbf{B}')\mathbf{P} + \mathbf{P}(\mathbf{A} - \mathbf{B}\mathbf{K}) + \mathbf{Q} + \mathbf{K}'\mathbf{T}'\mathbf{T}\mathbf{K} = 0$$

which can be rewritten as

$$\mathbf{A}'\mathbf{P} + \mathbf{P}\mathbf{A} + [\mathbf{T}\mathbf{K} - (\mathbf{T}')^{-1}\mathbf{B}'\mathbf{P}]'[\mathbf{T}\mathbf{K} - (\mathbf{T}')^{-1}\mathbf{B}'\mathbf{P}] - \mathbf{P}\mathbf{B}\mathbf{R}^{-1}\mathbf{B}'\mathbf{P} + \mathbf{Q} = 0$$

The minimization of J with respect to $\mathbf{K}$ requires the minimization of

$$\mathbf{x}'[\mathbf{T}\mathbf{K} - (\mathbf{T}')^{-1}\mathbf{B}'\mathbf{P}]'[\mathbf{T}\mathbf{K} - (\mathbf{T}')^{-1}\mathbf{B}'\mathbf{P}]\mathbf{x}$$

with respect to $\mathbf{K}$. (For the proof of this statement, refer, for example, to Reference 4 listed at the end of the book.) Since this last expression is nonnegative, the minimum occurs when it is zero, or when

$$\mathbf{TK} = (\mathbf{T}')^{-1}\mathbf{B}'\mathbf{P}$$

Hence

$$\mathbf{K} = \mathbf{T}^{-1}(\mathbf{T}')^{-1}\mathbf{B}'\mathbf{P} = \mathbf{R}^{-1}\mathbf{B}'\mathbf{P} \tag{4-7}$$

Equation (4-7) gives the optimal matrix $\mathbf{K}$. Thus the optimal control law to the quadratic optimal control problem when the performance index is given by Eq. (4-4) is linear and is given by

$$\mathbf{u}(t) = -\mathbf{K}\mathbf{x}(t) = -\mathbf{R}^{-1}\mathbf{B}'\mathbf{P}\mathbf{x}(t)$$

The matrix $\mathbf{P}$ in Eq. (4-7) must satisfy Eq. (4-5) or the following reduced equation:

$$\mathbf{A}'\mathbf{P} + \mathbf{P}\mathbf{A} - \mathbf{P}\mathbf{B}\mathbf{R}^{-1}\mathbf{B}'\mathbf{P} + \mathbf{Q} = 0 \tag{4-8}$$

Equation (4-8) is called the *reduced-matrix Riccati equation*. The design steps may be stated as follows:

1. Solve Eq. (4-8), the reduced-matrix Riccati equation, for the matrix $\mathbf{P}$. [If a positive definite matrix $\mathbf{P}$ exists (certain systems may not have positive definite matrix $\mathbf{P}$), the system is stable or matrix $\mathbf{A} - \mathbf{B}\mathbf{K}$ is stable.]
2. Substitute this matrix $\mathbf{P}$ into Eq. (4-7). The resulting matrix $\mathbf{K}$ is optimal.

MATLAB solution to quadratic optimal control problem

In MATLAB the command

$$\text{lqr}(A,B,Q,R)$$

solves the continuous-time linear quadratic regulator problem and the associated Riccati equation. This command calculates the optimal feedback gain matrix $\mathbf{K}$ such that the feedback control law

$$u = -\mathbf{K}\mathbf{x}$$

minimizes the performance index

$$J = \int_0^\infty (\mathbf{x}'\mathbf{Q}\mathbf{x} + \mathbf{u}'\mathbf{R}\mathbf{u})\, dt$$

subject to the constraint equation

$$\dot{\mathbf{x}} = \mathbf{A}\mathbf{x} + \mathbf{B}\mathbf{u}$$

Another command

$$[K,P,E] = \text{lqr}(A,B,Q,R)$$

also returns matrix **P**, the unique positive-definite solution to the associated matrix Riccati equation:

$$0 = PA + A'P - PBRB'P + Q$$

If matrix **A** − **BK** is a stable matrix, such a positive-definite solution **P** always exists. The closed-loop poles or eigenvalues of **A** − **BK** are also obtained by this command.

It is important to note that for certain systems matrix **A** − **BK** cannot be made a stable matrix, whatever **K** is chosen. In such a case there does not exist a positive-definite matrix **P** for the matrix Riccati equation. For such a case the commands

$$K = lqr(A,B,Q,R)$$

$$[K,P,E] = lqr(A,B,Q,R)$$

do not give the solution. See MATLAB Program 4-1.

EXAMPLE 4-1

Consider the system defined by

$$\begin{bmatrix} \dot{x}_1 \\ \dot{x}_2 \end{bmatrix} = \begin{bmatrix} -1 & 1 \\ 0 & 2 \end{bmatrix} \begin{bmatrix} x_1 \\ x_2 \end{bmatrix} + \begin{bmatrix} 1 \\ 0 \end{bmatrix} u$$

Show that the system cannot be stabilized by the state feedback control scheme

$$u = -\mathbf{Kx}$$

whatever matrix **K** is chosen.

Define

$$\mathbf{K} = [k_1 \quad k_2]$$

Then

$$\mathbf{A} - \mathbf{BK} = \begin{bmatrix} -1 & 1 \\ 0 & 2 \end{bmatrix} - \begin{bmatrix} 1 \\ 0 \end{bmatrix} [k_1 \quad k_2]$$

$$= \begin{bmatrix} -1 - k_1 & 1 - k_2 \\ 0 & 2 \end{bmatrix}$$

Hence the characteristic equation becomes

$$|s\mathbf{I} - \mathbf{A} + \mathbf{BK}| = \begin{vmatrix} s + 1 + k_1 & -1 + k_2 \\ 0 & s - 2 \end{vmatrix}$$

$$= (s + 1 + k_1)(s - 2) = 0$$

The closed-loop poles are located at

$$s = -1 - k_1, \qquad s = 2$$

Since the pole at $s = 2$ is in the right-half s plane, the system is unstable whatever **K** matrix is chosen. Hence quadratic optimal control techniques cannot be applied to this system.

Let us assume that matrices **Q** and **R** in the quadratic performance index are given by

$$\mathbf{Q} = \begin{bmatrix} 1 & 0 \\ 0 & 1 \end{bmatrix}, \qquad R = [1]$$

and that we write MATLAB Program 4-1. The resulting MATLAB solution is

$$K = [\text{NaN} \quad \text{NaN}]$$

(NaN means 'not a number'.) Whenever the solution to a quadratic optimal control problem does not exist, MATLAB tells us that matrix **K** consists of 'NaN'.

MATLAB Program 4–1

```
% ---------- Design of quadratic optimal regulator system ----------

% ***** Determination of feedback gain matrix K for quadratic
% optimal control *****

% ***** Enter state matrix A and control matrix B *****

A = [-1   1;0   2];
B = [1;0];

% ***** Enter matrices Q and R of the quadratic performance
% index *****

Q = [1   0;0   1];
R = [1];

% ***** To obtain optimal feedback gain matrix K, enter the
% following command *****

K = lqr(A,B,Q,R)

Warning: Matrix is singular to working precision.

K =

    NaN   NaN

% ***** If we enter the command [K,P,E] = lqr(A,B,Q,R), then *****

[K,P,E] = lqr(A,B,Q,R)

Warning: Matrix is singular to working precision.

K =

    NaN   NaN
```

P =

  -/ -/
  -/ -/

E =

  -2.0000
  -1.4142

EXAMPLE 4-2

Consider the system described by

$$\dot{\mathbf{x}} = \mathbf{A}\mathbf{x} + \mathbf{B}u$$

where

$$\mathbf{A} = \begin{bmatrix} 0 & 1 \\ 0 & -1 \end{bmatrix}, \qquad \mathbf{B} = \begin{bmatrix} 0 \\ 1 \end{bmatrix}$$

The performance index J is given by

$$J = \int_0^\infty (\mathbf{x}'\mathbf{Q}\mathbf{x} + u'Ru)\, dt$$

where

$$\mathbf{Q} = \begin{bmatrix} 1 & 0 \\ 0 & 1 \end{bmatrix}, \qquad R = [1]$$

Assume that the following control u is used.

$$u = -\mathbf{K}\mathbf{x}$$

Determine the optimal feedback gain matrix **K**.

The optimal feedback gain matrix **K** can be obtained by solving the following Riccati equation for a positive-definite matrix **P**:

$$\mathbf{A}'\mathbf{P} + \mathbf{P}\mathbf{A} - \mathbf{P}\mathbf{B}R^{-1}\mathbf{B}'\mathbf{P} + \mathbf{Q} = 0$$

The result is

$$\mathbf{P} = \begin{bmatrix} 2 & 1 \\ 1 & 1 \end{bmatrix}$$

Substituting this **P** matrix into the following equation gives the optimal **K** matrix:

$$\mathbf{K} = R^{-1}\mathbf{B}'\mathbf{P}$$

$$= [1][0 \quad 1]\begin{bmatrix} 2 & 1 \\ 1 & 1 \end{bmatrix} = [1 \quad 1]$$

Thus the optimal control signal is given by

$$u = -\mathbf{Kx} = -x_1 - x_2$$

MATLAB Program 4-2 yields the solution to this problem.

MATLAB Program 4–2

```
% ---------- Design of quadratic optimal regulator system ----------

% ***** Determination of feedback gain matrix K for quadratic
% optimal control *****

% ***** Enter state matrix A and control matrix B *****

A = [0  1;0  -1];
B = [0;1];

% ***** Enter matrices Q and R of the quadratic performance
% index *****

Q = [1  0;0  1];
R = [1];

% ***** The optimal feedback gain matrix K (if such matrix K
% exists) can be obtained by entering the following command *****

K = lqr(A,B,Q,R)

K =

    1.0000    1.0000
```

EXAMPLE 4-3

Consider the system given by

$$\dot{\mathbf{x}} = \mathbf{Ax} + \mathbf{B}u$$

where

$$\mathbf{A} = \begin{bmatrix} 0 & 1 & 0 \\ 0 & 0 & 1 \\ -35 & -27 & -9 \end{bmatrix}, \qquad \mathbf{B} = \begin{bmatrix} 0 \\ 0 \\ 1 \end{bmatrix}$$

The performance index J is given by

$$J = \int_0^\infty (\mathbf{x}'\mathbf{Qx} + u'Ru)\, dt$$

where

$$\mathbf{Q} = \begin{bmatrix} 1 & 0 & 0 \\ 0 & 1 & 0 \\ 0 & 0 & 1 \end{bmatrix}, \quad R = [1]$$

Obtain the positive-definite solution matrix **P** of the Riccati equation, optimal feedback gain matrix **K**, and eigenvalues of matrix **A** − **BK**.

A MATLAB program to solve this problem is given in MATLAB Program 4-3.

MATLAB Program 4–3

```
% ---------- Design of quadratic optimal regulator system ----------

% ***** Determination of feedback gain matrix K for quadratic
% optimal control *****

% ***** Enter state matrix A and control matrix B *****

A = [0  1  0;0  0  1;-35  -27  -9];
B = [0;0;1];

% ***** Enter matrices Q and R of the quadratic performance
% index *****

Q = [1  0  0;0  1  0;0  0  1];
R = [1];

% ***** The optimal feedback gain matrix K, solution P of Riccati
% equation, and closed-loop poles (that is, the eigenvalues
% of A - BK) can be obtained by entering the following
% command *****

[K,P,E] = lqr(A,B,Q,R)

K =

    0.0143    0.1107    0.0676


P =

    4.2625    2.4957    0.0143
    2.4957    2.8150    0.1107
    0.0143    0.1107    0.0676


E =

  -5.0958
  -1.9859 + 1.7110i
  -1.9859 - 1.7110i
```

EXAMPLE 4-4

Consider the system defined by the following state-space equations:

$$\dot{\mathbf{x}} = \mathbf{A}\mathbf{x} + \mathbf{B}u$$

$$y = \mathbf{C}\mathbf{x} + Du$$

where

$$\mathbf{A} = \begin{bmatrix} 0 & 1 & 0 \\ 0 & 0 & 1 \\ 0 & -2 & -3 \end{bmatrix}, \quad \mathbf{B} = \begin{bmatrix} 0 \\ 0 \\ 1 \end{bmatrix}, \quad \mathbf{C} = [1 \quad 0 \quad 0], \quad D = [0]$$

Assume that the control signal u is given by

$$u = k_1(r - x_1) - (k_2 x_2 + k_3 x_3) = k_1 r - (k_1 x_1 + k_2 x_2 + k_3 x_3)$$

as shown in Figure 4-2. In determining an optimal control law, we assume that the input is zero, or $r = 0$.

Let us determine the state feedback gain matrix $\mathbf{K}$, where

$$\mathbf{K} = [k_1 \quad k_2 \quad k_3]$$

such that the following performance index is minimized:

$$J = \int_0^\infty (\mathbf{x}'\mathbf{Q}\mathbf{x} + u'Ru)\,dt$$

where

$$\mathbf{Q} = \begin{bmatrix} q_{11} & 0 & 0 \\ 0 & q_{22} & 0 \\ 0 & 0 & q_{33} \end{bmatrix}, \quad R = 1, \quad \mathbf{x} = \begin{bmatrix} x_1 \\ x_2 \\ x_3 \end{bmatrix} = \begin{bmatrix} y \\ \dot{y} \\ \ddot{y} \end{bmatrix}$$

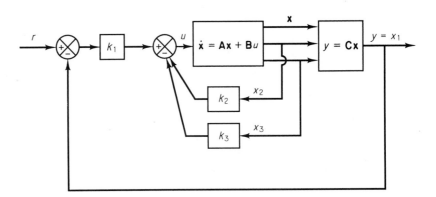

Figure 4-2

To get a fast response, q_{11} must be sufficiently large compared with q_{22}, q_{33}, and R. In this problem we choose

$$q_{11} = 100, \qquad q_{22} = q_{33} = 1, \qquad R = 0.01$$

To solve this problem with MATLAB, we use the command

$$K = \text{lqr}(A,B,Q,R)$$

MATLAB Program 4-4 yields the solution to this problem.

MATLAB Program 4–4

```
% ---------- Design of quadratic optimal control system ----------

% ***** We shall determine the optimal feedback gain matrix K that
% minimizes the performance index J *****

% ***** Enter state matrix A and control matrix B *****

A = [0  1  0;0  0  1;0  -2  -3];
B = [0;0;1];

% ***** Enter matrices Q and R of the quadratic performance
% index J *****

Q = [100  0  0;0  1  0;0  0  1];
R = [0.01];

% ***** To obtain the optimal state feedback gain matrix K,
% enter the following command *****

K = lqr(A,B,Q,R)

K =

   100.0000    53.1200    11.6711

k1 = K(1), k2 = K(2), k3 = K(3)

k1 =

   100.0000


k2 =

   53.1200


k3 =

   11.6711
```

Next we shall investigate the step-response characteristic of the designed system using the matrix $\mathbf{K}$ thus determined. The state equation for the designed system is

$$\dot{\mathbf{x}} = \mathbf{A}\mathbf{x} + \mathbf{B}u$$
$$= \mathbf{A}\mathbf{x} + \mathbf{B}(-\mathbf{K}\mathbf{x} + k_1 r)$$
$$= (\mathbf{A} - \mathbf{B}\mathbf{K})\mathbf{x} + \mathbf{B}k_1 r$$

and the output equation is

$$y = \mathbf{C}\mathbf{x} = \begin{bmatrix} 1 & 0 & 0 \end{bmatrix} \begin{bmatrix} x_1 \\ x_2 \\ x_3 \end{bmatrix}$$

To obtain the unit-step response, use the following command:

$$[y,x,t] = \text{step}(AA,BB,CC,DD)$$

where

$$AA = \mathbf{A} - \mathbf{B}\mathbf{K}, \qquad BB = \mathbf{B}k_1, \qquad CC = \mathbf{C}, \qquad DD = D$$

MATLAB Program 4-5 gives the unit-step response of the designed system. Figure 4-3 shows the output y versus time t. Figure 4-4 gives the response curves x_1, x_2, and x_3 versus t on one diagram. Figure 4-5 depicts the response x_2 versus t, and Figure 4-6 shows the response x_3 versus t.

MATLAB Program 4–5

```
% ---------- Unit-step response of designed system ----------

% ***** Using the optimal feedback gain matrix K determined in
% the preceding program, we shall obtain the unit-step response
% of the designed system *****

% ***** The state equation for the designed system is
% xdot = (A - BK)x + Bk1r and the output equation is
% y = Cx + Du, where matrices C and D are given by *****

C = [1  0  0];
D = [0];

% ***** Define the state matrix, control matrix, output matrix,
% and direct transmission matrix of the designed system as AA,
% BB, CC, and DD *****

AA = A - B*K;
BB = B*k1;
CC = C;
DD = D;
```

```
% ***** To obtain the unit-step response, enter the following
% command *****

[y,x,t] = step(AA,BB,CC,DD);

% ***** To plot the unit-step response curve y (= x1) versus
% t, enter the following command *****

plot(t,y)
grid
title('Unit-Step Response of Quadratic Optimal Control System')
xlabel('Sec')
ylabel('Output y = x1')

% ***** To plot curves x1, x2, x3 versus t on one diagram,
% enter the following command *****

plot(t,x)
grid
title('Response Curves x1, x2, x3 versus t')
xlabel('Sec')
ylabel('x1, x2, x3')
text(1.6,1.2,'x1')
text(0.7,1.2,'x2')
text(0.35,3.2,'x3')

% ***** To plot curve x2 versus t, enter the following command *****

x2 = [0   1   0]*x'; plot(t,x2)
grid
title('Response x2 versus t')
xlabel('Sec')
ylabel('x2')

% ***** To plot curve x3 versus t, enter the following command *****

x3 = [0   0   1]*x'; plot(t,x3)
grid
title('Response x3 versus t')
xlabel('Sec')
ylabel('x3')
```

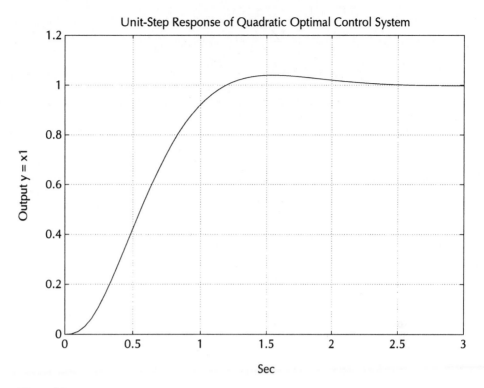

Figure 4-3

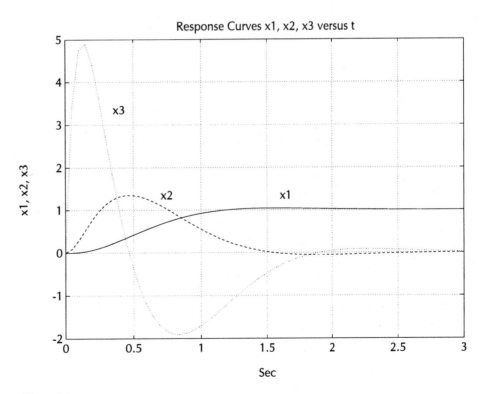

Figure 4-4

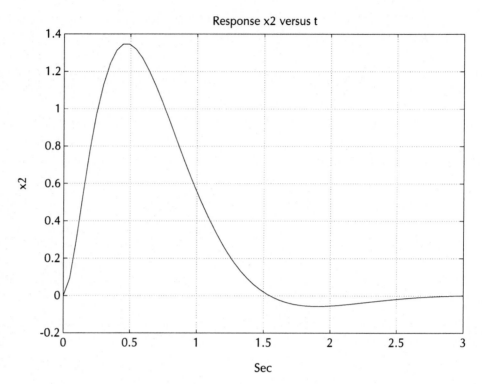

Figure 4-5

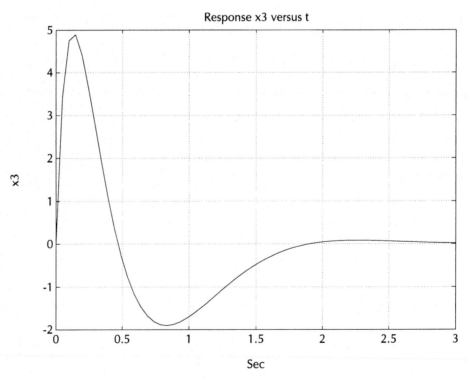

Figure 4-6

4-3 QUADRATIC OPTIMAL CONTROL OF DISCRETE-TIME SYSTEMS

In this section we shall first discuss the mathematical analysis of quadratic optimal control of discrete-time systems and derive the basic equations necessary for computer solution with MATLAB. Then we shall present MATLAB programs for solving quadratic optimal control problems involving discrete-time systems.

Quadratic optimal control problem

The quadratic optimal control problem may be stated as follows: Given a linear discrete-time control system

$$\mathbf{x}(k + 1) = \mathbf{G}\mathbf{x}(k) + \mathbf{H}\mathbf{u}(k), \qquad \mathbf{x}(0) = \mathbf{c} \tag{4-9}$$

where it is assumed to be completely state controllable and where

$$\mathbf{x}(k) = \text{state vector } (n\text{-vector})$$
$$\mathbf{u}(k) = \text{control vector } (r\text{-vector})$$
$$\mathbf{G} = n \times n \text{ nonsingular matrix}$$
$$\mathbf{H} = n \times r \text{ matrix}$$

find the optimal control sequence $\mathbf{u}(0), \mathbf{u}(1), \mathbf{u}(2), \ldots, \mathbf{u}(N - 1)$ that minimizes a quadratic performance index. An example of the quadratic performance indexes for a finite time process $(0 \le k \le N)$ is

$$J = \frac{1}{2}\mathbf{x}'(N)\mathbf{S}\mathbf{x}(N) + \frac{1}{2}\sum_{k=0}^{N-1}[\mathbf{x}'(k)\mathbf{Q}\mathbf{x}(k) + \mathbf{u}'(k)\mathbf{R}\mathbf{u}(k)] \tag{4-10}$$

where $\mathbf{Q} = n \times n$ positive definite or positive semidefinite Hermitian matrix (or real symmetric matrix)

$\mathbf{R} = r \times r$ positive definite Hermitian matrix (or real symmetric matrix)

$\mathbf{S} = n \times n$ positive definite or positive semidefinite Hermitian matrix (or real symmetric matrix)

Matrices $\mathbf{Q}$, $\mathbf{R}$, and $\mathbf{S}$ are selected to weigh the relative importance of the performance measures caused by the state vector $\mathbf{x}(k)$ $(k = 0, 1, 2, \ldots, N - 1)$, the control vector $\mathbf{u}(k)$ $(k = 0, 1, 2, \ldots, N - 1)$, and the final state $\mathbf{x}(N)$, respectively.

The initial state of the system is at some arbitrary state $\mathbf{x}(0) = \mathbf{c}$. The final state $\mathbf{x}(N)$ may be fixed, in which case the term $\frac{1}{2}\mathbf{x}'(N)\mathbf{S}\mathbf{x}(N)$ is removed from the performance index of Eq. (4-10) and, instead, the terminal condition $\mathbf{x}(N) = \mathbf{x}_f$ is imposed, where $\mathbf{x}_f$ is the fixed terminal state. If the final state $\mathbf{x}(N)$ is not fixed, the first term in Eq. (4-10) represents the weight of the performance measure due to the final state. Note that in the minimization problem the inclusion of the term $\frac{1}{2}\mathbf{x}'(N)\mathbf{S}\mathbf{x}(N)$ in the performance index J implies that we desire the final state $\mathbf{x}(N)$ to be as close to the origin as possible.

Solution by the conventional minimization method using Lagrange multipliers

The quadratic optimal control problem is a minimization problem involving a function of several variables. Thus it can be solved by the conventional minimization method. The minimization problem subjected to equality constraints may be solved by adjoining the constraints to the function to be minimized by use of Lagrange multipliers.

In the present optimization problem, we minimize J as given by Eq. (4-10), repeated here,

$$J = \frac{1}{2}\mathbf{x}'(N)\mathbf{S}\mathbf{x}(N) + \frac{1}{2}\sum_{k=0}^{N-1}[\mathbf{x}'(k)\mathbf{Q}\mathbf{x}(k) + \mathbf{u}'(k)\mathbf{R}\mathbf{u}(k)] \qquad (4\text{-}11)$$

when it is subjected to the constraint equation specified by Eq. (4-9),

$$\mathbf{x}(k+1) = \mathbf{G}\mathbf{x}(k) + \mathbf{H}\mathbf{u}(k) \qquad (4\text{-}12)$$

where $k = 0, 1, 2, \ldots, N - 1$, and where the initial condition on the state vector is specified as

$$\mathbf{x}(0) = \mathbf{c} \qquad (4\text{-}13)$$

Now, using a set of Lagrange multipliers $\boldsymbol{\lambda}(1), \boldsymbol{\lambda}(2), \ldots, \boldsymbol{\lambda}(N)$, we define a new performance index L as follows:

$$\begin{aligned}
L = \frac{1}{2}\,\mathbf{x}'(N)\mathbf{S}\mathbf{x}(N) + \frac{1}{2}\sum_{k=0}^{N-1}\Big\{ & [\mathbf{x}'(k)\mathbf{Q}\mathbf{x}(k) + \mathbf{u}'(k)\mathbf{R}\mathbf{u}(k)] \\
& + \boldsymbol{\lambda}'(k+1)[\mathbf{G}\mathbf{x}(k) + \mathbf{H}\mathbf{u}(k) - \mathbf{x}(k+1)] \\
& + [\mathbf{G}\mathbf{x}(k) + \mathbf{H}\mathbf{u}(k) - \mathbf{x}(k+1)]'\boldsymbol{\lambda}(k+1) \Big\}
\end{aligned} \qquad (4\text{-}14)$$

The reason for writing the terms involving the Lagrange multiplier in the form shown in Eq. (4-14) is to ensure that $L = L'$. (L is a real scalar quantity.) Note that

$$\boldsymbol{\lambda}'(0)[\mathbf{c} - \mathbf{x}(0)] + [\mathbf{c} - \mathbf{x}(0)]'\boldsymbol{\lambda}(0)$$

may be added to the performance index L. However, we shall not do so, to simplify the presentation. It is a well-known fact that minimization of the function L defined by Eq. (4-14) is equivalent to minimization of J as defined by Eq. (4-11) when it is subjected to the equality constraint defined by Eq. (4-12).

To minimize the function L, we need to differentiate L with respect to each component of vectors $\mathbf{x}(k)$, $\mathbf{u}(k)$, and $\boldsymbol{\lambda}(k)$ and set the results equal to zero. From the computational viewpoint, however, it is convenient to differentiate L with respect to $\bar{x}_i(k)$, $\bar{u}_i(k)$, and $\bar{\lambda}_i(k)$, where $\bar{x}_i(k)$, $\bar{u}_i(k)$, and $\bar{\lambda}_i(k)$ are, respectively, the complex conjugates of $x_i(k)$, $u_i(k)$, and $\lambda_i(k)$. (Note that the signal and its complex conjugate contain the same mathematical information.) Thus we set

$$\frac{\partial L}{\partial \bar{x}_i(k)} = 0, \qquad i = 1, 2, \ldots, n; k = 1, 2, \ldots, N$$

$$\frac{\partial L}{\partial \bar{u}_i(k)} = 0, \qquad i = 1, 2, \ldots, r; k = 0, 1, \ldots, N - 1$$

$$\frac{\partial L}{\partial \bar{\lambda}_i(k)} = 0, \qquad i = 1, 2, \ldots, n; k = 1, 2, \ldots, N$$

These equations are necessary conditions for L to have a minimum. Note that the simplified expressions for the preceding partial derivative equations are

$$\frac{\partial L}{\partial \overline{\mathbf{x}}(k)} = \mathbf{0}, \qquad k = 1, 2, \ldots, N \tag{4-15}$$

$$\frac{\partial L}{\partial \overline{\mathbf{u}}(k)} = \mathbf{0}, \qquad k = 0, 1, \ldots, N - 1 \tag{4-16}$$

$$\frac{\partial L}{\partial \overline{\boldsymbol{\lambda}}(k)} = \mathbf{0}, \qquad k = 1, 2, \ldots, N \tag{4-17}$$

Using the relationships

$$\frac{\partial}{\partial \overline{\mathbf{x}}} \mathbf{x}' \mathbf{A} \mathbf{x} = \mathbf{A} \mathbf{x} \qquad \text{and} \qquad \frac{\partial}{\partial \overline{\mathbf{x}}} \mathbf{x}' \mathbf{A} \mathbf{y} = \mathbf{A} \mathbf{y}$$

Equations (4-15), (4-16), and (4-17) may be rewritten as follows:

$$\frac{\partial L}{\partial \overline{\mathbf{x}}(k)} = \mathbf{0}: \qquad \mathbf{Q}\mathbf{x}(k) + \mathbf{G}'\boldsymbol{\lambda}(k + 1) - \boldsymbol{\lambda}(k) = \mathbf{0}, \quad k = 1, 2, \ldots, N - 1 \tag{4-18}$$

$$\frac{\partial L}{\partial \overline{\mathbf{x}}(N)} = \mathbf{0}: \qquad \mathbf{S}\mathbf{x}(N) - \boldsymbol{\lambda}(N) = \mathbf{0}, \tag{4-19}$$

$$\frac{\partial L}{\partial \overline{\mathbf{u}}(k)} = \mathbf{0}: \qquad \mathbf{R}\mathbf{u}(k) + \mathbf{H}'\boldsymbol{\lambda}(k + 1) = \mathbf{0}, \quad k = 0, 1, \ldots, N - 1 \tag{4-20}$$

$$\frac{\partial L}{\partial \overline{\boldsymbol{\lambda}}(k)} = \mathbf{0}: \quad \mathbf{G}\mathbf{x}(k - 1) + \mathbf{H}\mathbf{u}(k - 1) - \mathbf{x}(k) = \mathbf{0}, \quad k = 1, 2, \ldots, N \tag{4-21}$$

Equation (4-21) is simply the system state equation. Equation (4-19) specifies the final value of the Lagrange multiplier. Note that the Lagrange multiplier $\boldsymbol{\lambda}(k)$ is often called a *covector* or *adjoint vector*.

Now we shall simplify the equations just obtained. From Eq. (4-18) we have

$$\boldsymbol{\lambda}(k) = \mathbf{Q}\mathbf{x}(k) + \mathbf{G}'\boldsymbol{\lambda}(k + 1), \qquad k = 1, 2, 3, \ldots, N - 1 \tag{4-22}$$

with the final condition $\boldsymbol{\lambda}(N) = \mathbf{S}\mathbf{x}(N)$. By solving Eq. (4-20) for $\mathbf{u}(k)$ and noting that $\mathbf{R}^{-1}$ exists, we obtain

$$\mathbf{u}(k) = -\mathbf{R}^{-1}\mathbf{H}'\boldsymbol{\lambda}(k + 1), \qquad k = 0, 1, 2, \ldots, N - 1 \tag{4-23}$$

Equation (4-21) can be rewritten as

$$\mathbf{x}(k + 1) = \mathbf{G}\mathbf{x}(k) + \mathbf{H}\mathbf{u}(k), \qquad k = 0, 1, 2, \ldots, N - 1 \tag{4-24}$$

which is simply the state equation. Substitution of Eq. (4-23) into Eq. (4-24) results in

$$\mathbf{x}(k + 1) = \mathbf{G}\mathbf{x}(k) - \mathbf{H}\mathbf{R}^{-1}\mathbf{H}'\boldsymbol{\lambda}(k + 1) \tag{4-25}$$

with the initial condition $\mathbf{x}(0) = \mathbf{c}$.

To obtain the solution to the minimization problem, we need to solve Eqs. (4-22) and (4-25) simultaneously. Notice that for the system equation, Eq. (4-24), the initial condition $\mathbf{x}(0)$ is specified, while for the Lagrange multiplier equation, Eq. (4-22), the final condition $\boldsymbol{\lambda}(N)$ is specified. Thus the problem here becomes a two-point boundary-value problem.

If the two-point boundary-value problem is solved, the optimal values for the state vector and Lagrange multiplier vector may be determined, and the optimal control vector $\mathbf{u}(k)$ may be obtained in the open-loop form. However, if we employ the Riccati transformation, the optimal control vector $\mathbf{u}(k)$ can be obtained in the following closed-loop, or feedback, form:

$$\mathbf{u}(k) = -\mathbf{K}(k)\mathbf{x}(k)$$

where $\mathbf{K}(k)$ is the $r \times n$ feedback matrix.

In what follows, we shall obtain the optimal control vector $\mathbf{u}(k)$ in the closed-loop form by first obtaining the Riccati equation. Assume that $\boldsymbol{\lambda}(k)$ can be written in the following form:

$$\boldsymbol{\lambda}(k) = \mathbf{P}(k)\mathbf{x}(k) \tag{4-26}$$

where $\mathbf{P}(k)$ is an $n \times n$ Hermitian matrix (or an $n \times n$ real symmetric matrix). Substitution of Eq. (4-26) into Eq. (4-22) results in

$$\mathbf{P}(k)\mathbf{x}(k) = \mathbf{Q}\mathbf{x}(k) + \mathbf{G}'\mathbf{P}(k + 1)\mathbf{x}(k + 1) \tag{4-27}$$

and substitution of Eq. (4-26) into Eq. (4-25) gives

$$\mathbf{x}(k + 1) = \mathbf{G}\mathbf{x}(k) - \mathbf{H}\mathbf{R}^{-1}\mathbf{H}'\mathbf{P}(k + 1)\mathbf{x}(k + 1) \tag{4-28}$$

Notice that Eqs. (4-27) and (4-28) do not involve $\boldsymbol{\lambda}(k)$ and thus we have eliminated $\boldsymbol{\lambda}(k)$. The transformation process employed here is called the *Riccati transformation*. It is of extreme importance in solving such a two-point boundary-value problem.

From Eq. (4-28) we have

$$[\mathbf{I} + \mathbf{H}\mathbf{R}^{-1}\mathbf{H}'\mathbf{P}(k + 1)]\mathbf{x}(k + 1) = \mathbf{G}\mathbf{x}(k) \tag{4-29}$$

For completely state controllable systems, it can be shown that $\mathbf{P}(k + 1)$ is positive definite or positive semidefinite. For at least a positive-semidefinite matrix $\mathbf{P}(k + 1)$, we have

$$|\mathbf{I}_n + \mathbf{H}\mathbf{R}^{-1}\mathbf{H}'\mathbf{P}(k + 1)| = |\mathbf{I}_r + \mathbf{H}'\mathbf{P}(k + 1)\mathbf{H}\mathbf{R}^{-1}| = |\mathbf{I}_r + \mathbf{R}^{-1}\mathbf{H}'\mathbf{P}(k + 1)\mathbf{H}|$$

$$= |\mathbf{R}^{-1}||\mathbf{R} + \mathbf{H}'\mathbf{P}(k + 1)\mathbf{H}| \neq 0$$

where we have used the relationship

$$|\mathbf{I}_n + \mathbf{A}\mathbf{B}| = |\mathbf{I}_r + \mathbf{B}\mathbf{A}|, \qquad \mathbf{A} = n \times r \text{ matrix}, \qquad \mathbf{B} = r \times n \text{ matrix}$$

Hence the inverse of $\mathbf{I} + \mathbf{H}\mathbf{R}^{-1}\mathbf{H}'\mathbf{P}(k + 1)$ exists. Consequently, Eq. (4-29) can be written as follows:

$$\mathbf{x}(k + 1) = [\mathbf{I} + \mathbf{H}\mathbf{R}^{-1}\mathbf{H}'\mathbf{P}(k + 1)]^{-1}\mathbf{G}\mathbf{x}(k) \tag{4-30}$$

By substituting Eq. (4-30) into Eq. (4-27), we obtain

$$\mathbf{P}(k)\mathbf{x}(k) = \mathbf{Q}\mathbf{x}(k) + \mathbf{G}'\mathbf{P}(k + 1)[\mathbf{I} + \mathbf{H}\mathbf{R}^{-1}\mathbf{H}'\mathbf{P}(k + 1)]^{-1}\mathbf{G}\mathbf{x}(k)$$

or

$$\{\mathbf{P}(k) - \mathbf{Q} - \mathbf{G}'\mathbf{P}(k + 1)[\mathbf{I} + \mathbf{H}\mathbf{R}^{-1}\mathbf{H}'\mathbf{P}(k + 1)]^{-1}\mathbf{G}\}\mathbf{x}(k) = \mathbf{0}$$

This last equation must hold for all $\mathbf{x}(k)$. Hence we must have

$$\mathbf{P}(k) = \mathbf{Q} + \mathbf{G}'\mathbf{P}(k + 1)[\mathbf{I} + \mathbf{H}\mathbf{R}^{-1}\mathbf{H}'\mathbf{P}(k + 1)]^{-1}\mathbf{G} \qquad (4\text{-}31)$$

Equation (4-31) may be modified. By using the matrix inversion lemma

$$(\mathbf{A} + \mathbf{B}\mathbf{D})^{-1} = \mathbf{A}^{-1} - \mathbf{A}^{-1}\mathbf{B}(\mathbf{I} + \mathbf{D}\mathbf{A}^{-1}\mathbf{B})^{-1}\mathbf{D}\mathbf{A}^{-1}$$

and making the substitutions

$$\mathbf{A} = \mathbf{I}, \qquad \mathbf{B} = \mathbf{H}\mathbf{R}^{-1}, \qquad \mathbf{D} = \mathbf{H}'\mathbf{P}(k + 1)$$

we obtain

$$[\mathbf{I} + \mathbf{H}\mathbf{R}^{-1}\mathbf{H}'\mathbf{P}(k + 1)]^{-1} = \mathbf{I} - \mathbf{H}\mathbf{R}^{-1}[\mathbf{I} + \mathbf{H}'\mathbf{P}(k + 1)\mathbf{H}\mathbf{R}^{-1}]^{-1}\mathbf{H}'\mathbf{P}(k + 1)$$
$$= \mathbf{I} - \mathbf{H}[\mathbf{R} + \mathbf{H}'\mathbf{P}(k + 1)\mathbf{H}]^{-1}\mathbf{H}'\mathbf{P}(k + 1)$$

Hence Eq. (4-31) can be modified to

$$\mathbf{P}(k) = \mathbf{Q} + \mathbf{G}'\mathbf{P}(k + 1)\mathbf{G}$$
$$- \mathbf{G}'\mathbf{P}(k + 1)\mathbf{H}[\mathbf{R} + \mathbf{H}'\mathbf{P}(k + 1)\mathbf{H}]^{-1}\mathbf{H}'\mathbf{P}(k + 1)\mathbf{G} \qquad (4\text{-}32)$$

Equation (4-32) is called the *Riccati equation*. Referring to Eqs. (4-19) and (4-26), notice that at $k = N$ we have

$$\mathbf{P}(N)\mathbf{x}(N) = \boldsymbol{\lambda}(N) = \mathbf{S}\mathbf{x}(N)$$

or

$$\mathbf{P}(N) = \mathbf{S} \qquad (4\text{-}33)$$

Hence Eq. (4-31) or (4-32) can be solved uniquely backward from $k = N$ to $k = 0$. That is, we can obtain $\mathbf{P}(N), \mathbf{P}(N - 1), \ldots, \mathbf{P}(0)$ starting from $\mathbf{P}(N)$, which is known.

By referring to Eqs. (4-22) and (4-26), the optimal control vector $\mathbf{u}(k)$, given by Eq. (4-23), now becomes

$$\mathbf{u}(k) = -\mathbf{R}^{-1}\mathbf{H}'\boldsymbol{\lambda}(k + 1) = -\mathbf{R}^{-1}\mathbf{H}'(\mathbf{G}')^{-1}[\boldsymbol{\lambda}(k) - \mathbf{Q}\mathbf{x}(k)]$$
$$= -\mathbf{R}^{-1}\mathbf{H}'(\mathbf{G}')^{-1}[\mathbf{P}(k) - \mathbf{Q}]\mathbf{x}(k) = -\mathbf{K}(k)\mathbf{x}(k) \qquad (4\text{-}34)$$

where

$$\mathbf{K}(k) = \mathbf{R}^{-1}\mathbf{H}'(\mathbf{G}')^{-1}[\mathbf{P}(k) - \mathbf{Q}] \qquad (4\text{-}35)$$

Equation (4-34) gives the closed-loop form, or feedback form, for the optimal control vector $\mathbf{u}(k)$. Notice that the optimal control vector is proportional to the state vector.

Note that the optimal control vector $\mathbf{u}(k)$ can be given in a few different forms. Referring to Eqs. (4-26) and (4-30), $\mathbf{u}(k)$ may be given by

$$
\begin{aligned}
\mathbf{u}(k) &= -\mathbf{R}^{-1}\mathbf{H}'\boldsymbol{\lambda}(k+1) = -\mathbf{R}^{-1}\mathbf{H}'\mathbf{P}(k+1)\mathbf{x}(k+1) \\
&= -\mathbf{R}^{-1}\mathbf{H}'\mathbf{P}(k+1)[\mathbf{I} + \mathbf{H}\mathbf{R}^{-1}\mathbf{H}'\mathbf{P}(k+1)]^{-1}\mathbf{G}\mathbf{x}(k) \\
&= -\mathbf{R}^{-1}\mathbf{H}'[\mathbf{P}^{-1}(k+1) + \mathbf{H}\mathbf{R}^{-1}\mathbf{H}']^{-1}\mathbf{G}\mathbf{x}(k) \\
&= -\mathbf{K}(k)\mathbf{x}(k)
\end{aligned}
\tag{4-36}
$$

where

$$
\mathbf{K}(k) = \mathbf{R}^{-1}\mathbf{H}'[\mathbf{P}^{-1}(k+1) + \mathbf{H}\mathbf{R}^{-1}\mathbf{H}']^{-1}\mathbf{G} \tag{4-37}
$$

A slightly different form of the optimal control vector $\mathbf{u}(k)$ can be given by

$$
\begin{aligned}
\mathbf{u}(k) &= -[\mathbf{R} + \mathbf{H}'\mathbf{P}(k+1)\mathbf{H}]^{-1}\mathbf{H}'\mathbf{P}(k+1)\mathbf{G}\mathbf{x}(k) \\
&= -\mathbf{K}(k)\mathbf{x}(k)
\end{aligned}
\tag{4-38}
$$

where

$$
\mathbf{K}(k) = [\mathbf{R} + \mathbf{H}'\mathbf{P}(k+1)\mathbf{H}]^{-1}\mathbf{H}'\mathbf{P}(k+1)\mathbf{G} \tag{4-39}
$$

Equation (4-39) can be derived as follows: Since

$$
\begin{aligned}
&[\mathbf{R} + \mathbf{H}'\mathbf{P}(k+1)\mathbf{H}]^{-1}\mathbf{H}'\mathbf{P}(k+1)[\mathbf{P}^{-1}(k+1) + \mathbf{H}\mathbf{R}^{-1}\mathbf{H}'] \\
&= [\mathbf{R} + \mathbf{H}'\mathbf{P}(k+1)\mathbf{H}]^{-1}\mathbf{H}'[\mathbf{I} + \mathbf{P}(k+1)\mathbf{H}\mathbf{R}^{-1}\mathbf{H}'] \\
&= [\mathbf{R} + \mathbf{H}'\mathbf{P}(k+1)\mathbf{H}]^{-1}[\mathbf{R} + \mathbf{H}'\mathbf{P}(k+1)\mathbf{H}]\mathbf{R}^{-1}\mathbf{H}' = \mathbf{R}^{-1}\mathbf{H}'
\end{aligned}
$$

we have

$$
\mathbf{R}^{-1}\mathbf{H}'[\mathbf{P}^{-1}(k+1) + \mathbf{H}\mathbf{R}^{-1}\mathbf{H}']^{-1} = [\mathbf{R} + \mathbf{H}'\mathbf{P}(k+1)\mathbf{H}]^{-1}\mathbf{H}'\mathbf{P}(k+1)
$$

As shown above, the expressions for $\mathbf{K}(k)$, given by Eqs. (4-35), (4-37), and (4-39), are equivalent. Equations (4-34), (4-36), and (4-38) clearly indicate that the optimal control law requires feedback of the state vector with time-varying gain $\mathbf{K}(k)$.

Note that a property of the feedback gain matrix $\mathbf{K}(k)$ is that it is almost constant, except near the end of the process at $k = N$.

Evaluation of the minimum performance index

We shall next evaluate the minimum value of the performance index:

$$
\min J = \min\left\{ \frac{1}{2}\mathbf{x}'(N)\mathbf{S}\mathbf{x}(N) + \frac{1}{2}\sum_{k=0}^{N-1}[\mathbf{x}'(k)\mathbf{Q}\mathbf{x}(k) + \mathbf{u}'(k)\mathbf{R}\mathbf{u}(k)] \right\}
$$

Premultiplying both sides of Eq. (4-27) by $\mathbf{x}'(k)$, we have

$$
\mathbf{x}'(k)\mathbf{P}(k)\mathbf{x}(k) = \mathbf{x}'(k)\mathbf{Q}\mathbf{x}(k) + \mathbf{x}'(k)\mathbf{G}'\mathbf{P}(k+1)\mathbf{x}(k+1)
$$

Substituting Eq. (4-29) into this last equation, we obtain

$$
\begin{aligned}
\mathbf{x}'(k)\mathbf{P}(k)\mathbf{x}(k) &= \mathbf{x}'(k)\mathbf{Q}\mathbf{x}(k) + \mathbf{x}'(k+1)[\mathbf{I} + \mathbf{H}\mathbf{R}^{-1}\mathbf{H}'\mathbf{P}(k+1)]'\mathbf{P}(k+1)\mathbf{x}(k+1) \\
&= \mathbf{x}'(k)\mathbf{Q}\mathbf{x}(k) + \mathbf{x}'(k+1)[\mathbf{I} + \mathbf{P}(k+1)\mathbf{H}\mathbf{R}^{-1}\mathbf{H}']\mathbf{P}(k+1)\mathbf{x}(k+1)
\end{aligned}
$$

Hence

$$\mathbf{x}'(k)\mathbf{Q}\mathbf{x}(k) = \mathbf{x}'(k)\mathbf{P}(k)\mathbf{x}(k) - \mathbf{x}'(k+1)\mathbf{P}(k+1)\mathbf{x}(k+1)$$
$$- \mathbf{x}'(k+1)\mathbf{P}(k+1)\mathbf{H}\mathbf{R}^{-1}\mathbf{H}'\mathbf{P}(k+1)\mathbf{x}(k+1) \quad (4\text{-}40)$$

Also, from Eqs. (4-23) and (4-26) we have

$$\mathbf{u}(k) = -\mathbf{R}^{-1}\mathbf{H}'\mathbf{P}(k+1)\mathbf{x}(k+1)$$

Hence

$$\mathbf{u}'(k)\mathbf{R}\mathbf{u}(k) = [-\mathbf{x}'(k+1)\mathbf{P}(k+1)\mathbf{H}\mathbf{R}^{-1}]\mathbf{R}[-\mathbf{R}^{-1}\mathbf{H}'\mathbf{P}(k+1)\mathbf{x}(k+1)]$$
$$= \mathbf{x}'(k+1)\mathbf{P}(k+1)\mathbf{H}\mathbf{R}^{-1}\mathbf{H}'\mathbf{P}(k+1)\mathbf{x}(k+1) \quad (4\text{-}41)$$

By adding Eqs. (4-40) and (4-41), we have

$$\mathbf{x}'(k)\mathbf{Q}\mathbf{x}(k) + \mathbf{u}'(k)\mathbf{R}\mathbf{u}(k) = \mathbf{x}'(k)\mathbf{P}(k)\mathbf{x}(k) - \mathbf{x}'(k+1)\mathbf{P}(k+1)\mathbf{x}(k+1) \quad (4\text{-}42)$$

By substituting Eq. (4-42) into Eq. (4-11), we obtain

$$J_{\min} = \frac{1}{2}\mathbf{x}'(N)\mathbf{S}\mathbf{x}(N) + \frac{1}{2}\sum_{k=0}^{N-1}[\mathbf{x}'(k)\mathbf{P}(k)\mathbf{x}(k) - \mathbf{x}'(k+1)\mathbf{P}(k+1)\mathbf{x}(k+1)]$$
$$= \frac{1}{2}\mathbf{x}'(N)\mathbf{S}\mathbf{x}(N) + \frac{1}{2}[\mathbf{x}'(0)\mathbf{P}(0)\mathbf{x}(0) - \mathbf{x}'(1)\mathbf{P}(1)\mathbf{x}(1) + \mathbf{x}'(1)\mathbf{P}(1)\mathbf{x}(1)$$
$$- \mathbf{x}'(2)\mathbf{P}(2)\mathbf{x}(2) + \cdots + \mathbf{x}'(N-1)\mathbf{P}(N-1)\mathbf{x}(N-1)$$
$$- \mathbf{x}'(N)\mathbf{P}(N)\mathbf{x}(N)]$$
$$= \frac{1}{2}\mathbf{x}'(N)\mathbf{S}\mathbf{x}(N) + \frac{1}{2}\mathbf{x}'(0)\mathbf{P}(0)\mathbf{x}(0) - \frac{1}{2}\mathbf{x}'(N)\mathbf{P}(N)\mathbf{x}(N) \quad (4\text{-}43)$$

Notice that from Eq. (4-33) we have $\mathbf{P}(N) = \mathbf{S}$. Hence Eq. (4-43) becomes

$$J_{\min} = \frac{1}{2}\mathbf{x}'(0)\mathbf{P}(0)\mathbf{x}(0) \quad (4\text{-}44)$$

Thus the minimum value of the performance index J is given by Eq. (4-44). It is a function of $\mathbf{P}(0)$ and the initial state $\mathbf{x}(0)$.

EXAMPLE 4-5

Consider a discrete-time control system defined by

$$x(k+1) = 0.3679x(k) + 0.6321u(k), \qquad x(0) = 1$$

Determine the optimal control law to minimize the following performance index:

$$J = \frac{1}{2}[x(10)]^2 + \frac{1}{2}\sum_{k=0}^{9}[x^2(k) + u^2(k)]$$

Note in this example that $S = 1$, $Q = 1$, and $R = 1$. Also, determine the minimum value of the performance index J.

Referring to Eq. (4-31), we obtain $P(k)$ as follows:

$$P(k) = 1 + (0.3679)P(k + 1)[1 + (0.6321)(1)(0.6321)P(k + 1)]^{-1}(0.3679)$$

which can be simplified to

$$P(k) = 1 + 0.1354P(k + 1)[1 + 0.3996P(k + 1)]^{-1}$$

The boundary condition for $P(k)$ is specified by Eq. (4-33), and in this example

$$P(N) = P(10) = S = 1$$

We now compute $P(k)$ backward from $k = 9$ to $k = 0$:

$$P(9) = 1 + 0.1354 \times 1(1 + 0.3996 \times 1)^{-1} = 1.0967$$
$$P(8) = 1 + 0.1354 \times 1.0967(1 + 0.3996 \times 1.0967)^{-1} = 1.1032$$
$$P(7) = 1 + 0.1354 \times 1.1032(1 + 0.3996 \times 1.1032)^{-1} = 1.1036$$
$$P(6) = 1 + 0.1354 \times 1.1036(1 + 0.3996 \times 1.1036)^{-1} = 1.1037$$
$$P(k) = 1.1037, \quad k = 5, 4, 3, 2, 1, 0$$

Notice that the values of $P(k)$ rapidly approach the steady-state value. The steady-state value P_{ss} can be obtained from

$$P_{ss} = 1 + 0.1354P_{ss}(1 + 0.3996P_{ss})^{-1}$$

or

$$0.3996P_{ss}^2 + 0.4650P_{ss} - 1 = 0$$

Solving this last equation for P_{ss}, we have

$$P_{ss} = 1.1037 \quad \text{or} \quad -2.2674$$

Since $P(k)$ must be positive, we find the steady-state value for $P(k)$ to be 1.1037. The feedback gain $K(k)$ can be computed from Eq. (4-35):

$$K(k) = (1)(0.6321)(0.3679)^{-1}[P(k) - 1] = 1.7181[P(k) - 1]$$

By substituting the values of $P(k)$ that we have obtained, we get

$$K(10) = 1.7181(1 - 1) = 0$$
$$K(9) = 1.7181(1.0967 - 1) = 0.1662$$
$$K(8) = 1.7181(1.1032 - 1) = 0.1773$$
$$K(7) = 1.7181(1.1036 - 1) = 0.1781$$
$$K(6) = K(5) = \cdots = K(0) = 0.1781$$

The optimal control law is given by

$$u(k) = -K(k)x(k)$$

Since

$$x(k + 1) = 0.3679x(k) + 0.6321u(k) = [0.3679 - 0.6321K(k)]x(k)$$

we obtain

$$x(1) = [0.3679 - 0.6321K(0)]x(0)$$
$$= (0.3679 - 0.6321 \times 0.1781) \times 1 = 0.2553$$
$$x(2) = (0.3679 - 0.6321 \times 0.1781) \times 0.2553 = 0.0652$$
$$x(3) = (0.3679 - 0.6321 \times 0.1781) \times 0.0652 = 0.0166$$
$$x(4) = (0.3679 - 0.6321 \times 0.1781) \times 0.0166 = 0.00424$$

The values of $x(k)$ for $k = 5, 6, \ldots, 10$ approach zero rapidly.

The optimal control sequence $u(k)$ is now obtained as follows:

$$u(0) = -K(0)x(0) = -0.1781 \times 1 = -0.1781$$
$$u(1) = -K(1)x(1) = -0.1781 \times 0.2553 = -0.0455$$
$$u(2) = -K(2)x(2) = -0.1781 \times 0.0652 = -0.0116$$
$$u(3) = -K(3)x(3) = -0.1781 \times 0.0166 = -0.00296$$
$$u(4) = -K(4)x(4) = -0.1781 \times 0.00424 = -0.000756$$
$$u(k) \doteq 0, \qquad k = 5, 6, \ldots, 10$$

Finally, the minimum value of the performance index J can be obtained from Eq. (4-44):

$$J_{\min} = \frac{1}{2}x'(0)P(0)x(0) = \frac{1}{2}(1 \times 1.1037 \times 1) = 0.5518$$

MATLAB Program 4-6 gives the solution to this example problem. The values of $P(k)$, $K(k)$, $x(k)$, and $u(k)$ are obtained. Also, the minimum value of the performance index J is computed, and plots of $P(k)$ versus k and $K(k)$ versus k are obtained. Figure 4-7 shows a plot of $P(k)$ versus k, and Figure 4-8 depicts a plot of $K(k)$ versus k. Notice that the values of $P(k)$ and $K(k)$ are almost constant except for the last few stages.

```
MATLAB Program 4-6

% ---------- Quadratic optimal control ----------

% ***** Solving Riccati equation and finding optimal feedback
% gain matrix K *****

% ***** Enter matrices G, H, S, Q, and R *****

G = [0.3679];
H = [0.6321];
S = [1];
Q = [1];
R = [1];

% ***** Enter boundary condition for P, equation for determining
% matrix K, and Riccati equation *****
```

```
P = [1]; P10 = P;
K = inv(R)*H'*inv(G')*(P - Q); K10 = K;
P = Q + G'*P*G - G'*P*H*inv(R + H'*P*H)*H'*P*G; P9 = P;
```

```
% ***** Enter repeatedly equations for K and P until K = K0
% and P = P0 *****
```

```
K = inv(R)*H'*inv(G')*(P - Q); K9 = K;
P = Q + G'*P*G - G'*P*H*inv(R + H'*P*H)*H'*P*G; P8 = P;
K = inv(R)*H'*inv(G')*(P - Q); K8 = K;
P = Q + G'*P*G - G'*P*H*inv(R + H'*P*H)*H'*P*G; P7 = P;
K = inv(R)*H'*inv(G')*(P - Q); K7 = K;
P = Q + G'*P*G - G'*P*H*inv(R + H'*P*H)*H'*P*G; P6 = P;
K = inv(R)*H'*inv(G')*(P - Q); K6 = K;
P = Q + G'*P*G - G'*P*H*inv(R + H'*P*H)*H'*P*G; P5 = P;
K = inv(R)*H'*inv(G')*(P - Q); K5 = K;
P = Q + G'*P*G - G'*P*H*inv(R + H'*P*H)*H'*P*G; P4 = P;
K = inv(R)*H'*inv(G')*(P - Q); K4 = K;
P = Q + G'*P*G - G'*P*H*inv(R + H'*P*H)*H'*P*G; P3 = P;
K = inv(R)*H'*inv(G')*(P - Q); K3 = K;
P = Q + G'*P*G - G'*P*H*inv(R + H'*P*H)*H'*P*G; P2 = P;
K = inv(R)*H'*inv(G')*(P - Q); K2 = K;
P = Q + G'*P*G - G'*P*H*inv(R + H'*P*H)*H'*P*G; P1 = P;
K = inv(R)*H'*inv(G')*(P - Q); K1 = K;
P = Q + G'*P*G - G'*P*H*inv(R + H'*P*H)*H'*P*G; P0 = P;
K = inv(R)*H'*inv(G')*(P - Q); K0 = K;
```

```
% ***** Printout P0, P1, P2, ..., P10 *****
```

```
P = [P0  P1  P2  P3  P4  P5  P6  P7  P8  P9  P10]'
```

```
P =
```

```
    1.1037
    1.1037
    1.1037
    1.1037
    1.1037
    1.1037
    1.1037
    1.1036
    1.1032
    1.0967
    1.0000
```

```
% ***** Printout K0, K1, K2, ..., K10 *****
```

```
K = [K0  K1  K2  K3  K4  K5  K6  K7  K8  K9  K10]'
```

```
K =

    0.1781
    0.1781
    0.1781
    0.1781
    0.1781
    0.1781
    0.1781
    0.1781
    0.1773
    0.1662
         0

% ***** Enter initial state x(0) and initial control u(0) *****

x = [1]; x0 = x;
u = - K0*x; u0 = u;

% ***** Enter state equation for x1, x2, x3, ..., x10; enter
% also control equation for u1, u2, u3, ..., u10 *****

x = G*x + H*u; x1 = x;
u = - K1*x; u1 = u;
x = G*x + H*u; x2 = x;
u = - K2*x; u2 = u;
x = G*x + H*u; x3 = x;
u = - K3*x; u3 = u;
x = G*x + H*u; x4 = x;
u = - K4*x; u4 = u;
x = G*x + H*u; x5 = x;
u = - K5*x; u5 = u;
x = G*x + H*u; x6 = x;
u = - K6*x; u6 = u;
x = G*x + H*u; x7 = x;
u = - K7*x; u7 = u;
x = G*x + H*u; x8 = x;
u = - K8*x; u8 = u;
x = G*x + H*u; x9 = x;
u = - K9*x; u9 = u;
x = G*x + H*u; x10 = x;
u = - K10*x; u10 = u;

% ***** Printout x0, x1, x2, ..., x10 *****

[x0  x1  x2  x3  x4  x5  x6  x7  x8  x9  x10]'
```

ans =

    1.0000
    0.2553
    0.0652
    0.0166
    0.0042
    0.0011
    0.0003
    0.0001
    0.0000
    0.0000
    0.0000

% ***** Printout u0, u1, u2, ..., u10 *****

[u0 u1 u2 u3 u4 u5 u6 u7 u8 u9 u10]'

ans =

   -0.1781
   -0.0455
   -0.0116
   -0.0030
   -0.0008
   -0.0002
   -0.0000
   -0.0000
   -0.0000
   -0.0000
         0

% ***** Computation of the minimum value of the performance
% index J *****

% ***** The minimum value of J can be obtained from the
% following equation *****

Jmin = 0.5*x0'*P0*x0

Jmin =

    0.5518

% ***** To plot P(k) versus k and K(k) versus k, enter the
% following program *****

```
k = 0:10;
v = [0  10  0  1.2];
axis(v);
plot(k,P,'o')
grid
title('Plot of P(k) versus k');
xlabel('k')
ylabel('P(k)')

v = [0  10  0  0.2];
axis(v);
plot(k,K,'o')
grid
title('Plot of K(k) versus k');
xlabel('k')
ylabel('K(k)')
```

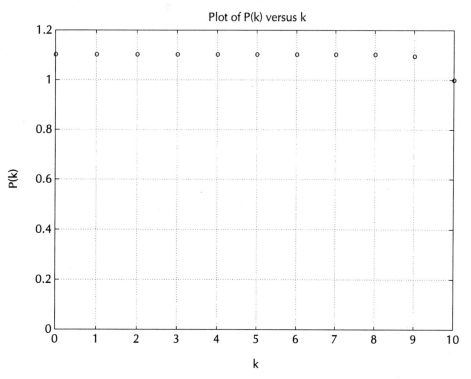

Figure 4-7

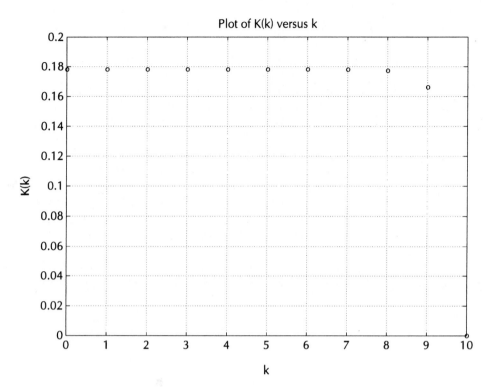

Figure 4-8

Comments on MATLAB Program 4-6

In MATLAB Program 4-6 we presented a program that is easy to follow. If, however, the number N of stages is large, then *for* loops may be used to shorten the program. In what follows we discuss a program for solving this problem by use of *for* loops. See the following MATLAB program.

```
G = 0.3679; H = 0.6321; Q = 1; R = 1; S = 1; x0 = 1;
N = 11; p(N) = S; x(1) = 1; Pnext = S;

for i = N-1:-1:1,
  P = Q+G'*Pnext*G-G'*Pnext*H*inv(R+H'*Pnext*H)*H'*Pnext*G;
  p(i) = P; Pnext = P;
end
for i = N:-1:1,
  K = inv(R)*H'*inv(G')*(p(i)-Q);
  k(i) = K;
end
for i = 1:N-1,
  xnext = (G-H*k(i))*x(i);
  x(i+1) =xnext;
end
for i = 1:N,
  u(i) = -k(i)*x(i);
end
```

It is important to point out that if we define

$$P = [p(1)\quad p(2)\quad p(3)\quad p(4)\quad p(5)\quad p(6)\quad p(7)\quad p(8)\quad p(9)\quad p(10)\quad p(11)]$$

then $p(1)$ is the first element of P, which is P0 in MATLAB Program 4-6. $p(11)$ is the last element of P, which is P10 in MATLAB Program 4-6. Similarly, $k(1) =$ K0, $k(2) = $ K1, ..., $k(11) = $ K10; $x(1) = $ x0, $x(2) = $ x1, ..., $x(11) = $ x10; $u(1) = $ u0, $u(2) = $ u1, ..., $u(11) = $ u10. (Note that we set N = 11, rather than N = 10, in writing *for* loops.) Any error [such as entering N = 10, $x(0) = 1$, or $p(10) = 1$ in the program] will result in an incorrect solution.

To print out the values of P0, P1, ..., P10 [which correspond to $p(1)$, $p(2)$, ..., $p(11)$], K0, K1, ..., K10 [which correspond to $k(1), k(2), ..., k(11)$], x0, x1, ..., x10 [which correspond to $x(1), x(2), ..., x(11)$], and u0, u1, ..., u10 [which correspond to $u(1), u(2), ..., u(11)$], we enter the printout statement as follows.

```
% ***** Printout P, K, x, and u *****

M = [p'  k'  x'  u']

M =

     1.1037     0.1781     1.0000    -0.1781
     1.1037     0.1781     0.2553    -0.0455
     1.1037     0.1781     0.0652    -0.0116
     1.1037     0.1781     0.0166    -0.0030
     1.1037     0.1781     0.0042    -0.0008
     1.1037     0.1781     0.0011    -0.0002
     1.1037     0.1781     0.0003    -0.0000
     1.1036     0.1781     0.0001    -0.0000
     1.1032     0.1773     0.0000    -0.0000
     1.0967     0.1662     0.0000    -0.0000
     1.0000          0     0.0000          0
```

The first column of matrix M gives from top to bottom the values of P0, P1, ..., P10. Similarly, the second, third, and fourth columns give K0, K1, ..., K10; x0, x1, ..., x10; and u0, u1, ..., u10; respectively.

EXAMPLE 4-6

Consider the discrete-time control system defined by

$$\mathbf{x}(k + 1) = \mathbf{G}\mathbf{x}(k) + \mathbf{H}u(k)$$

where

$$\mathbf{G} = \begin{bmatrix} 1 & 1 \\ 1 & 0 \end{bmatrix}, \qquad \mathbf{H} = \begin{bmatrix} 1 \\ 0 \end{bmatrix}, \qquad \mathbf{x}(0) = \begin{bmatrix} 1 \\ 0 \end{bmatrix}$$

Determine the optimal control sequence $u(k)$ that will minimize the following performance index:

$$J = \frac{1}{2}\mathbf{x}'(8)\mathbf{S}\mathbf{x}(8) + \frac{1}{2}\sum_{k=0}^{7}[\mathbf{x}'(k)\mathbf{Q}\mathbf{x}(k) + u'(k)Ru(k)]$$

where

$$\mathbf{Q} = \begin{bmatrix} 1 & 0 \\ 0 & 1 \end{bmatrix}, \qquad R = 1, \qquad \mathbf{S} = \begin{bmatrix} 1 & 0 \\ 0 & 1 \end{bmatrix}$$

Referring to Eq. (4-31), we have

$$\mathbf{P}(k) = \mathbf{Q} + \mathbf{G}'\mathbf{P}(k+1)[\mathbf{I} + \mathbf{H}R^{-1}\mathbf{H}'\mathbf{P}(k+1)]^{-1}\mathbf{G}$$

$$= \begin{bmatrix} 1 & 0 \\ 0 & 1 \end{bmatrix} + \begin{bmatrix} 1 & 1 \\ 1 & 0 \end{bmatrix}\begin{bmatrix} p_{11}(k+1) & p_{12}(k+1) \\ p_{12}(k+1) & p_{22}(k+1) \end{bmatrix}$$

$$\times \left\{ \begin{bmatrix} 1 & 0 \\ 0 & 1 \end{bmatrix} + \begin{bmatrix} 1 & 0 \\ 0 & 0 \end{bmatrix}\begin{bmatrix} p_{11}(k+1) & p_{12}(k+1) \\ p_{12}(k+1) & p_{22}(k+1) \end{bmatrix} \right\}^{-1}\begin{bmatrix} 1 & 1 \\ 1 & 0 \end{bmatrix}$$

The boundary condition for $\mathbf{P}(k)$ is specified by Eq. (4-33) and is given by

$$\mathbf{P}(N) = \mathbf{P}(8) = \mathbf{S} = \begin{bmatrix} 1 & 0 \\ 0 & 1 \end{bmatrix}$$

Now we compute $\mathbf{P}(k)$ backward from $\mathbf{P}(7)$ to $\mathbf{P}(0)$:

$$\mathbf{P}(7) = \begin{bmatrix} 1 & 0 \\ 0 & 1 \end{bmatrix} + \begin{bmatrix} 1 & 1 \\ 1 & 0 \end{bmatrix}\begin{bmatrix} 1 & 0 \\ 0 & 1 \end{bmatrix}\left\{ \begin{bmatrix} 1 & 0 \\ 0 & 1 \end{bmatrix} \right.$$

$$\left. + \begin{bmatrix} 1 & 0 \\ 0 & 0 \end{bmatrix}\begin{bmatrix} 1 & 0 \\ 0 & 1 \end{bmatrix} \right\}^{-1}\begin{bmatrix} 1 & 1 \\ 1 & 0 \end{bmatrix}$$

$$= \begin{bmatrix} \frac{5}{2} & \frac{1}{2} \\ \frac{1}{2} & \frac{3}{2} \end{bmatrix} = \begin{bmatrix} 2.5 & 0.5 \\ 0.5 & 1.5 \end{bmatrix}$$

$$\mathbf{P}(6) = \begin{bmatrix} 1 & 0 \\ 0 & 1 \end{bmatrix} + \begin{bmatrix} 1 & 1 \\ 1 & 0 \end{bmatrix}\begin{bmatrix} 2.5 & 0.5 \\ 0.5 & 1.5 \end{bmatrix}\left\{ \begin{bmatrix} 1 & 0 \\ 0 & 1 \end{bmatrix} \right.$$

$$\left. + \begin{bmatrix} 1 & 0 \\ 0 & 0 \end{bmatrix}\begin{bmatrix} 2.5 & 0.5 \\ 0.5 & 1.5 \end{bmatrix} \right\}^{-1}\begin{bmatrix} 1 & 1 \\ 1 & 0 \end{bmatrix}$$

$$= \begin{bmatrix} \frac{24}{7} & \frac{6}{7} \\ \frac{6}{7} & \frac{12}{7} \end{bmatrix} = \begin{bmatrix} 3.4286 & 0.8571 \\ 0.8571 & 1.7143 \end{bmatrix}$$

Similarly, $\mathbf{P}(5), \mathbf{P}(4), \ldots, \mathbf{P}(0)$ can be computed as shown in Table 4-1.

Next we shall determine the feedback gain matrix $\mathbf{K}(k)$. Referring to Eq. (4-35), matrix $\mathbf{K}(k)$ can be given as follows:

$$\mathbf{K}(k) = R^{-1}\mathbf{H}'(\mathbf{G}')^{-1}[\mathbf{P}(k) - \mathbf{Q}]$$

$$= [1][1 \quad 0]\begin{bmatrix} 1 & 1 \\ 1 & 0 \end{bmatrix}^{-1}[\mathbf{P}(k) - \mathbf{Q}]$$

$$= [0 \quad 1]\begin{bmatrix} p_{11}(k) - 1 & p_{12}(k) \\ p_{12}(k) & p_{22}(k) - 1 \end{bmatrix}$$

$$= [p_{12}(k) \quad p_{22}(k) - 1]$$

Thus

$$\mathbf{K}(8) = [p_{12}(8) \quad p_{22}(8) - 1] = [0.0000 \quad 0.0000]$$

$$\mathbf{K}(7) = [p_{12}(7) \quad p_{22}(7) - 1] = [0.5000 \quad 0.5000]$$

Similarly, $\mathbf{K}(6), \mathbf{K}(5), \ldots, \mathbf{K}(0)$ can be computed to give the values shown in Table 4-1.

Next we shall compute $\mathbf{x}(k)$. Let us write

$$\mathbf{K}(k) = [K_1(k) \quad K_2(k)]$$

Table 4-1 $P(k)$, $K(k)$, $x(k)$, AND $u(k)$ FOR $k = 0, 1, 2, \ldots, 8$, RESPECTIVELY, FOR THE SYSTEM CONSIDERED IN EXAMPLE 4-6

k	$\mathbf{P}(k)$	$\mathbf{K}(k)$	$\mathbf{x}(k)$	$u(k)$
0	$\begin{bmatrix} 3.7913 & 1.0000 \\ 1.0000 & 1.7913 \end{bmatrix}$	$[1.0000 \quad 0.7913]$	$\begin{bmatrix} 1.0000 \\ 0.0000 \end{bmatrix}$	-1.0000
1	$\begin{bmatrix} 3.7911 & 0.9999 \\ 0.9999 & 1.7913 \end{bmatrix}$	$[0.9999 \quad 0.7913]$	$\begin{bmatrix} 0.0000 \\ 1.0000 \end{bmatrix}$	-0.7913
2	$\begin{bmatrix} 3.7905 & 0.9997 \\ 0.9997 & 1.7911 \end{bmatrix}$	$[0.9997 \quad 0.7911]$	$\begin{bmatrix} 0.2087 \\ 0.0000 \end{bmatrix}$	-0.2087
3	$\begin{bmatrix} 3.7877 & 0.9986 \\ 0.9986 & 1.7905 \end{bmatrix}$	$[0.9986 \quad 0.7905]$	$\begin{bmatrix} 0.0001 \\ 0.2087 \end{bmatrix}$	-0.1651
4	$\begin{bmatrix} 3.7740 & 0.9932 \\ 0.9932 & 1.7877 \end{bmatrix}$	$[0.9932 \quad 0.7877]$	$\begin{bmatrix} 0.0437 \\ 0.0001 \end{bmatrix}$	-0.0435
5	$\begin{bmatrix} 3.7097 & 0.9677 \\ 0.9677 & 1.7742 \end{bmatrix}$	$[0.9677 \quad 0.7742]$	$\begin{bmatrix} 0.0003 \\ 0.0437 \end{bmatrix}$	-0.0342
6	$\begin{bmatrix} 3.4286 & 0.8571 \\ 0.8571 & 1.7143 \end{bmatrix}$	$[0.8571 \quad 0.7143]$	$\begin{bmatrix} 0.0099 \\ 0.0003 \end{bmatrix}$	-0.0087
7	$\begin{bmatrix} 2.5000 & 0.5000 \\ 0.5000 & 1.5000 \end{bmatrix}$	$[0.5000 \quad 0.5000]$	$\begin{bmatrix} 0.0015 \\ 0.0099 \end{bmatrix}$	-0.0057
8	$\begin{bmatrix} 1.0000 & 0.0000 \\ 0.0000 & 1.0000 \end{bmatrix}$	$[0.0000 \quad 0.0000]$	$\begin{bmatrix} 0.0057 \\ 0.0015 \end{bmatrix}$	0.0000

Then

$$\mathbf{x}(k + 1) = \mathbf{G}\mathbf{x}(k) + \mathbf{H}u(k)$$

$$= [\mathbf{G} - \mathbf{H}\mathbf{K}(k)]\mathbf{x}(k)$$

$$= \begin{bmatrix} 1 - K_1(k) & 1 - K_2(k) \\ 1 & 0 \end{bmatrix} \begin{bmatrix} x_1(k) \\ x_2(k) \end{bmatrix}$$

Since the initial state is

$$\mathbf{x}(0) = \begin{bmatrix} 1 \\ 0 \end{bmatrix}$$

$\mathbf{x}(k)$, where $k = 1, 2, \ldots, 8$, can be obtained as follows:

$$\mathbf{x}(1) = \begin{bmatrix} 1 - 1 & 1 - 0.7913 \\ 1 & 0 \end{bmatrix} \begin{bmatrix} 1 \\ 0 \end{bmatrix} = \begin{bmatrix} 0.0000 \\ 1.0000 \end{bmatrix}$$

$$\mathbf{x}(2) = \begin{bmatrix} 1 - 0.9999 & 1 - 0.7913 \\ 1 & 0 \end{bmatrix} \begin{bmatrix} 0.0000 \\ 1.0000 \end{bmatrix} = \begin{bmatrix} 0.2087 \\ 0.0000 \end{bmatrix}$$

Similarly, $\mathbf{x}(3), \mathbf{x}(4), \ldots, \mathbf{x}(8)$ can be computed. The results are shown in Table 4-1. Finally, the optimal control sequence $u(k)$ can be obtained from Eq. (4-36):

$$u(k) = -\mathbf{K}(k)\mathbf{x}(k)$$

That is,

$$u(0) = -\mathbf{K}(0)\mathbf{x}(0) = -[1 \quad 0.7913]\begin{bmatrix} 1 \\ 0 \end{bmatrix} = -1.0000$$

$$u(1) = -\mathbf{K}(1)\mathbf{x}(1) = -[0.9999 \quad 0.7913]\begin{bmatrix} 0 \\ 1 \end{bmatrix} = -0.7913$$

Similarly, $u(2), u(3), \ldots, u(8)$ can be computed to give the values shown in Table 4-1.

As mentioned earlier, the feedback gain matrix $\mathbf{K}(k)$ is almost constant except for the last several values of k. Thus, if the number of stages is not 8 but 100, then $\mathbf{K}(0)$, $\mathbf{K}(1), \ldots, \mathbf{K}(93)$ will be constant matrices, and $\mathbf{K}(94), \mathbf{K}(95), \ldots, \mathbf{K}(100)$ will vary. This fact is important, because if the number of stages N is sufficiently large, then the feedback gain matrix becomes a constant matrix, and so the designer is able to use a constant feedback gain matrix to approximate the time-varying optimal gain matrix.

The minimum value of J is obtained from Eq. (4-44) as follows:

$$J_{\min} = \frac{1}{2}\mathbf{x}'(0)\mathbf{P}(0)\mathbf{x}(0) = \frac{1}{2}[1 \quad 0]\begin{bmatrix} 3.7913 & 1.0000 \\ 1.0000 & 1.7913 \end{bmatrix}\begin{bmatrix} 1 \\ 0 \end{bmatrix}$$

$$= 1.8956$$

MATLAB Program 4-7 may be used to obtain the solution of this quadratic optimal control problem. This MATLAB program yields $\mathbf{P}(k)$, $\mathbf{K}(k)$, $\mathbf{x}(k)$, $u(k)$, and the minimum value of the performance index J.

MATLAB Program 4–7

```
% ---------- Quadratic optimal control ----------

% ***** Solving Riccati equation and finding optimal feedback
% gain matrix K *****

% ***** Enter matrices G, H, S, Q, and R *****

G = [1   1;1   0];
H = [1;0];
S = [1   0;0   1];
Q = [1   0;0   1];
R = [1];

% ***** Enter boundary condition for P, equation for
% determining matrix K, and Riccati equation.  Define
% 2x2 identity matrix I *****

P = [1   0;0   1]; P8 = P;
K = inv(R)*H'*inv(G')*(P - Q); K8 = K;
I = [1   0;0   1];
P = Q + G'*P*inv(I+H*inv(R)*H'*P)*G; P7 = P;

% ***** Enter repeatedly equations for K and P until K = K0
% and P = P0 *****

K = inv(R)*H'*inv(G')*(P - Q); K7 = K;
P = Q + G'*P*inv(I+H*inv(R)*H'*P)*G; P6 = P;
```

```
K = inv(R)*H'*inv(G')*(P - Q); K6 = K;
P = Q + G'*P*inv(I+H*inv(R)*H'*P)*G; P5 = P;
K = inv(R)*H'*inv(G')*(P - Q); K5 = K;
P = Q + G'*P*inv(I+H*inv(R)*H'*P)*G; P4 = P;
K = inv(R)*H'*inv(G')*(P - Q); K4 = K;
P = Q + G'*P*inv(I+H*inv(R)*H'*P)*G; P3 = P;
K = inv(R)*H'*inv(G')*(P - Q); K3 = K;
P = Q + G'*P*inv(I+H*inv(R)*H'*P)*G; P2 = P;
K = inv(R)*H'*inv(G')*(P - Q); K2 = K;
P = Q + G'*P*inv(I+H*inv(R)*H'*P)*G; P1 = P;
K = inv(R)*H'*inv(G')*(P - Q); K1 = K;
P = Q + G'*P*inv(I+H*inv(R)*H'*P)*G; P0 = P;
K = inv(R)*H'*inv(G')*(P - Q); K0 = K;

% ***** Printout P0, P1, P2, ..., P8 *****

P0, P1, P2, P3, P4, P5, P6, P7, P8


P0 =

    3.7913      1.0000
    1.0000      1.7913


P1 =

    3.7911      0.9999
    0.9999      1.7913


P2 =

    3.7905      0.9997
    0.9997      1.7911


P3 =

    3.7877      0.9986
    0.9986      1.7905


P4 =

    3.7740      0.9932
    0.9932      1.7877


P5 =

    3.7097      0.9677
    0.9677      1.7742
```

P6 =

3.4286	0.8571
0.8571	1.7143

P7 =

2.5000	0.5000
0.5000	1.5000

P8 =

1	0
0	1

% ***** Printout K0, K1, K2, ..., K8 *****

K0, K1, K2, K3, K4, K5, K6, K7, K8

K0 =

1.0000	0.7913

K1 =

0.9999	0.7913

K2 =

0.9997	0.7911

K3 =

0.9986	0.7905

K4 =

0.9932	0.7877

K5 =

0.9677	0.7742

K6 =

0.8571	0.7143

```
K7 =

    0.5000      0.5000


K8 =

    0       0

% ***** Enter initial state x(0) and initial control u(0) *****

x = [1;0]; x0 = x;
u = - K0*x; u0 = u;

% ***** Enter state equations for x1, x2, x3, ..., x8; enter
% also control equations for u1, u2, u3, ..., u8 *****

x = G*x + H*u; x1 = x;
u = - K1*x; u1 = u;
x = G*x + H*u; x2 = x;
u = - K2*x; u2 = u;
x = G*x + H*u; x3 = x;
u = - K3*x; u3 = u;
x = G*x + H*u; x4 = x;
u = - K4*x; u4 = u;
x = G*x + H*u; x5 = x;
u = - K5*x; u5 = u;
x = G*x + H*u; x6 = x;
u = - K6*x; u6 = u;
x = G*x + H*u; x7 = x;
u = - K7*x; u7 = u;
x = G*x + H*u; x8 = x;
u = - K8*x; u8 = u;

% ***** Printout x0, x1, x2, ..., x8 *****

x0, x1, x2, x3, x4, x5, x6, x7, x8

x0 =

    1
    0


x1 =

    0.0000
    1.0000


x2 =

    0.2087
    0.0000
```

x3 =

    0.0001
    0.2087

x4 =

    0.0437
    0.0001

x5 =

    0.0003
    0.0437

x6 =

    0.0099
    0.0003

x7 =

    0.0015
    0.0099

x8 =

    0.0057
    0.0015

% ***** Printout u0, u1, u2, ..., u8 *****

u0, u1, u2, u3, u4, u5, u6, u7, u8

u0 =

    -1.0000

u1 =

    -0.7913

u2 =

    -0.2087

u3 =

   -0.1651

u4 =

   -0.0435

u5 =

   -0.0342

u6 =

   -0.0087

u7 =

   -0.0057

u8 =

   0

% ***** Computation of the minimum value of the performance
% index J *****

% ***** The minimum value of J can be obtained from the
% following equation *****

Jmin = 0.5*x0'*P0*x0

Jmin =

   1.8956

Comments on MATLAB Program 4-7

Comments similar to those given to MATLAB Program 4-6 apply to MATLAB Program 4-7. This program may be written using *for* loops as shown below.

```
G = [1   1;1   0]; H = [1;0]; Q = [1   0;0   1]; R = 1; S = [1   0;0   1];
x0 = [1;0]; N = 9;
p11(N) = 1; p12(N) = 0; p22(N) = 1; x1(1) = 1; x2(1) = 0; Pnext = S;

for i = N−1:−1:1,
  P = Q+G'*Pnext*inv(eye(2)+H*inv(R)*H'*Pnext)*G;
```

```
      p11(i) = P(1,1); p12(i) = P(1,2); p22(i) = P(2,2); Pnext = P;
   end
   for i = N:-1:1,
      K = inv(R)*H'*inv(G')*([p11(i)   p12(i);p12(i)   p22(i)]-Q);
      k1(i) = K(1); k2(i) = K(2);
   end
   for i = 1:N-1,
      xnext = (G-H*[k1(i)   k2(i)])*[x1(i);x2(i)];
      x1(i+1) = xnext(1); x2(i+1) = xnext(2);
   end
   for i = 1:N,
      u(i) = -[k1(i)   k2(i)]*[x1(i);x2(i)];
   end
```

Using this program, matrix P, matrix K, vector x, and vector u can be obtained as shown next.

```
% ***** Printout P, K, x, and u *****

P = [p11;p12;p12;p22]

P =

Columns 1 through 7

     3.7913    3.7911    3.7905    3.7877    3.7740    3.7097    3.4286
     1.0000    0.9999    0.9997    0.9986    0.9932    0.9677    0.8571
     1.0000    0.9999    0.9997    0.9986    0.9932    0.9677    0.8571
     1.7913    1.7913    1.7911    1.7905    1.7877    1.7742    1.7143

Columns 8 through 9

     2.5000    1.0000
     0.5000         0
     0.5000         0
     1.5000    1.0000

K = [k1;k2]'

K =

     1.0000    0.7913
     0.9999    0.7913
     0.9997    0.7911
     0.9986    0.7905
     0.9932    0.7877
     0.9677    0.7742
     0.8571    0.7143
     0.5000    0.5000
          0         0

x = [x1;x2]
```

x =

Columns 1 through 7

| 1.0000 | 0.0000 | 0.2087 | 0.0001 | 0.0437 | 0.0003 | 0.0099 |
| 0 | 1.0000 | 0.0000 | 0.2087 | 0.0001 | 0.0437 | 0.0003 |

Columns 8 through 9

| 0.0015 | 0.0057 |
| 0.0099 | 0.0015 |

u = u'

u =

$$
\begin{array}{r}
-1.0000 \\
-0.7913 \\
-0.2087 \\
-0.1651 \\
-0.0435 \\
-0.0342 \\
-0.0087 \\
-0.0057 \\
0
\end{array}
$$

In this printout, P0, P1, ..., P8 are given as column vectors. The first column of matrix P gives P0, the second column gives P1, and so forth. In each column the first row gives p11, the second and third row give p12, and the fourth row gives p22. K0, K1, ..., K8 are given as row vectors in matrix K. The first row corresponds to K0 and the last row corresponds to K8. x0, x1, ..., x8 are given as columns of matrix x. The first column corresponds to x0 and the last column corresponds to x8. u0, u1, ..., u8 are given as the first, second, ..., ninth row of vector u.

4-4 STEADY-STATE QUADRATIC OPTIMAL CONTROL OF DISCRETE-TIME SYSTEMS

Consider the control system defined by Eq. (4-9):

$$\mathbf{x}(k + 1) = \mathbf{G}\mathbf{x}(k) + \mathbf{H}\mathbf{u}(k) \tag{4-45}$$

We have seen that, when the control process is finite (when N is finite), the feedback gain matrix $\mathbf{K}(k)$ becomes a time-varying matrix.

Let us now consider the quadratic optimal control problem for which the process continues without bound, or $N = \infty$ (that is, the process is an infinite-stage process). As N approaches infinity, the optimal control solution becomes a steady-state solution, and the time-varying gain matrix $\mathbf{K}(k)$ becomes a constant gain matrix. Such a constant gain matrix $\mathbf{K}(k)$ is called a steady-state gain matrix and is written as $\mathbf{K}$.

For $N = \infty$, the performance index may be modified to

$$J = \frac{1}{2} \sum_{k=0}^{\infty} [\mathbf{x}'(k)\mathbf{Q}\mathbf{x}(k) + \mathbf{u}'(k)\mathbf{R}\mathbf{u}(k)] \tag{4-46}$$

The term $\frac{1}{2}\mathbf{x}'(N)\mathbf{Sx}(N)$, which appeared in Eq. (4-10), is not included in this representation of J. This is because, if the optimal control system is stable so that the value of J converges to a constant, $\mathbf{x}(\infty)$ becomes zero and $\frac{1}{2}\mathbf{x}'(\infty)\mathbf{Sx}(\infty) = 0$.

Let us now define the steady-state matrix $\mathbf{P}(k)$ as $\mathbf{P}$. Referring to Eq. (4-31), matrix $\mathbf{P}$ can be determined as follows:

$$\mathbf{P} = \mathbf{Q} + \mathbf{G}'\mathbf{P}(\mathbf{I} + \mathbf{HR}^{-1}\mathbf{H}'\mathbf{P})^{-1}\mathbf{G}$$

$$= \mathbf{Q} + \mathbf{G}'(\mathbf{P}^{-1} + \mathbf{HR}^{-1}\mathbf{H}')^{-1}\mathbf{G} \qquad (4\text{-}47)$$

Clearly, matrix $\mathbf{P}$ is determined by matrices $\mathbf{G}$, $\mathbf{H}$, $\mathbf{Q}$, and $\mathbf{R}$. A slightly different expression for $\mathbf{P}$ can be derived from Eq. (4-32):

$$\mathbf{P} = \mathbf{Q} + \mathbf{G}'\mathbf{PG} - \mathbf{G}'\mathbf{PH}(\mathbf{R} + \mathbf{H}'\mathbf{PH})^{-1}\mathbf{H}'\mathbf{PG} \qquad (4\text{-}48)$$

The steady-state gain matrix $\mathbf{K}$ can be obtained in terms of $\mathbf{P}$ as follows. From Eq. (4-35),

$$\mathbf{K} = \mathbf{R}^{-1}\mathbf{H}'(\mathbf{G}')^{-1}(\mathbf{P} - \mathbf{Q}) \qquad (4\text{-}49)$$

From Eq. (4-37),

$$\mathbf{K} = \mathbf{R}^{-1}\mathbf{H}'(\mathbf{P}^{-1} + \mathbf{HR}^{-1}\mathbf{H}')^{-1}\mathbf{G} \qquad (4\text{-}50)$$

Still another expression for $\mathbf{K}$ is possible. From Eq. (4-39),

$$\mathbf{K} = (\mathbf{R} + \mathbf{H}'\mathbf{PH})^{-1}\mathbf{H}'\mathbf{PG} \qquad (4\text{-}51)$$

Any of the expressions given by Eqs. (4-49), (4-50), and (4-51) may be used to obtain the steady-state gain matrix $\mathbf{K}$. (All expressions yield the same numerical result.)

The optimal control law for steady-state operation is given by

$$\mathbf{u}(k) = -\mathbf{Kx}(k)$$

If, for example, Eq. (4-51) is substituted into this last equation, we obtain

$$\mathbf{u}(k) = -(\mathbf{R} + \mathbf{H}'\mathbf{PH})^{-1}\mathbf{H}'\mathbf{PGx}(k) \qquad (4\text{-}52)$$

and the control system becomes an optimal regulator system:

$$\mathbf{x}(k + 1) = [\mathbf{G} - \mathbf{H}(\mathbf{R} + \mathbf{H}'\mathbf{PH})^{-1}\mathbf{H}'\mathbf{PG}]\mathbf{x}(k)$$

$$= (\mathbf{I} + \mathbf{HR}^{-1}\mathbf{H}'\mathbf{P})^{-1}\mathbf{Gx}(k) \qquad (4\text{-}53)$$

where we have used the matrix inversion lemma

$$(\mathbf{A} + \mathbf{BC})^{-1} = \mathbf{A}^{-1} - \mathbf{A}^{-1}\mathbf{B}(\mathbf{I} + \mathbf{CA}^{-1}\mathbf{B})^{-1}\mathbf{CA}$$

with $\mathbf{A} = \mathbf{I}$, $\mathbf{B} = \mathbf{H}$, and $\mathbf{C} = \mathbf{R}^{-1}\mathbf{H}'\mathbf{P}$.

The performance index J associated with the steady-state optimal control law can be obtained from Eq. (4-44) by substituting $\mathbf{P}$ for $\mathbf{P}(0)$:

$$J_{\min} = \frac{1}{2}\mathbf{x}'(0)\mathbf{Px}(0) \qquad (4\text{-}54)$$

In many practical systems, instead of using a time-varying gain matrix $\mathbf{K}(k)$, we approximate such a gain matrix by the constant gain matrix $\mathbf{K}$. Deviations from the optimal performance due to the approximation will appear only near the end of the control process.

Steady-state Riccati equation

In implementing the steady-state (or time-invariant) optimal controller, we require the steady-state solution of the Riccati equation. There are several ways to obtain the steady-state solution.

One way to solve the steady-state Riccati equation given by Eq. (4-48),

$$\mathbf{P} = \mathbf{Q} + \mathbf{G}'\mathbf{PG} - \mathbf{G}'\mathbf{PH}(\mathbf{R} + \mathbf{H}'\mathbf{PH})^{-1}\mathbf{H}'\mathbf{PG}$$

is to start with the following nonsteady-state Riccati equation, which was given by Eq. (4-32):

$$\mathbf{P}(k) = \mathbf{Q} + \mathbf{G}'\mathbf{P}(k + 1)\mathbf{G}$$
$$- \mathbf{G}'\mathbf{P}(k + 1)\mathbf{H}[\mathbf{R} + \mathbf{H}'\mathbf{P}(k + 1)\mathbf{H}]^{-1}\mathbf{H}'\mathbf{P}(k + 1)\mathbf{G} \quad (4\text{-}55)$$

By reversing the direction of time, we may modify Eq. (4-55) to read

$$\mathbf{P}(k + 1) = \mathbf{Q} + \mathbf{G}'\mathbf{P}(k)\mathbf{G} - \mathbf{G}'\mathbf{P}(k)\mathbf{H}[\mathbf{R} + \mathbf{H}'\mathbf{P}(k)\mathbf{H}]^{-1}\mathbf{H}'\mathbf{P}(k)\mathbf{G} \quad (4\text{-}56)$$

and begin the solution with $\mathbf{P}(0) = \mathbf{0}$ and iterate the equation until a stationary solution is obtained. In computing the numerical solution, it is important to note that matrix $\mathbf{P}$ is either a Hermitian or a real symmetric matrix and is positive definite.

EXAMPLE 4-7

Consider the system

$$\mathbf{x}(k + 1) = \mathbf{Gx}(k) + \mathbf{H}u(k)$$

where

$$\mathbf{G} = \begin{bmatrix} 0.2 & 0 \\ 0 & 0.4 \end{bmatrix}, \quad \mathbf{H} = \begin{bmatrix} 1 \\ 1 \end{bmatrix}$$

The performance index J is given by

$$J = \frac{1}{2} \sum_{k=0}^{\infty} [\mathbf{x}'(k)\mathbf{Qx}(k) + u'(k)Ru(k)]$$

where

$$\mathbf{Q} = \begin{bmatrix} 1 & 0 \\ 0 & 0.5 \end{bmatrix}, \quad R = 1$$

The control law that minimizes J can be given by

$$u(k) = -\mathbf{Kx}(k)$$

Determine the steady-state gain matrix $\mathbf{K}$.

MATLAB Program 4-8 determines the steady-state gain matrix **K** for this problem. In this program we show how matrix **P** (the solution to the steady-state Riccati equation) approaches a steady-state matrix starting with **P** = **0**. By several iterations, matrix **P** reaches the steady-state matrix. Using this steady-state matrix **P**, the steady-state matrix **K** can be determined as given in the program.

MATLAB Program 4–8

```
% ---------- Steady-state quadratic optimal control ----------

% ***** Solving steady-state Riccati equation and finding
% optimal feedback gain matrix K *****

% ***** Enter matrices G, H, Q, and R *****

G = [0.2  0;0  0.4];
H = [1;1];
Q = [1  0;0  0.5];
R = [1];

% ***** Start with the solution of steady-state Riccati equation
% with P = [0  0;0  0] *****

P = [0  0;0  0];
P = Q + G'*P*G - G'*P*H*inv(R+H'*P*H)*H'*P*G

P =

     1.0000          0
          0     0.5000

P = Q + G'*P*G - G'*P*H*inv(R+H'*P*H)*H'*P*G

P =

     1.0240     -0.0160
    -0.0160      0.5640

P = Q + G'*P*G - G'*P*H*inv(R+H'*P*H)*H'*P*G

P =

     1.0251     -0.0186
    -0.0186      0.5714

P = Q + G'*P*G - G'*P*H*inv(R+H'*P*H)*H'*P*G

P =

     1.0252     -0.0189
    -0.0189      0.5723

P = Q + G'*P*G - G'*P*H*inv(R+H'*P*H)*H'*P*G
```

P =

       1.0252   -0.0189
      -0.0189   0.5724

P = Q + G'*P*G - G'*P*H*inv(R+H'*P*H)*H'*P*G

P =

       1.0252   -0.0189
      -0.0189   0.5724

% ***** When P matrix stays constant, steady state is reached.
% Steady-state P matrix is *****

P

P =

       1.0252   -0.0189
      -0.0189   0.5724

% ***** Optimal feedback gain matrix K is obatined from *****

K = inv(R + H'*P*H)*H'*P*G

K =

       0.0786   0.0865

MATLAB Program 4-9 is an improved version of MATLAB Program 4-8. In this program the solution **P** of the steady-state Riccati equation is checked every 10 iterations. After the first 10 iterations, we get matrix **P** as follows:

$$\mathbf{P} = \begin{bmatrix} 1.0252 & -0.0189 \\ -0.0189 & 0.5724 \end{bmatrix}$$

To check if this matrix **P** is the steady-state solution of the Riccati equation, we make another 10 (or 20) iterations. If the resulting matrix **P** is exactly the same as the previously obtained **P** matrix, we stop the iteration process. Using the steady-state matrix **P** thus obtained, we compute the steady-state matrix **K**.

MATLAB Program 4–9

% ---------- Steady-state quadratic optimal control ----------

% ***** Solving steady-state Riccati equation and finding
% optimal feedback gain matrix K *****

% ***** Enter matrices G, H, Q, and R *****

G = [0.2   0;0   0.4];
H = [1;1];

```
Q = [1  0;0  0.5];
R = [1];

% ***** Start with the solution of steady-state Riccati equation
% with P = [0  0;0  0] *****

P = [0  0;0  0];
P = Q + G'*P*G - G'*P*H*inv(R+H'*P*H)*H'*P*G;

% ***** Check solution P every 10 or 20 steps of iteration.
% Stop iteration when P stays constant *****

for i = 1:10,
  P = Q + G'*P*G - G'*P*H*inv(R+H'*P*H)*H'*P*G;
end
P

P =

      1.0252     -0.0189
     -0.0189      0.5724

for i = 1:10,
  P = Q + G'*P*G - G'*P*H*inv(R+H'*P*H)*H'*P*G;
end
P

P =

      1.0252     -0.0189
     -0.0189      0.5724

% ***** P matrix stays constant.  Thus steady state has been
% reached.  The steady-state P matrix is *****

P

P =

      1.0252     -0.0189
     -0.0189      0.5724

% ***** Optimal feedback gain matrix K is obatined from *****

K = inv(R + H'*P*H)*H'*P*G

K =

      0.0786      0.0865
```

EXAMPLE 4-8: Design of a Servo System

Consider the design of the servo system shown in Figure 4-9. The plant does not involve an integrator and, therefore, an integral controller is included in the loop. The sampling period T is 0.1 sec.

From Figure 4-9 we obtain the following equations:

$$x(k + 1) = 0.5x(k) + 2u(k)$$

$$u(k) = k_1 v(k) - k_2 x(k)$$

$$v(k) = r(k) - y(k) + v(k - 1)$$

$$y(k) = x(k)$$

where k_1 is the integral gain constant and k_2 is the feedback gain constant. In this design problem, k_1 and k_2 are variables and must be determined such that the system is stable and will exhibit an acceptable transient response to the unit step input.

Since

$$v(k + 1) = r(k + 1) - y(k + 1) + v(k)$$

$$= -0.5x(k) + v(k) - 2u(k) + r(k + 1)$$

we obtain

$$\begin{bmatrix} x(k + 1) \\ v(k + 1) \end{bmatrix} = \begin{bmatrix} 0.5 & 0 \\ -0.5 & 1 \end{bmatrix} \begin{bmatrix} x(k) \\ v(k) \end{bmatrix} + \begin{bmatrix} 2 \\ -2 \end{bmatrix} u(k) + \begin{bmatrix} 0 \\ 1 \end{bmatrix} r(k + 1) \tag{4-57}$$

For $k = \infty$, we have

$$\begin{bmatrix} x(\infty) \\ v(\infty) \end{bmatrix} = \begin{bmatrix} 0.5 & 0 \\ -0.5 & 1 \end{bmatrix} \begin{bmatrix} x(\infty) \\ v(\infty) \end{bmatrix} + \begin{bmatrix} 2 \\ -2 \end{bmatrix} u(\infty) + \begin{bmatrix} 0 \\ 1 \end{bmatrix} r(\infty) \tag{4-58}$$

For any step input, $r(k + 1) = r(\infty) = r$. Define

$$x_e(k) = x(k) - x(\infty)$$

$$v_e(k) = v(k) - v(\infty)$$

$$u_e(k) = u(k) - u(\infty)$$

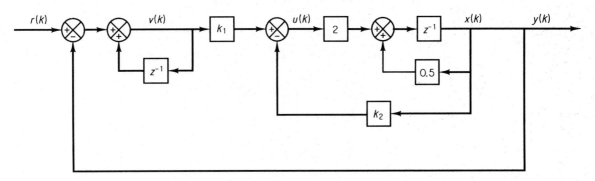

Figure 4-9

Subtracting Eq. (4-58) from Eq. (4-57), we obtain

$$\begin{bmatrix} x_e(k+1) \\ v_e(k+1) \end{bmatrix} = \begin{bmatrix} 0.5 & 0 \\ -0.5 & 1 \end{bmatrix} \begin{bmatrix} x_e(k) \\ v_e(k) \end{bmatrix} + \begin{bmatrix} 2 \\ -2 \end{bmatrix} u_e(k) \qquad (4\text{-}59)$$

Note that

$$u_e(k) = k_1 v_e(k) - k_2 x_e(k)$$

Define

$$x_1(k) = x_e(k)$$
$$x_2(k) = v_e(k)$$
$$w(k) = u_e(k)$$

Then Eq. (4-59) can be written as follows:

$$\begin{bmatrix} x_1(k+1) \\ x_2(k+1) \end{bmatrix} = \begin{bmatrix} 0.5 & 0 \\ -0.5 & 1 \end{bmatrix} \begin{bmatrix} x_1(k) \\ x_2(k) \end{bmatrix} + \begin{bmatrix} 2 \\ -2 \end{bmatrix} w(k)$$

where

$$w(k) = -[k_2 \quad -k_1] \begin{bmatrix} x_1(k) \\ x_2(k) \end{bmatrix}$$

Rewriting, we have

$$\mathbf{x}(k+1) = \mathbf{G}\mathbf{x}(k) + \mathbf{H}w(k)$$
$$w(k) = -\mathbf{K}\mathbf{x}(k)$$

where

$$\mathbf{x}(k) = \begin{bmatrix} x_1(k) \\ x_2(k) \end{bmatrix}, \qquad \mathbf{G} = \begin{bmatrix} 0.5 & 0 \\ -0.5 & 1 \end{bmatrix}, \qquad \mathbf{H} = \begin{bmatrix} 2 \\ -2 \end{bmatrix}, \qquad \mathbf{K} = [k_2 \quad -k_1]$$

To design a stable system and to have reasonable step-response characteristics, we may use the quadratic optimal control scheme. (Note that, if we use the quadratic optimal control scheme for this system, the resulting system is always stable.) Let us assume the following performance index:

$$J = \frac{1}{2} \sum_{k=0}^{\infty} [\mathbf{x}(k)'\mathbf{Q}\mathbf{x}(k) + w(k)'Rw(k)]$$

If $\mathbf{Q}$ and R are chosen to be positive definite, the resulting system is stable. For this case, we choose

$$\mathbf{Q} = \begin{bmatrix} 100 & 0 \\ 0 & 1 \end{bmatrix}, \qquad R = 1$$

Note that the present $\mathbf{Q}$ and R are only one possible set. Other positive-definite $\mathbf{Q}$ and R may be chosen. The resulting system is stable but different for each different set of $\mathbf{Q}$ and R.
        MATLAB Program 4-10 may be used to determine matrix $\mathbf{K}$.

```
MATLAB Program 4–10
```

```
% ---------- Design of a servo system based on minimization
% of a quadratic performance index ----------

% ***** The following program solves steady-state Riccati equation and gives
% optimal feedback gain matrix K *****

% ***** Enter matrices G, H, Q, and R *****

G = [0.5   0;-0.5   1];
H = [2;-2];
Q = [100   0;0   1];
R = [1];

% ***** Start with the solution of steady-state Riccati equation
% with P = [0   0;0   0] *****

P = [0   0;0   0];
P = Q + G'*P*G - G'*P*H*inv(R+H'*P*H)*H'*P*G;

% ***** Check solution P every 10 or 20 steps of iteration.
% Stop iteration when P stays constant *****

for i = 1:20,
   P = Q + G'*P*G - G'*P*H*inv(R+H'*P*H)*H'*P*G;
end
P

P =

   100.0624      -0.0115
    -0.0115      10.1892

for i = 1:20,
   P = Q + G'*P*G - G'*P*H*inv(R+H'*P*H)*H'*P*G;
end
P

P =

   100.0624      -0.0119
    -0.0119      10.5107

for i = 1:20,
   P = Q + G'*P*G - G'*P*H*inv(R+H'*P*H)*H'*P*G;
end
P

P =

   100.0624      -0.0119
    -0.0119      10.5167
```

```
for i = 1:20,
  P = Q + G'*P*G - G'*P*H*inv(R+H'*P*H)*H'*P*G;
end
P

P =

   100.0624      -0.0119
    -0.0119      10.5168

for i = 1:20,
  P = Q + G'*P*G - G'*P*H*inv(R+H'*P*H)*H'*P*G;
end
P

P =

   100.0624      -0.0119
    -0.0119      10.5168

% ***** P matrix stays constant.  Thus steady state has
% been reached.  The steady state P matrix is *****

P

P =

   100.0624      -0.0119
    -0.0119      10.5168

% ***** Optimal feedback gain matrix K is obtained from *****

K = inv(R + H'*P*H)*H'*P*G

K =

    0.2494      -0.0475

k1 = -K(2)

k1 =

    0.0475

k2 = K(1)

k2 =

    0.2494
```

To obtain the unit-step response curve [$y(k)$ versus k], we may proceed as follows [for a step input, $r(k)$ may be written as r]: Since

$$x(k + 1) = 0.5x(k) + 2u(k)$$
$$= 0.5x(k) + 2[-k_2 x(k) + k_1 v(k)]$$
$$= (0.5 - 2k_2)x(k) + 2k_1 v(k)$$

and

$$v(k + 1) = v(k) + r(k + 1) - y(k + 1)$$
$$= v(k) + r - (0.5 - 2k_2)x(k) - 2k_1 v(k)$$
$$= (1 - 2k_1)v(k) + (-0.5 + 2k_2)x(k) + r$$

we get

$$\begin{bmatrix} x(k + 1) \\ v(k + 1) \end{bmatrix} = \begin{bmatrix} 0.5 - 2k_2 & 2k_1 \\ -0.5 + 2k_2 & 1 - 2k_1 \end{bmatrix} \begin{bmatrix} x(k) \\ v(k) \end{bmatrix} + \begin{bmatrix} 0 \\ 1 \end{bmatrix} r \qquad (4\text{-}60)$$

$$y(k) = x(k) = \begin{bmatrix} 1 & 0 \end{bmatrix} \begin{bmatrix} x(k) \\ v(k) \end{bmatrix} + [0]r \qquad (4\text{-}61)$$

For a unit-step input, $r = 1$.

The unit-step response $y(k)$ versus k can be obtained by first converting the state-space equations [Eqs. (4-60) and (4-61)] into the pulse transfer function $Y(z)/R(z)$:

$$[\text{num,den}] = \text{ss2tf(GG,HH,CC,DD)}$$

where

$$\text{GG} = [0.5 - 2k_2 \quad 2k_1 \; ; \; -0.5 + 2k_2 \quad 1 - 2k_1]$$

$$\text{HH} = [0;1]$$

$$\text{CC} = [1 \quad 0]$$

$$\text{DD} = [0]$$

and then using the command filter as follows:

$$y = \text{filter(num,den,r)}$$

where r is a unit-step function.

To obtain the response $v(k)$, first note that

$$v(k) = \begin{bmatrix} 0 & 1 \end{bmatrix} \begin{bmatrix} x(k) \\ v(k) \end{bmatrix} = \mathbf{FF} \begin{bmatrix} x(k) \\ v(k) \end{bmatrix}$$

where $\mathbf{FF} = \begin{bmatrix} 0 & 1 \end{bmatrix}$. Then use the following command:

$$[\text{numv,denv}] = \text{ss2tf(GG,HH,FF,DD)}$$

$$v = \text{filter(numv,denv,r)}$$

MATLAB Program 4-11 yields the response $y(k)$ versus k and $v(k)$ versus k. The unit-step response $y(k)$ versus k is shown in Figure 4-10. The response $v(k)$ versus k is shown in Figure 4-11.

Notice that the system is stable and exhibits nonoscillatory response characteristics. The response characteristics depend on a set of $\mathbf{Q}$ and R chosen in the performance index J.

MATLAB Program 4–11

```
% ---------- Unit-step response of designed system ----------

% ***** This program calculates the response of the system
% when subjected to a unit-step input.  The values that are
% used for k1 and k2 are computed in MATLAB Program 4-10.  The
% response is obtained using the method to convert the discrete-
% time state-space equations into pulse transfer function form.  The
% response is then found with the conventional 'filter' command *****

% ***** Enter values of k1 and k2 *****

k1 = 0.0475; k2 = 0.2494;

% ***** Enter matrices GG,HH,CC,FF,DD *****

GG = [0.5-2*k2   2*k1;-0.5+2*k2   1-2*k1];
HH = [0;1];
CC = [1   0];
FF = [0   1];
DD = [0];

% ***** To obtain the response y(k), convert state-space equations
% into pulse transfer function Y(z)/R(z) *****

[num,den] = ss2tf(GG,HH,CC,DD);

% ***** Enter command to obtain unit-step response y(k) *****

r = ones(1,101);
axis([0   100   0   1.2]);
k = 0:100;
y = filter(num,den,r);
plot(k,y,'o',k,y,'-')
grid
title('Output y(k) to Unit-Step Input')
xlabel('k')
ylabel('y(k)')

% ***** To obtain the response v(k), convert state-space equations
% into pulse transfer function V(z)/R(z) *****

[numv,denv] = ss2tf(GG,HH,FF,DD);

% ***** Enter command to obtain v(k) *****

axis([0   100   0   12]);
k = 0:100;
v = filter(numv,denv,r);
plot(k,v,'o',k,v,'-')
grid
```

```
title('Output v(k) of Integrator')
xlabel('k')
ylabel('v(k)')
```

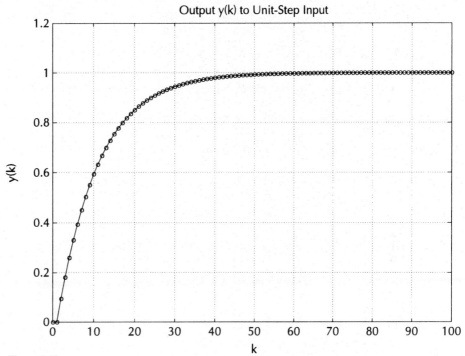

Figure 4-10

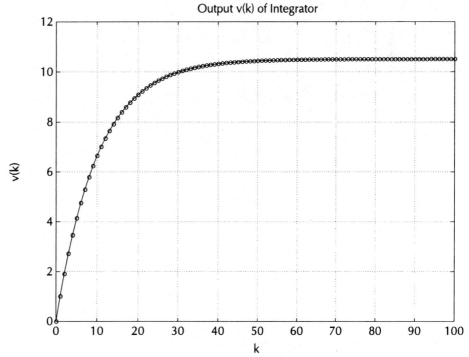

Figure 4-11

EXAMPLE 4-9

Consider the inverted pendulum system shown in Figure 4-12. (This system is the same as that discussed in Example 3-3.) Design a digital controller for this inverted pendulum control system. Since the plant (inverted pendulum with cart) does not involve an integrator, we need to include an integral controller. We choose the sampling period T to be 0.1 sec. If we implement this system as a servo system, the block diagram may take the form shown in Figure 4-13. The controller to be designed will include state feedback and an integrator in the closed loop.

To design a stable controller, the quadratic optimal control scheme may be used. (Note that the system designed based on the minimization of the quadratic performance index will be a stable system.) In this example, we shall demonstrate this approach.

Define state variables x_1, x_2, x_3, and x_4 as follows:

$$x_1 = \theta$$
$$x_2 = \dot{\theta}$$
$$x_3 = x$$
$$x_4 = \dot{x}$$

We shall assume the same numerical values for M, m, and l as we used in Example 3-3. (That is, $M = 2$ kg, $m = 0.1$ kg, and $l = 0.5$ m.) The discretized system state equation and output equation were derived in Example 3-3. Using those derived equations, we have

$$\mathbf{x}(k + 1) = \mathbf{G}\mathbf{x}(k) + \mathbf{H}u(k)$$
$$y(k) = \mathbf{C}\mathbf{x}(k) + Du(k)$$

where

$$\mathbf{G} = \begin{bmatrix} 1.1048 & 0.1035 & 0 & 0 \\ 2.1316 & 1.1048 & 0 & 0 \\ -0.0025 & -0.0001 & 1 & 0.1 \\ -0.0508 & -0.0025 & 0 & 1 \end{bmatrix}$$

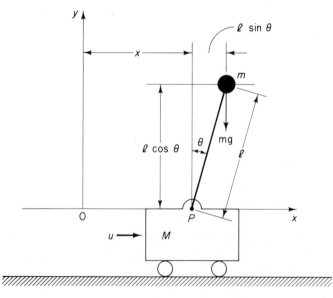

Figure 4-12

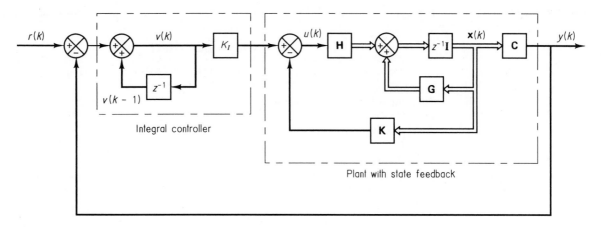

Figure 4-13

$$\mathbf{H} = \begin{bmatrix} -0.0051 \\ -0.1035 \\ 0.0025 \\ 0.0501 \end{bmatrix}, \qquad \mathbf{C} = [0 \quad 0 \quad 1 \quad 0], \qquad D = [0]$$

The state-space representation for the entire control system is given by

$$\mathbf{x}(k+1) = \mathbf{Gx}(k) + \mathbf{H}u(k)$$
$$y(k) = \mathbf{Cx}(k)$$
$$v(k) = v(k-1) + r(k) - y(k)$$
$$u(k) = -\mathbf{Kx}(k) + K_I v(k)$$

where

$$\mathbf{K} = [k_1 \quad k_2 \quad k_3 \quad k_4]$$

Since

$$v(k+1) = v(k) + r(k+1) - y(k+1)$$
$$= v(k) + r(k+1) - \mathbf{C}[\mathbf{Gx}(k) + \mathbf{H}u(k)]$$
$$= -\mathbf{CGx}(k) + v(k) - \mathbf{CH}u(k) + r(k+1)$$

we have

$$\begin{bmatrix} \mathbf{x}(k+1) \\ v(k+1) \end{bmatrix} = \begin{bmatrix} \mathbf{G} & \mathbf{0} \\ -\mathbf{CG} & 1 \end{bmatrix} \begin{bmatrix} \mathbf{x}(k) \\ v(k) \end{bmatrix} + \begin{bmatrix} \mathbf{H} \\ -\mathbf{CH} \end{bmatrix} u(k) + \begin{bmatrix} \mathbf{0} \\ 1 \end{bmatrix} r(k+1)$$

Let us assume that the input r is a step function, or

$$r(k) = r(k+1) = r$$

Then, as k approaches infinity,

$$\begin{bmatrix} \mathbf{x}(\infty) \\ v(\infty) \end{bmatrix} = \begin{bmatrix} \mathbf{G} & \mathbf{0} \\ -\mathbf{CG} & 1 \end{bmatrix} \begin{bmatrix} x(\infty) \\ v(\infty) \end{bmatrix} + \begin{bmatrix} \mathbf{H} \\ -\mathbf{CH} \end{bmatrix} u(\infty) + \begin{bmatrix} \mathbf{0} \\ 1 \end{bmatrix} r(\infty)$$

Define

$$\mathbf{x}_e(k) = \mathbf{x}(k) - \mathbf{x}(\infty)$$
$$v_e(k) = v(k) - v(\infty)$$

Then the error equation becomes

$$\begin{bmatrix} \mathbf{x}_e(k+1) \\ v_e(k+1) \end{bmatrix} = \begin{bmatrix} \mathbf{G} & \mathbf{0} \\ -\mathbf{CG} & 1 \end{bmatrix} \begin{bmatrix} \mathbf{x}_e(k) \\ v_e(k) \end{bmatrix} + \begin{bmatrix} \mathbf{H} \\ -\mathbf{CH} \end{bmatrix} u_e(k)$$

Note that

$$u_e(k) = -\mathbf{K}\mathbf{x}_e(k) + K_I v_e(k) = -[\mathbf{K} \quad -K_I] \begin{bmatrix} \mathbf{x}_e(k) \\ v_e(k) \end{bmatrix}$$

Now define

$$\hat{\mathbf{G}} = \begin{bmatrix} \mathbf{G} & \mathbf{0} \\ -\mathbf{CG} & 1 \end{bmatrix}, \quad \hat{\mathbf{H}} = \begin{bmatrix} \mathbf{H} \\ -\mathbf{CH} \end{bmatrix}, \quad \hat{\mathbf{K}} = [\mathbf{K} \quad -K_I], \quad w(k) = u_e(k)$$

$$\boldsymbol{\xi}(k) = \begin{bmatrix} \mathbf{x}_e(k) \\ v_e(k) \end{bmatrix} = \begin{bmatrix} x_{1e}(k) \\ x_{2e}(k) \\ x_{3e}(k) \\ x_{4e}(k) \\ x_{5e}(k) \end{bmatrix}$$

where $x_{5e}(k) = v_e(k)$. Then we have

$$\boldsymbol{\xi}(k+1) = \hat{\mathbf{G}}\boldsymbol{\xi}(k) + \hat{\mathbf{H}}w(k)$$
$$w(k) = -\hat{\mathbf{K}}\boldsymbol{\xi}(k)$$

Our problem becomes that of determining the matrix $\hat{\mathbf{K}}$ such that the following quadratic performance index is minimized:

$$J = \frac{1}{2} \sum_{k=0}^{\infty} [\boldsymbol{\xi}'\mathbf{Q}\boldsymbol{\xi} + w'Rw]$$

where $\mathbf{Q}$ and R should be chosen properly so that the response of the system is acceptable. (The purpose of using the quadratic performance index is to assure the stability of the system.)
Let us choose $\mathbf{Q}$ and R as follows:

$$\mathbf{Q} = \begin{bmatrix} 10 & 0 & 0 & 0 & 0 \\ 0 & 1 & 0 & 0 & 0 \\ 0 & 0 & 100 & 0 & 0 \\ 0 & 0 & 0 & 1 & 0 \\ 0 & 0 & 0 & 0 & 1 \end{bmatrix}, \quad R = [1]$$

Our emphasis is on state variables x_{3e} and x_{1e}. (Note that many different sets of $\mathbf{Q}$ and R may be used.) In the MATLAB program for solving this problem, we shall use the notations

$$\text{G1} = \hat{\mathbf{G}}, \quad \text{H1} = \hat{\mathbf{H}}, \quad \text{KK} = \hat{\mathbf{K}}$$

MATLAB Program 4-12 yields the solution $\mathbf{P}$ of the steady-state Riccati equation and the feedback gain matrix $\mathbf{K}$ and the integral gain constant K_I.

MATLAB Program 4–12

```
% ---------- Design of an inverted pendulum control system
% based on minimization of a quadratic performance index ----------

% ***** The following program solves steady-state Riccati
% equation and gives optimal feedback gain matrix K *****

% ***** Enter matrices G, H, C, and D *****

G = [1.1048    0.1035    0    0
      2.1316    1.1048    0    0
     -0.0025   -0.0001    1    0.1
     -0.0508   -0.0025    0    1];
H = [-0.0051
     -0.1035
      0.0025
      0.0501];
C = [0   0   1   0];
D = [0];

% ***** Enter matrices G1, H1, Q and R *****

G1 = [G  zeros(4,1);-C*G  1];
H1 = [H;-C*H];
Q = [10   0     0   0   0
      0   1     0   0   0
      0   0   100   0   0
      0   0     1   0   0
      0   0     0   0   1];
R = [1];

% ***** Start solving steady-state Riccati equation
% for P with P = diag(0,4) *****

P = diag(0,4);
P = Q + G1'*P*G1 - G1'*P*H1*inv(R+H1'*P*H1)*H1'*P*G1;

% ***** Check solution P every 20 steps of iteration.
% Stop iteration when P stays constant *****

for i = 1:20,
  P = Q + G1'*P*G1 - G1'*P*H1*inv(R+H1'*P*H1)*H1'*P*G1;
end
P

P =

  1.0e + 003 *

    9.6887    2.1677    3.4319    2.4341   -0.1741
    2.1677    0.4876    0.7743    0.5490   -0.0393
```

```
   3.4319      0.7743      2.2988      1.1788     -0.1312
   2.4341      0.5490      1.1788      0.7824     -0.0625
  -0.1741     -0.0393     -0.1312     -0.0625      0.0185
```

```
for i = 1:20,
  P = Q + G1'*P*G1 - G1'*P*H1*inv(R+H1'*P*H1)*H1'*P*G1;
end
P
```

P =

  1.0e + 004 *

```
   1.0707      0.2397      0.3996      0.2772     -0.0220
   0.2397      0.0539      0.0902      0.0625     -0.0050
   0.3996      0.0902      0.2617      0.1367     -0.0158
   0.2772      0.0625      0.1367      0.0895     -0.0078
  -0.0220     -0.0050     -0.0158     -0.0078      0.0021
```

```
for i = 1:20,
  P = Q + G1'*P*G1 - G1'*P*H1*inv(R+H1'*P*H1)*H1'*P*G1;
end
P
```

P =

  1.0e + 004 *

```
   1.0724      0.2401      0.4006      0.2778     -0.0221
   0.2401      0.0540      0.0904      0.0627     -0.0050
   0.4006      0.0904      0.2623      0.1371     -0.0158
   0.2778      0.0627      0.1371      0.0897     -0.0078
  -0.0221     -0.0050     -0.0158     -0.0078      0.0021
```

```
for i = 1:20,
  P = Q + G1'*P*G1 - G1'*P*H1*inv(R+H1'*P*H1)*H1'*P*G1;
end
P
```

P =

  1.0e + 004 *

```
   1.0724      0.2401      0.4006      0.2778     -0.0221
   0.2401      0.0540      0.0904      0.0627     -0.0050
   0.4006      0.0904      0.2623      0.1371     -0.0158
   0.2778      0.0627      0.1371      0.0897     -0.0078
  -0.0221     -0.0050     -0.0158     -0.0078      0.0021
```

```
% ***** P matrix stays constant. Thus steady state has
% been reached.  The steady-state P matrix is *****
```

P

```
P =

  1.0e + 004 *

    1.0724    0.2401    0.4006    0.2778   -0.0221
    0.2401    0.0540    0.0904    0.0627   -0.0050
    0.4006    0.0904    0.2623    0.1371   -0.0158
    0.2778    0.0627    0.1371    0.0897   -0.0078
   -0.0221   -0.0050   -0.0158   -0.0078    0.0021

% ***** Optimal feedback gain matrix KK is obatined from *****

KK = inv(R + H1'*P*H1)*H1'*P*G1

KK =

  -64.9346  -14.4819  -10.8475   -9.2871   0.5189

K = [KK(1)  KK(2)  KK(3)  KK(4)]

K =

  -64.9346  -14.4819  -10.8475   -9.2871

KI = -KK(5)

KI =

  -0.5189
```

Transient-response characteristics of the designed system. To check the transient-response characteristics of the designed system, we shall examine the unit-step response of the system. To obtain the unit-step response, we proceed as follows: Since

$$\mathbf{x}(k + 1) = \mathbf{Gx}(k) + \mathbf{H}[-\mathbf{Kx}(k) + K_I v(k)]$$

$$= (\mathbf{G} - \mathbf{HK})\mathbf{x}(k) + \mathbf{H}K_I v(k)$$

$$v(k + 1) = v(k) + r(k + 1) - y(k + 1)$$

$$= v(k) + r(k + 1) - \mathbf{C}[\mathbf{Gx}(k) + \mathbf{H}u(k)]$$

$$= (-\mathbf{CG} + \mathbf{CHK})\mathbf{x}(k) + (1 - \mathbf{CH}K_I)v(k) + r$$

we obtain

$$\begin{bmatrix} \mathbf{x}(k + 1) \\ v(k + 1) \end{bmatrix} = \begin{bmatrix} \mathbf{G} - \mathbf{HK} & \mathbf{H}K_I \\ -\mathbf{CG} + \mathbf{CHK} & 1 - \mathbf{CH}K_I \end{bmatrix} \begin{bmatrix} \mathbf{x}(k) \\ v(k) \end{bmatrix} + \begin{bmatrix} \mathbf{0} \\ 1 \end{bmatrix} r \qquad (4\text{-}62)$$

$$y(k) = [\mathbf{C} \quad 0] \begin{bmatrix} \mathbf{x}(k) \\ v(k) \end{bmatrix} + [0]r \qquad (4\text{-}63)$$

where $r = 1$. To determine the unit-step response $y(k)$ (the cart position), first define

$$\mathbf{GG} = \begin{bmatrix} \mathbf{G} - \mathbf{HK} & \mathbf{HK}_I \\ -\mathbf{CG} + \mathbf{CHK} & 1 - \mathbf{CHK}_I \end{bmatrix}$$

$$\mathbf{HH} = \begin{bmatrix} \mathbf{0} \\ 1 \end{bmatrix}$$

$$\mathbf{CC} = [\mathbf{C} \quad 0] = [0 \quad 0 \quad 1 \quad 0 \quad 0]$$

$$DD = [D] = [0]$$

and then convert the state-space equations [Eqs. (4-62) and (4-63)] into the pulse transfer function $Y(z)/R(z)$ by using the following MATLAB command:

$$[\text{num,den}] = \text{ss2tf(GG,HH,CC,DD)}$$

Then use the *filter* command:

$$y = \text{filter(num,den,r)}$$

where r = unit step input.

To obtain the response $x_1(k)$, we note that

$$x_1(k) = [1 \quad 0 \quad 0 \quad 0 \quad 0] \begin{bmatrix} \mathbf{x}(k) \\ v(k) \end{bmatrix}$$

Define

$$\mathbf{FF} = [1 \quad 0 \quad 0 \quad 0 \quad 0]$$

Then

$$x_1(k) = \mathbf{FF} \begin{bmatrix} \mathbf{x}(k) \\ v(k) \end{bmatrix} \tag{4-64}$$

Convert the state-space equations [Eqs. (4-62) and (4-64)] into the pulse transfer function $X_1(z)/R(z)$ using the command

$$[\text{num1,den1}] = \text{ss2tf(GG,HH,FF,DD)}$$

Then use the filter command

$$x1 = \text{filter(num1,den1,r)}$$

Similarly, to obtain the response $x_2(k)$, we note that

$$x_2(k) = [0 \quad 1 \quad 0 \quad 0 \quad 0] \begin{bmatrix} \mathbf{x}(k) \\ v(k) \end{bmatrix} \tag{4-65}$$

Define

$$\mathbf{JJ} = [0 \quad 1 \quad 0 \quad 0 \quad 0]$$

Then convert the state-space equations [Eqs. (4-62) and (4-65)] into the pulse transfer function $X_2(z)/R(z)$ using the command

$$[\text{num2,den2}] = \text{ss2tf(GG,HH,JJ,DD)}$$

Then use the filter command

$$x2 = \text{filter}(num2,den2,r)$$

Similarly, by defining

$$\mathbf{LL} = [0 \quad 0 \quad 0 \quad 1 \quad 0]$$

$$\mathbf{MM} = [0 \quad 0 \quad 0 \quad 0 \quad 1]$$

the responses $x_4(k)$ and $x_5(k) = v(k)$ can be obtained using the commands

$$[num4,den4] = \text{ss2tf}(GG,HH,LL,DD)$$

$$x4 = \text{filter}(num4,den4,r)$$

and

$$[num5,den5] = \text{ss2tf}(GG,HH,MM,DD)$$

$$x5 = \text{filter}(num5,den5,r)$$

MATLAB Program 4-13 yields $y(k)$, $x_1(k)$, $x_2(k)$, $x_4(k)$, and $x_5(k)$ when the unit-step input $(r = 1)$ is given.

MATLAB Program 4–13

```
% ---------- Step response of the designed system ----------

% ***** This program calculates the response of the system
% when subjected to a unit-step input.  The values that are
% used for K and KI are computed in MATLAB Program 4-12.  The
% response is obtained using the method to convert the discrete-
% time state-space equations into pulse transfer-function form.  The
% response is then found with the conventional 'filter' command *****

% ***** Enter matrices K, KI, GG, HH, CC, FF, JJ, LL, MM, DD *****

K = [-64.9346  -14.4819  -10.8475  -9.2871];
KI = -0.5189;
GG = [G-H*K   H*KI;-C*G+C*H*K   1-C*H*KI];
HH = [0;0;0;0;1];
CC = [0  0  1  0  0];
FF = [1  0  0  0  0];
JJ  = [0  1  0  0  0];
LL = [0  0  0  1  0];
MM = [0  0  0  0  1];
DD = [0];

% ***** To obtain y(k) convert state-space equations into pulse
% transfer function X3(z)/R(z) *****

[num,den] = ss2tf(GG,HH,CC,DD);

% ***** Enter command to obtain unit-step response *****
```

```
r = ones(1,101);
axis([0  100  -0.2  1.2]);
k = 0:100;
y = filter(num,den,r);
plot(k,y,'o',k,y,'-')
grid
title('Position of Cart : y(k) = x3(k)')
xlabel('k')
ylabel('y(k) = x3(k)')

% ***** To obtain x1(k) convert state-space equations into pulse
% transfer function X1(z)/R(z) *****

[num1,den1] = ss2tf(GG,HH,FF,DD);

% ***** Enter command to obtain unit-step response *****

axis([0  100  -0.1  0.2]);
x1 = filter(num1,den1,r);
plot(k,x1,'o',k,x1,'-')
grid
title('Angular Displacement Theta : x1(k)')
xlabel('k')
ylabel('x1(k)')

% ***** To obtain x2(k) convert state-space equations into pulse
% transfer function X2(z)/R(z) *****

[num2,den2] = ss2tf(GG,HH,JJ,DD);

% ***** Enter command to obtain unit-step response *****

axis([0  100  -0.5  0.5]);
x2 = filter(num2,den2,r);
plot(k,x2,'o',k,x2,'-')
grid
title('Angular Velocity Theta Dot : x2(k)')
xlabel('k')
ylabel('x2(k)')

% ***** To obtain x4(k) convert state-space equations into pulse
% transfer function X4(z)/R(z) *****

[num4,den4] = ss2tf(GG,HH,LL,DD);

% ***** Enter command to obtain unit-step response *****

axis([0  100  -0.5  1]);
x4 = filter(num4,den4,r);
plot(k,x4,'o',k,x4,'-')
grid
title('Velocity of Cart : x4(k)')
```

```
xlabel('k')
ylabel('x4(k)')

% ***** To obtain x5(k) convert state-space equations into pulse
% transfer function X5(z)/R(z) *****

[num5,den5] = ss2tf(GG,HH,MM,DD);

% ***** Enter command to obtain unit-step response *****

axis([0  100  -5  30]);
x5 = filter(num5,den5,r);
plot(k,x5,'o',k,x5,'-')
grid
title('Output of Integrator : x5(k) = v(k)')
xlabel('k')
ylabel('x5(k) = v(k)')
```

Based on MATLAB computations, the position of the cart [$y(k)$ versus k] can be obtained as shown in Figure 4-14. (Notice that the initial move of the cart is in the negative direction.) Figure 4-15 depicts the angular displacement of the pendulum, $x1(k) = \theta(k)$ plotted versus k. Figure 4-16 shows the angular velocity of the pendulum, $x2(k)$ plotted versus k. Figure 4-17 shows the velocity of the cart, $x4(k)$ plotted versus k. The output of the integrator, $v(k)$ versus k, is shown in Figure 4-18. Since in the present system the sampling period T is 0.1 sec, it takes approximately 6 sec to reach steady state. (Compare this system with that designed in Example 3-3.)

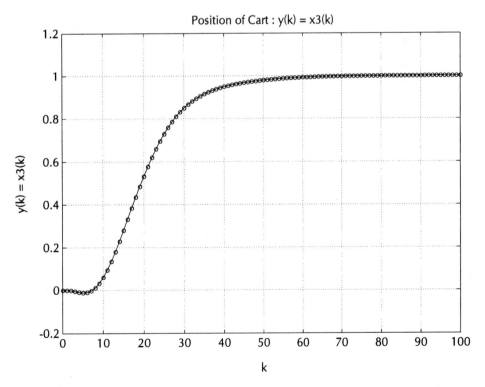

Figure 4-14

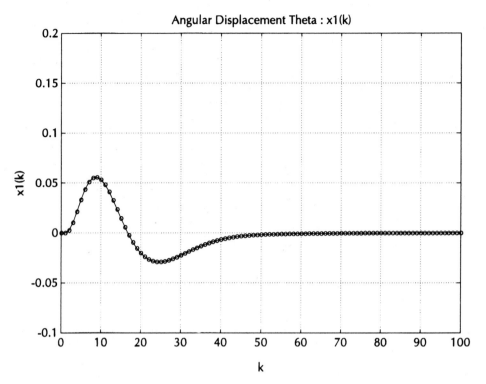

Figure 4-15

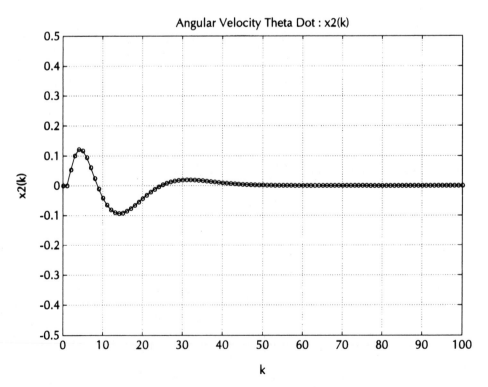

Figure 4-16

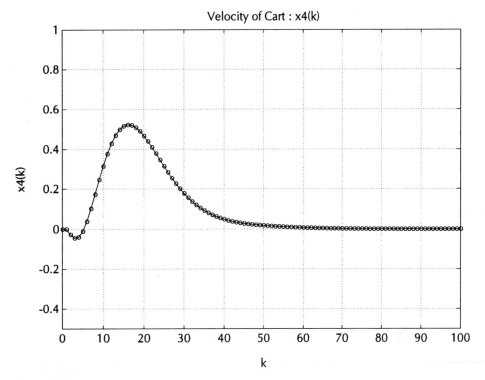

Figure 4-17

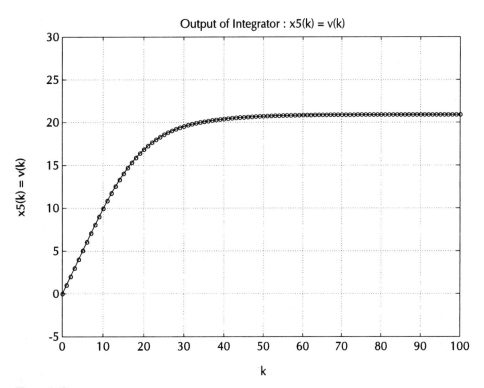

Figure 4-18

4-5 MINIMUM-ENERGY CONTROL PROBLEM

In discussing minimum-energy control systems, pseudoinverses play an important role. In this section we shall first review pseudoinverses and then solve a minimum-energy control problem.

Pseudoinverses

The concept of pseudoinverses of a matrix is a generalization of the notion of an inverse. It is useful for finding a 'solution' to a set of algebraic equations in which the number of unknown variables and the number of independent linear equations are not equal.

In what follows, we shall consider pseudoinverses that enable us to determine minimum-norm solutions.

Minimum-norm solution that minimizes $\|x\|$

Consider a linear algebraic equation

$$x_1 + 5x_2 = 1$$

Since we have two variables and only one equation, no unique solution exists. Instead, there exist an infinite number of solutions. Graphically, any point on line $x_1 + 5x_2 = 1$, as shown in Figure 4-19, is a possible solution. However, if we decide to pick the point that is closest to the origin, the solution becomes unique.

Consider the vector–matrix equation

$$\mathbf{Ax} = \mathbf{b} \tag{4-66}$$

where $\mathbf{A}$ is an $n \times m$ matrix, $\mathbf{x}$ is an m-vector, and $\mathbf{b}$ is an n-vector. We assume that $m > n$ (that is, the number of unknown variables is greater than the number of equations) and that the equation has an infinite number of solutions. Let us find the unique solution $\mathbf{x}$ that is located closest to the origin, or that has the minimum norm $\|\mathbf{x}\|$.

Let us define the minimum-norm solution as $\mathbf{x}^\circ$. That is, $\mathbf{x}^\circ$ satisfies the condition that $\mathbf{Ax}^\circ = \mathbf{b}$ and $\|\mathbf{x}^\circ\| \leq \|\mathbf{x}\|$ for all $\mathbf{x}$ that satisfy $\mathbf{Ax} = \mathbf{b}$. This means that the solution point $\mathbf{x}^\circ$ is nearest to the origin of the m-dimensional space among all possible solutions of Eq. (4-66). We shall obtain such a minimum-norm solution in the following.

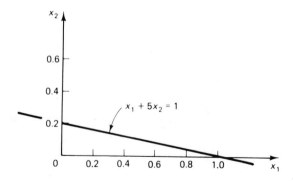

Figure 4-19

Right pseudoinverse matrix

For a vector–matrix equation

$$\mathbf{A}\mathbf{x} = \mathbf{b}$$

where $\mathbf{A}$ is an $n \times m$ matrix having rank n, $\mathbf{x}$ is an m-vector, and $\mathbf{b}$ is an n-vector, the solution that minimizes the norm $\|\mathbf{x}\|$ is given by

$$\mathbf{x}^{\circ} = \mathbf{A}^{RM}\mathbf{b}$$

where $\mathbf{A}^{RM} = \mathbf{A}'(\mathbf{A}\mathbf{A}')^{-1}$ provided the indicated inverse exists.

This can be proved as follows. First, note that norm $\|\mathbf{x}\|$ can be written as

$$\|\mathbf{x}\| = \|\mathbf{x} - \mathbf{x}^{\circ} + \mathbf{x}^{\circ}\| = \|\mathbf{x}^{\circ}\| + \|\mathbf{x} - \mathbf{x}^{\circ}\| + 2(\mathbf{x}^{\circ})'(\mathbf{x} - \mathbf{x}^{\circ})$$

The last term, $2(\mathbf{x}^{\circ})'(\mathbf{x} - \mathbf{x}^{\circ})$, can be shown to be zero, since

$$\begin{aligned}
(\mathbf{x}^{\circ})'(\mathbf{x} - \mathbf{x}^{\circ}) &= [\mathbf{A}'(\mathbf{A}\mathbf{A}')^{-1}\mathbf{b}]'[\mathbf{x} - \mathbf{A}'(\mathbf{A}\mathbf{A}')^{-1}\mathbf{b}] \\
&= \mathbf{b}'(\mathbf{A}\mathbf{A}')^{-1}\mathbf{A}[\mathbf{x} - \mathbf{A}'(\mathbf{A}\mathbf{A}')^{-1}\mathbf{b}] \\
&= \mathbf{b}'(\mathbf{A}\mathbf{A}')^{-1}[\mathbf{A}\mathbf{x} - (\mathbf{A}\mathbf{A}')(\mathbf{A}\mathbf{A}')^{-1}\mathbf{b}] \\
&= \mathbf{b}'(\mathbf{A}\mathbf{A}')^{-1}(\mathbf{b} - \mathbf{b}) \\
&= 0
\end{aligned}$$

Hence

$$\|\mathbf{x}\| = \|\mathbf{x}^{\circ}\| + \|\mathbf{x} - \mathbf{x}^{\circ}\|$$

which can be rewritten as

$$\|\mathbf{x}\| - \|\mathbf{x}^{\circ}\| = \|\mathbf{x} - \mathbf{x}^{\circ}\|$$

Since $\|\mathbf{x} - \mathbf{x}^{\circ}\| \geq 0$, we obtain

$$\|\mathbf{x}\| \geq \|\mathbf{x}^{\circ}\|$$

Thus we have shown that $\mathbf{x}^{\circ}$ is the solution that gives the minimum norm $\|\mathbf{x}\|$.

The matrix $\mathbf{A}^{RM} = \mathbf{A}'(\mathbf{A}\mathbf{A}')^{-1}$ that yields the minimum-norm solution ($\|\mathbf{x}^{\circ}\| = $ minimum) is called the *right pseudoinverse* or *minimal right inverse* of $\mathbf{A}$.

As shown in the preceding discussions, the right pseudoinverse $\mathbf{A}^{RM}$ gives the solution $\mathbf{x}^{\circ} = \mathbf{A}^{RM}\mathbf{b}$ that minimizes the norm, or gives $\|\mathbf{x}^{\circ}\| = $ minimum. Note that the right pseudoinverse $\mathbf{A}^{RM}$ is an $m \times n$ matrix, since $\mathbf{A}$ is an $n \times m$ matrix and

$$\begin{aligned}
\mathbf{A}^{RM} &= \mathbf{A}'(\mathbf{A}\mathbf{A}')^{-1} \\
&= (m \times n \text{ matrix})(n \times n \text{ matrix})^{-1} \\
&= m \times n \text{ matrix}, \qquad m > n
\end{aligned}$$

Notice that the dimension of $\mathbf{A}\mathbf{A}'$ is smaller than the dimension of vector $\mathbf{x}$, which is m. Notice also that the right pseudoinverse $\mathbf{A}^{RM}$ possesses the property that it is indeed an "inverse" matrix if premultiplied by $\mathbf{A}$:

$$\mathbf{A}\mathbf{A}^{RM} = \mathbf{A}[\mathbf{A}'(\mathbf{A}\mathbf{A}')^{-1}] = \mathbf{A}\mathbf{A}'(\mathbf{A}\mathbf{A}')^{-1} = \mathbf{I}_n$$

EXAMPLE 4-10: Right Pseudoinverse

Consider the vector–matrix equation

$$\mathbf{Ax = b}$$

where

$$\mathbf{A} = \begin{bmatrix} 1 & 2 & 3 \\ 4 & 5 & 6 \end{bmatrix}, \qquad \mathbf{x} = \begin{bmatrix} x_1 \\ x_2 \\ x_3 \end{bmatrix}, \qquad \mathbf{b} = \begin{bmatrix} 10 \\ 20 \end{bmatrix}$$

Since no unique solution exists for this equation, we shall find the minimum-norm solution that minimizes $\|\mathbf{x}\|$. Such a solution is given by

$$\mathbf{x}^\circ = \mathbf{A}^{RM}\mathbf{b}$$

where

$$\mathbf{A}^{RM} = \mathbf{A}'(\mathbf{AA}')^{-1}$$

Hence

$$\mathbf{x}^\circ = \mathbf{A}^{RM}\mathbf{b} = \begin{bmatrix} 1 & 4 \\ 2 & 5 \\ 3 & 6 \end{bmatrix}\left\{\begin{bmatrix} 1 & 2 & 3 \\ 4 & 5 & 6 \end{bmatrix}\begin{bmatrix} 1 & 4 \\ 2 & 5 \\ 3 & 6 \end{bmatrix}\right\}^{-1}\begin{bmatrix} 10 \\ 20 \end{bmatrix}$$

$$= \begin{bmatrix} -0.5556 \\ 1.1111 \\ 2.7778 \end{bmatrix}$$

A MATLAB program for solving this problem is given in MATLAB Program 4-14.

MATLAB Program 4–14

```
% ---------- Right pseudoinverse matrix ----------

% ***** In this program we find minimum-norm solution xopt
% to equation Ax = b, where the number of unknown variables
% is greater than the number of equations.  The minimum-
% norm solution xopt minimizes norm IIxII.  That is, the
% minimum-norm solution xopt is closest to the origin among
% many other solutions *****

% ***** Enter matrices A and b *****

A = [ 1  2  3;4  5  6];
b = [10;20];

% ***** The minimum-norm solution is given by xopt = ARM*b *****

ARM = A'*inv(A*A')
```

```
ARM =

        -0.9444      0.4444
        -0.1111      0.1111
         0.7222     -0.2222

xopt = ARM*b

xopt =

        -0.5556
         1.1111
         2.7778

% ***** Notice that A*ARM is a 2x2 identity matrix, while
% ARM*A is a 3x3 matrix *****

A*ARM

ans =

         1.0000           0
        -0.0000      1.0000

ARM*A

ans =

         0.8333      0.3333     -0.1667
         0.3333      0.3333      0.3333
        -0.1667      0.3333      0.8333
```

Solution that minimizes $\|Ax - b\|$

Consider a vector–matrix equation

$$\mathbf{Ax} = \mathbf{b} \tag{4-67}$$

where $\mathbf{A}$ is an $n \times m$ matrix, $\mathbf{x}$ is an m-vector, and $\mathbf{b}$ is an n-vector. Here we assume that $n > m$. That is, the number of unknown variables is smaller than the number of equations. In the classical sense, there may or may not exist any solution.

If no solution exists, we may wish to find a unique 'solution' that minimizes the norm $\|\mathbf{Ax} - \mathbf{b}\|$. Let us define a 'solution' to Eq. (4-67) that will minimize $\|\mathbf{Ax} - \mathbf{b}\|$ as $\mathbf{x}°$. In other words, $\mathbf{x}°$ satisfies the condition

$$\|\mathbf{Ax} - \mathbf{b}\| \geq \|\mathbf{Ax}° - \mathbf{b}\|, \qquad \text{for all } \mathbf{x}$$

Note that $\mathbf{x}°$ is not a solution in the classical sense, since it does not satisfy the original vector–matrix equation $\mathbf{Ax} = \mathbf{b}$. Therefore, we may call $\mathbf{x}°$ an 'approximate solution' in that it minimizes norm $\|\mathbf{Ax} - \mathbf{b}\|$. We shall obtain such an approximate solution in the following.

Left pseudoinverse matrix

For a vector–matrix equation

$$\mathbf{Ax} = \mathbf{b}$$

where $\mathbf{A}$ is an $n \times m$ matrix having rank m, $\mathbf{x}$ is an m-vector, and $\mathbf{b}$ is an n-vector, the vector $\mathbf{x}^\circ$ that minimizes the norm $\|\mathbf{Ax} - \mathbf{b}\|$ is given by

$$\mathbf{x}^\circ = \mathbf{A}^{LM}\mathbf{b} = (\mathbf{A}'\mathbf{A})^{-1}\mathbf{A}'\mathbf{b}$$

where $\mathbf{A}^{LM} = (\mathbf{A}'\mathbf{A})^{-1}\mathbf{A}'$ provided the indicated inverse exists.

To verify this, first note that

$$\|\mathbf{Ax} - \mathbf{b}\| = \|\mathbf{A}(\mathbf{x} - \mathbf{x}^\circ) + \mathbf{Ax}^\circ - \mathbf{b}\|$$
$$= \|\mathbf{A}(\mathbf{x} - \mathbf{x}^\circ)\| + \|\mathbf{Ax}^\circ - \mathbf{b}\| + 2[\mathbf{A}(\mathbf{x} - \mathbf{x}^\circ)]'(\mathbf{Ax}^\circ - \mathbf{b})$$

The last term can be shown to be zero as follows:

$$[\mathbf{A}(\mathbf{x} - \mathbf{x}^\circ)]'(\mathbf{Ax}^\circ - \mathbf{b}) = (\mathbf{x} - \mathbf{x}^\circ)'\mathbf{A}'[\mathbf{A}(\mathbf{A}'\mathbf{A})^{-1}\mathbf{A}' - \mathbf{I}_n]\mathbf{b}$$
$$= (\mathbf{x} - \mathbf{x}^\circ)'[(\mathbf{A}'\mathbf{A})(\mathbf{A}'\mathbf{A})^{-1}\mathbf{A}' - \mathbf{A}']\mathbf{b}$$
$$= (\mathbf{x} - \mathbf{x}^\circ)(\mathbf{A}' - \mathbf{A}')\mathbf{b}$$
$$= 0$$

Hence

$$\|\mathbf{Ax} - \mathbf{b}\| = \|\mathbf{A}(\mathbf{x} - \mathbf{x}^\circ)\| + \|\mathbf{Ax}^\circ - \mathbf{b}\|$$

Noting that $\|\mathbf{A}(\mathbf{x} - \mathbf{x}^\circ)\| \geq 0$, we obtain

$$\|\mathbf{Ax} - \mathbf{b}\| - \|\mathbf{Ax}^\circ - \mathbf{b}\| = \|\mathbf{A}(\mathbf{x} - \mathbf{x}^\circ)\| \geq 0$$

or

$$\|\mathbf{Ax} - \mathbf{b}\| \geq \|\mathbf{Ax}^\circ - \mathbf{b}\|$$

Thus

$$\mathbf{x}^\circ = \mathbf{A}^{LM}\mathbf{b} = (\mathbf{A}'\mathbf{A})^{-1}\mathbf{A}'\mathbf{b}$$

minimizes $\|\mathbf{Ax} - \mathbf{b}\|$.

The matrix $\mathbf{A}^{LM} = (\mathbf{A}'\mathbf{A})^{-1}\mathbf{A}'$ is called the *left pseudoinverse* or *minimal left inverse* of matrix $\mathbf{A}$. Note tht $\mathbf{A}^{LM}$ is indeed the inverse matrix of $\mathbf{A}$, in that if postmultiplied by $\mathbf{A}$ it will give an identity matrix $\mathbf{I}_m$:

$$\mathbf{A}^{LM}\mathbf{A} = (\mathbf{A}'\mathbf{A})^{-1}\mathbf{A}'\mathbf{A} = (\mathbf{A}'\mathbf{A})^{-1}(\mathbf{A}'\mathbf{A}) = \mathbf{I}_m$$

EXAMPLE 4-11: Left Pseudoinverse

Consider the following vector–matrix equation:

$$\mathbf{Ax} = \mathbf{b}$$

where

$$
\mathbf{A} = \begin{bmatrix} 1 & 1 \\ 1 & 2 \\ 1 & 4 \end{bmatrix}, \qquad \mathbf{x} = \begin{bmatrix} x_1 \\ x_2 \end{bmatrix}, \qquad \mathbf{b} = \begin{bmatrix} 1 \\ 2 \\ 3 \end{bmatrix}
$$

We shall find the minimum-norm solution that minimizes $\| \mathbf{A}\mathbf{x} - \mathbf{b} \|$. Such a minimum-norm solution is given by

$$
\mathbf{x}^\circ = \mathbf{A}^{LM}\mathbf{b}
$$

where

$$
\mathbf{A}^{LM} = (\mathbf{A}'\mathbf{A})^{-1}\mathbf{A}'
$$

Hence

$$
\mathbf{x}^\circ = (\mathbf{A}'\mathbf{A})^{-1}\mathbf{A}'\mathbf{b}
$$

$$
= \left\{ \begin{bmatrix} 1 & 1 & 1 \\ 1 & 2 & 4 \end{bmatrix} \begin{bmatrix} 1 & 1 \\ 1 & 2 \\ 1 & 4 \end{bmatrix} \right\}^{-1} \begin{bmatrix} 1 & 1 & 1 \\ 1 & 2 & 4 \end{bmatrix} \begin{bmatrix} 1 \\ 2 \\ 3 \end{bmatrix} = \begin{bmatrix} 0.5000 \\ 0.6429 \end{bmatrix}
$$

MATLAB Program 4-15 yields the solution to the problem discussed in Example 4-11.

MATLAB Program 4–15

```
% ---------- Left pseudoinverse matrix ----------

% ***** In this program we find minimum-norm solution xopt
% to equation Ax = b, where the number of unknown variables
% is smaller than the number of equations.  The minimum-
% norm solution xopt minimizes norm ||Ax - b|| *****

% ***** Enter matrices A and b *****

A = [ 1  1;1  2;1  4];
b = [1;2;3];

% ***** The minimum-norm solution is given by xopt = ALM*b *****

ALM = inv(A'*A)*A'

ALM =

        1.0000     0.5000    -0.5000
       -0.2857    -0.0714     0.3571

xopt = ALM*b

xopt =

        0.5000
        0.6429
```

```
% ***** Notice that ALM*A is a 2x2 identity matrix, while
% A*ALM is a 3x3 matrix *****

ALM*A

ans =

      1.0000    0.0000
     -0.0000    1.0000

A*ALM

ans =

      0.7143    0.4286   -0.1429
      0.4286    0.3571    0.2143
     -0.1429    0.2143    0.9286
```

Minimum-energy control problem

If an nth-order, linear, single-input, single-output discrete-time control system is completely state controllable, and if the control signal is chosen properly, then we need at most n sampling periods to bring an arbitrary initial state to the desired final state, provided the control vector is not constrained. Hence, if we allow N (where $N > n$) sampling periods, we have extra freedom to satisfy additional constraints.

The amount of control energy needed depends on the time period (number of sampling periods) allowed for control. If the number of sampling periods allowed is n, the order of the system, then the time-optimal control sequence $u(0), u(1), \ldots, u(n-1)$ is unique. However, if N sampling periods ($N > n$) are allowed, then more than one possible control sequence is possible. Each possible control sequence requires a certain amount of control energy. In many industrial applications, if many control sequences are possible, it is desirable to accomplish control tasks using the minimum amount of control energy.

In this problem, we treat the problem of transferring the state from an arbitrary initial state to the desired final state (which we assume to be the origin of the state space) in N sampling periods and at the same time using the minimum control energy.

Consider the discrete-time control system defined by

$$\mathbf{x}(k+1) = \mathbf{G}\mathbf{x}(k) + \mathbf{H}u(k) \tag{4-68}$$

where $\mathbf{x}(k)$ = state vector (n-vector) at kth sampling instant
$\quad\quad u(k)$ = control signal (scalar) at kth sampling instant
$\quad\quad\quad \mathbf{G} = n \times n$ nonsingular matrix
$\quad\quad\quad \mathbf{H} = n \times 1$ matrix

Let us determine the control law that will bring the system state from an arbitrary initial state to the origin in N sampling periods (where $N > n$) using a minimum amount of control energy, where the control energy is measured by

$$\frac{1}{2} \sum_{k=0}^{N-1} u^2(k)$$

Assume that the system is completely state controllable.

The state $\mathbf{x}(N)$ of Eq. (4-68) can be given by

$$\mathbf{x}(N) = \mathbf{G}^N\mathbf{x}(0) + \mathbf{G}^{N-1}\mathbf{H}u(0) + \mathbf{G}^{N-2}\mathbf{H}u(1) + \cdots + \mathbf{GH}u(N-2) + \mathbf{H}u(N-1)$$

Substituting $\mathbf{0}$ for $\mathbf{x}(N)$ in this last equation yields

$$\mathbf{x}(0) = -\mathbf{G}^{-1}\mathbf{H}u(0) - \mathbf{G}^{-2}\mathbf{H}u(1)$$
$$- \cdots - \mathbf{G}^{-N+1}\mathbf{H}u(N-2) - \mathbf{G}^{-N}\mathbf{H}u(N-1) \qquad (4\text{-}69)$$

Define

$$\mathbf{f}_i = \mathbf{G}^{-i}\mathbf{H}$$

Then Eq. (4-69) becomes

$$\mathbf{x}(0) = -\mathbf{f}_1 u(0) - \mathbf{f}_2 u(1) - \cdots - \mathbf{f}_{N-1} u(N-2) - \mathbf{f}_N u(N-1) \qquad (4\text{-}70)$$

Since the system is completely state controllable, the vectors $\mathbf{f}_1, \mathbf{f}_2, \ldots, \mathbf{f}_n$ are linearly independent. (The remaining $N - n$ vectors can be expressed as linear combinations of these n linearly independent vectors.) Equation (4-70) can be rewritten as

$$\mathbf{x}(0) = -\mathbf{FU} \qquad (4\text{-}71)$$

where

$$\mathbf{F} = [\mathbf{f}_1 \vdots \mathbf{f}_2 \vdots \cdots \vdots \mathbf{f}_N], \qquad \mathbf{U} = \begin{bmatrix} u(0) \\ u(1) \\ \vdots \\ u(N-1) \end{bmatrix}$$

We shall now find the control sequence that satisfies Eq. (4-71) and at the same time minimizes the total control energy. Note that matrix $\mathbf{F}$ is an $n \times N$ matrix and has rank n. Since $\mathbf{F}$ is not a square matrix, the inverse of matrix $\mathbf{F}$ is not defined. Notice that since $N > n$ the number of unknown control signals $u(0), u(1), \ldots, u(N-1)$ in Eq. (4-71) is greater than the number n of component scalar equations. A set of scalar equations in such a situation is said to be *underdetermined* and possesses an indefinite number of solutions. However, in the present case we have a constraint that a set of N unknown variables $u(0), u(1), \ldots, u(N-1)$ gives a minimum norm:

$$\frac{1}{2} \sum_{k=0}^{N-1} u^2(k) = \text{minimum}$$

Then there is a unique solution. Such a unique solution gives the control sequence that brings an arbitrary initial state $\mathbf{x}(0)$ to the origin in N sampling periods and in so doing minimizes the total energy of control.

The minimizing solution in such a problem, for which the number of unknown variables is greater than the number of equations, can be obtained in terms of the right pseudoinverse $\mathbf{F}^{RM}$, where

$$\mathbf{F}^{RM} = \mathbf{F}'(\mathbf{FF}')^{-1} \qquad (4\text{-}72)$$

By using the right pseudoinverse, the minimum-energy control sequence $u(0)$,

$u(1), \ldots, u(N - 1)$ that transfers an arbitrary initial state $\mathbf{x}(0)$ to the origin can be given by

$$\mathbf{U} = -\mathbf{F}^{RM}\mathbf{x}(0) = -\mathbf{F}'(\mathbf{F}\mathbf{F}')^{-1}\mathbf{x}(0) \qquad (4\text{-}73)$$

Note that $\mathbf{F}'(\mathbf{F}\mathbf{F}')^{-1}$ is an $N \times n$ matrix. Hence $\mathbf{F}'(\mathbf{F}\mathbf{F}')^{-1}$ postmultiplied by $\mathbf{x}(0)$ is an $N \times 1$ matrix. Equation (4-73) can be rewritten as

$$\begin{bmatrix} u(0) \\ u(1) \\ \vdots \\ u(N - 1) \end{bmatrix} = -\mathbf{F}'(\mathbf{F}\mathbf{F}')^{-1}\mathbf{x}(0) \qquad (4\text{-}74)$$

The control sequence given by Eq. (4-74) will bring an arbitrary initial state to the origin in N sampling periods and will require the minimum control energy among all possible control sequences requiring N sampling periods.

EXAMPLE 4-12

Consider the system

$$\mathbf{x}(k + 1) = \mathbf{G}\mathbf{x}(k) + \mathbf{H}u(k) \qquad (4\text{-}75)$$

where

$$\mathbf{G} = \begin{bmatrix} 1 & 0.6321 \\ 0 & 0.3679 \end{bmatrix}, \quad \mathbf{H} = \begin{bmatrix} 0.3679 \\ 0.6321 \end{bmatrix}, \quad \begin{bmatrix} x_1(0) \\ x_2(0) \end{bmatrix} = \begin{bmatrix} 5 \\ -5 \end{bmatrix}$$

It is desired to bring the initial state to the origin in three sampling periods. (The sampling period is assumed to be 1 sec.) Among infinitely many possible choices for the control sequence, determine the optimal control sequence that will minimize the control energy, or will minimize the following performance index:

$$J = \frac{1}{2} \sum_{k=0}^{2} u^2(k)$$

From Eq. (4-70), the initial state $\mathbf{x}(0)$ can be written as follows:

$$\mathbf{x}(0) = -\mathbf{f}_1 u(0) - \mathbf{f}_2 u(1) - \mathbf{f}_3 u(2)$$

where

$$\mathbf{f}_1 = \mathbf{G}^{-1}\mathbf{H} = \begin{bmatrix} -0.7181 \\ 1.7181 \end{bmatrix}, \quad \mathbf{f}_2 = \mathbf{G}^{-2}\mathbf{H} = \begin{bmatrix} -3.6701 \\ 4.6701 \end{bmatrix}, \quad \mathbf{f}_3 = \mathbf{G}^{-3}\mathbf{H} = \begin{bmatrix} -11.6939 \\ 12.6939 \end{bmatrix}$$

Hence

$$\begin{bmatrix} x_1(0) \\ x_2(0) \end{bmatrix} = -\begin{bmatrix} -0.7181 \\ 1.7181 \end{bmatrix}u(0) - \begin{bmatrix} -3.6701 \\ 4.6701 \end{bmatrix}u(1) - \begin{bmatrix} -11.6939 \\ 12.6939 \end{bmatrix}u(2)$$

or

$$\begin{bmatrix} x_1(0) \\ x_2(0) \end{bmatrix} = -\begin{bmatrix} -0.7181 & -3.6701 & -11.6939 \\ 1.7181 & 4.6701 & 12.6939 \end{bmatrix}\begin{bmatrix} u(0) \\ u(1) \\ u(2) \end{bmatrix} \qquad (4\text{-}76)$$

By use of the right pseudoinverse, we can give the minimum norm solution to Eq. (4-76) as

$$\begin{bmatrix} u(0) \\ u(1) \\ u(2) \end{bmatrix} = -\mathbf{F}^{RM}\mathbf{x}(0) = -\mathbf{F}'(\mathbf{F}\mathbf{F}')^{-1}\begin{bmatrix} x_1(0) \\ x_2(0) \end{bmatrix}$$

where

$$\mathbf{F} = \begin{bmatrix} -0.7181 & -3.6701 & -11.6939 \\ 1.7181 & 4.6701 & 12.6939 \end{bmatrix}$$

The right pseudoinverse $\mathbf{F}^{RM}$ is determined as follows:

$$\mathbf{F}^{RM} = \mathbf{F}'(\mathbf{F}\mathbf{F}')^{-1} = \begin{bmatrix} -0.7181 & 1.7181 \\ -3.6701 & 4.6701 \\ -11.6939 & 12.6939 \end{bmatrix}\begin{bmatrix} 150.7326 & -166.8147 \\ -166.8147 & 185.8968 \end{bmatrix}^{-1}$$

$$= \begin{bmatrix} 0.7910 & 0.7191 \\ 0.5000 & 0.4738 \\ -0.2910 & -0.1929 \end{bmatrix}$$

Hence

$$\begin{bmatrix} u(0) \\ u(1) \\ u(2) \end{bmatrix} = -\begin{bmatrix} 0.7910 & 0.7191 \\ 0.5000 & 0.4738 \\ -0.2910 & -0.1929 \end{bmatrix}\begin{bmatrix} 5 \\ -5 \end{bmatrix} = \begin{bmatrix} -0.3598 \\ -0.1310 \\ 0.4908 \end{bmatrix} \qquad (4\text{-}77)$$

The control sequence given by Eq. (4-77) will bring the state to the origin in three sampling periods and will also minimize the total control energy.

By using the optimal control sequence given by Eq. (4-77), the state can be transferred as follows:

$$\begin{bmatrix} x_1(1) \\ x_2(1) \end{bmatrix} = \begin{bmatrix} 1 & 0.6321 \\ 0 & 0.3679 \end{bmatrix}\begin{bmatrix} 5 \\ -5 \end{bmatrix} + \begin{bmatrix} 0.3679 \\ 0.6321 \end{bmatrix}[-0.3598] = \begin{bmatrix} 1.7071 \\ -2.0669 \end{bmatrix}$$

$$\begin{bmatrix} x_1(2) \\ x_2(2) \end{bmatrix} = \begin{bmatrix} 1 & 0.6321 \\ 0 & 0.3679 \end{bmatrix}\begin{bmatrix} 1.7071 \\ -2.0669 \end{bmatrix} + \begin{bmatrix} 0.3679 \\ 0.6321 \end{bmatrix}[-0.1310] = \begin{bmatrix} 0.3524 \\ -0.8432 \end{bmatrix}$$

$$\begin{bmatrix} x_1(3) \\ x_2(3) \end{bmatrix} = \begin{bmatrix} 1 & 0.6321 \\ 0 & 0.3679 \end{bmatrix}\begin{bmatrix} 0.3524 \\ -0.8432 \end{bmatrix} + \begin{bmatrix} 0.3679 \\ 0.6321 \end{bmatrix}[0.4908] = \begin{bmatrix} 0 \\ 0 \end{bmatrix}$$

The minimum energy required for this control is

$$J_{\min} = \frac{1}{2}\sum_{k=0}^{2} u^2(k) = \frac{1}{2}[u^2(0) + u^2(1) + u^2(2)] = \frac{1}{2}[(-0.3598)^2 + (-0.1310)^2 + (0.4908)^2]$$

$$= 0.1937$$

A MATLAB program for solving this minimum-energy control problem is given in MATLAB Program 4-16.

MATLAB Program 4–16

```
% ---------- Minimum-energy control problem ----------

% ***** Solution of minimum-energy control problem, where
% the number of unknown variables is greater than that of
% equations, is obtained by use of the right pseudoinverse *****

% ***** Enter matrices G, H, and x0 *****

G = [1   0.6321;0   0.3679];
H = [0.3679;0.6321];
x0 = [5;-5];

% ***** Enter matrices f1, f2, and f3 *****

f1 = inv(G)*H;
f2 = inv(G)^2*H;
f3 = inv(G)^3*H;

% ***** Enter matrix F = [f1  f2  f3] and compute the right
% pseudoinverse FRM = F'*inv(F*F') *****

F = [f1  f2  f3];
FRM = F'*inv(F*F')
FRM =

        0.7910      0.7191
        0.5000      0.4738
       -0.2910     -0.1929

% ***** Optimal control uopt can be given by *****

uopt = - FRM*x0

uopt =

      -0.3598
      -0.1310
       0.4908

u0 = uopt(1), u1 = uopt(2), u2 = uopt(3)

u0 =

    -0.3598

u1 =

    -0.1310
```

u2 =

    0.4908

% ***** The minimum value of performance index J can be
% given by *****

Jmin = 0.5*uopt'*uopt

Jmin =

    0.1937

% ***** To verify that the state reaches the origin in
% three sampling periods, enter the following equations
% and compute x3 *****

x1 = G*x0 + H*u0

x1 =

    1.7071
   -2.0669

x2 = G*x1 + H*u1

x2 =

    0.3524
   -0.8432

x3 = G*x2 + H*u2

x3 =

   1.0e - 014 *

   -0.7105
    0.3053

References

1. MathWorks, Inc., *The Student Edition of MATLAB*. Englewood Cliffs, N.J.: Prentice Hall, 1992.

2. MathWorks, Inc., *MATLAB User's Guide*. Natick, Mass.: MathWorks, Inc., 1990.

3. Ogata, K., *Discrete-Time Control Systems*. Englewood Cliffs, N.J.: Prentice Hall, 1987.

4. Ogata, K., *Modern Control Engineering*, 2nd ed. Englewood Cliffs, N.J.: Prentice Hall, 1990.

5. Ogata, K., *Solving Control Engineering Problems with MATLAB*. Englewood Cliffs, N.J.: Prentice Hall, 1994.

Index